The Waite Group®

FRACTALS
FOR WINDOWS

Tim Wegner
Bert Tyler
Mark Peterson
Pieter Branderhorst

Editorial Director: Scott Calamar
Development Editor: Mitchell Waite
Managing Editor: Joel Fugazzotto
Design: Pat Rogondino
Cover Design: Michael Rogondino
Production Director: Julianne Ososke
Production: Cecelia Morales

Wegner, Tim (Timothy I.)
    Fractals for sindows / Tim Wegner & Bert Tyler.
      p.   c.
    Includes bibliographical references and index.
    ISBN 1-878739-25-5
    1. Winfract. 2. Fractals--Data processing 3. Microsoft Windows
(Computer file)   I. Tyler, Bert.   II. Title.
QA614.86.W43 1992
514' .74--dc20
                                      92-38012
                                         CIP

ACKNOWLEDGMENTS

The authors would like to acknowledge all those who have contributed to the Winfract and Fractint programs in one way or another. We have been blessed with a steady stream of ideas, bug reports, code contributions, and fractal recipes from the four corners of the globe. As a result of these contributions, Winfract/Fractint can truly be called a community project, and the "Stone Soup Group" a lively international body of fractal enthusiasts that goes far beyond we four main authors.

Mitchell Waite and the Waite Group Press have provided limitless enthusiasm and vision for this project. We hereby award Mitch the Stone Soup "Power User" award for all the hours he has spent generating images and sharing ideas with us. Thanks to Joel Fugazzotto and Julianne Ososke for their capable guidance throughout the writing and production of this book.

Thanks once again are due to Larry Wood, whose computer art forum on CompuServe (GO GRAPHDEV) is the online home of Winfract.

Last but not least, we thank the fractal artists whose images appear in these pages. They are Michael Coddington, BG Dodson, Dan Farmer, Richard Hughes, Ronald C. Lewen, Bill Potter, Richard H. Sherry, and Lee H. Skinner. (The cover image is by Eli Boyajian.)

Tim Wegner
Bert Tyler
Mark Peterson
Pieter Branderhorst

Preface

FRACTALS FOR WINDOWS—A GUIDEBOOK FOR FRACTAL EXPLORERS

This book is about creating fractals—dazzling and colorful images of infinite detail—on your PC. This is a hands-on book that comes bundled with Winfract, the preeminent Windows fractal-generating program. All the images in the color plate section of the book were created with this powerful program, which is the result of collaborative effort by an international team of volunteer fractal enthusiasts. With this software and a PC, you can quickly and easily begin creating your own fractals from any of the built-in fractal types. As you become more proficient, you will discover an inexhaustible number of options for coloring and transforming your images to suit your imagination. A beginner can create images of striking complexity and beauty. But even an expert will find more than enough controls and tools to challenge his or her adventurous creativity.

Fractals for Windows consists of this preface, an introduction, six chapters, and two appendices.

INSTALLATION

This section tells you how to get Winfract up and running on your PC. If you are an experienced computer user eager to begin creating fractals, you may find that the quick start in this section is all you need to begin using the program. A more detailed guided tour is provided in Chapter 2.

CHAPTER 1: FRACTALS: A PRIMER

The first chapter describes fractals, the different varieties of fractals, how they are generated, and their significance. The background provided here will enhance your enjoyment of creating fractals by providing insight into what fractals are and how they are generated.

CHAPTER 2: WINFRACT TUTORIAL

The Winfract tutorial is an extensive tour of the main features of Winfract. You will go on a step-by-step tour through Winfract's basic functions right up to some of the more advanced functions. By the end of the tour, you will know how to make many of those spectacular color plate images.

CHAPTER 3: FRACTAL RECIPES

In this chapter, you can sample a gourmet feast of the very best fractal recipes created by devoted Winfract users. You can learn by example the hints and tricks that the experts use to make dazzling fractal images.

CHAPTER 4: WINFRACT REFERENCE

Winfract is a multifeatured software program. This chapter tells you how to access all the basic functions and unlock the secrets of Winfract's advanced fractal-generation options.

CHAPTER 5: FRACTAL TYPES

Winfract can generate the most extensive variety of fractals of any fractal program. At last count, the main fractal type screen, which lists the different kinds of fractals generated by Winfract, had 78 entries. As you will discover, the actual number of possible kinds of fractals you can create with Winfract is much larger than that. This chapter tells you about all of those different kinds of fractals, and it is filled with dozens of examples that you can try.

CHAPTER 6: WINFRACT'S SOURCE CODE

If you are curious about the inner workings of Winfract, you will find what you are looking for in Chapter 6. The programmers tell you how to compile the program, and they walk you through key sections of code with explanations of how the fractal magic is accomplished.

APPENDICES

There are two appendices, Appendix A: *Winfract and Windows Video Drivers*, and Appendix B: *The Graphics Interchange Format*. These appendices explain how Windows video drivers affect Winfract users, and they give background on the main file format that Winfract uses to store graphics.

Dear Reader:

This book is the continuation of a story. Close to two years ago I became entranced with a program called Fractint, a powerful fractal processor that lit up my computer with infinitely detailed patterns, ran at what seemed like the speed of light, and required no programming knowledge. I was blown away by its capabilties and asked The Stone Soup Group if they would write a book about their program.

That book, Fractal Creations, became an immediate success even though it came out at an odd time. It was a DOS-based program in a world that was increasingly moving toward Windows. Although the output of the program was nothing short of miraculous, the input was beginning to look a little ... dated. It was a command-line interface in what was quick becoming a GUI world.

I asked Tim Wegner if the Stone Soup Group had considered writing a Windows version of Fractint and he told me that one already existed. In fact, WINFRACT was tucked away on Compuserve, waiting to be discovered. It was a fantastic enhancement to Fractint; it was mouse and menu driven and provided a really easy-to-use zoom box to magnify each fractal. It also included a number of new fractal types.

WAITE
GROUP
PRESS™

As the sales of Fractal Creations grew , and Windows 3.1 caught on like wildfile, requests for a book about WINFRACT came pouring in. So I asked Tim, Bert, Mark, and Pieter if they would once again go back to the drawing board. You are now holding the fruits of their labor. In addition to the program, which is easier to use then ever, we have included a number of other touches including the source code, a section of "fractal recipes" and a beautiful color plate section.

We'd like to hear what you think. Fill out and return our Reader Satisfaction Card at the back of this book to obtain a catalog and see what else we are brewing up for you!

Sincerely,

Mitchell Waite

Mitchell Waite
Publisher

INTRODUCTION

The fascinating world of fractals awaits you! Whether you are new to this world or are an experienced fractal explorer, this book is for you. *Fractals for Windows* has been designed to be read while you try the examples on your computer using the Winfract program. The companion disk contains both the Winfract software package and the supporting example files. The goal of this book is to introduce you to the dazzling fractal universe and enable you to create spectacular fractal images with your PC. You will find everything you need to begin exploring an endless variety of fractal images. After you become experienced you will find this book is a handy reference for Winfract that will continue to provide many hours of pleasure.

This introduction briefly describes the resources contained in this book and how best to utilize them depending on your experience and interests.

INSTALLING THE SOFTWARE

Your first priority should be to get Winfract up and running. The Installation section contains the information needed to install the Winfract software on your hard disk. Winfract will run on any PC that can run Windows 3.0 or later in the standard or 386 enhanced modes.

To get the most out of Winfract your Windows environment should be configured with a video driver for at least 256 colors. This is briefly discussed in the Installation section, and then again in more detail in the Appendices.

If you want to jump right in and begin playing with Winfract, you will find a quick start in the Installation section.

LEARNING ABOUT FRACTALS

You will find a discussion of what fractals are, how they are generated, and the ideas behind them in Chapter 1. This is the one chapter in the book that does not require a computer—the only prerequisite is a lively curiosity.

FOR THOSE NEW TO WINFRACT

The first two chapters provide a logical sequence for those encountering Winfract for the first time. These chapters take you from installation of Winfract and background about fractals to a guided tour of Winfract's many capabilities.

WINFRACT AND FRACTINT USERS

If you are already familiar with the Winfract program, you can start with Chapter 1 to learn more about fractals, and then try out the fractal recipes in Chapter 3. If you are already familiar with Fractint, the DOS-based sister program of Winfract, you will want to familiarize yourself with the way Winfract's user interface works, described in Chapter 4. There you will also learn how to access Fractint-style menus.

REFERENCE INFORMATION

This book contains two chapters of useful reference information. Chapter 4 documents the Winfract's functions, commands, and menus. Chapter 5 provides a comprehensive description of Winfract's fractal types.

FOR PROGRAMMERS

You don't have to be a programmer to enjoy this book, but if you are, you will find a wealth of useful information about programming fractals. The complete source for Winfract is included on the distribution disk. The Fractal Types chapter (Chapter 5) tells you where to find the routines used to generate each kind of fractal. Chapter 6 provides an overview of the code, tells you how to compile Winfract, and describes the step-by-step process of adding a new fractal to Winfract.

TABLE OF CONTENTS

CONTENTS

INSTALLATION

This chapter describes how to install the Winfract program that is bundled with this book. It also includes quick-start instructions for those who want to immediately begin generating fractals. A more complete guided tour is in Chapter 2.

HARDWARE AND SOFTWARE REQUIREMENTS

Winfract requires an IBM-compatible personal computer with an 80286-or-better CPU and Windows 3.0 or higher with at least 500K of free user memory under Windows. Winfract requires that Windows be running in either standard mode or 386 enhanced mode. Winfract will not run under Windows in "real mode." The Winfract program and the associated files distributed with it use up about 1MB on your hard disk. The installation process temporarily requires another 0.5MB (which means you'll need a total of 1.5MB of free disk space to run the installation program)—that extra 0.5MB is freed up as soon as the installation process is complete.

Winfract is distributed on a high-density 3 1/2-inch disk, so you will need a 3 1/2-inch disk drive to install it. If all of the files on this 3 1/2-inch disk are copied to a high-density 5 1/4-inch disk, you will be able to use that disk to install Winfract from a high-density 5 1/4-inch disk drive. You won't quite have room for all the files on the 5 1/4-inch disk, so copy all the files except WINSRC.EXE to the second disk. That file contains the programming source code for Winfract and is not involved in the installation process, nor is it needed to run Winfract.

INSTALLING WINFRACT

Before installing any software package on your computer, it is always a good idea to make a backup copy of the distribution floppy. After you've made your backup copy, start up your copy of Windows, insert either the Winfract distribution disk or its backup copy into drive A: (or another floppy drive), select FILE and then RUN from Windows' Program manager, and then type A:\INSTALL and press (ENTER) at the RUN command prompt.

The INSTALL program will bring up an INITIALIZING, PLEASE WAIT message box (and the wait can be considerable on slower PCs—up to 75 seconds on a 16MHZ 386SX—so please be patient), eventually followed by a larger WELCOME window with a background of a Mandelbrot image.

Press (ENTER), and a second message box informs you in which directory and Program Group INSTALL is going to place your Winfract program. You may change either entry, if you like. Press (ENTER) when you're done, and INSTALL will complete the installation process, copying all of the relevant files on the distribution floppy to the destination directory, creating the Program Group if it doesn't already exist, and adding Winfract to that Program Group. When INSTALL is done, it displays a final INSTALL SUCCEEDED messagebox.

WINFRACT QUICK START

To start Winfract while Windows is running, simply double-click on its icon. Winfract will display a small window which is already generating its default Mandelbrot set using its default 320x200 image size (see Figure I-1). When the image is complete, Winfract will beep at you and remove the CALCULATING message from its Titlebar. You do not have to wait for images to complete before you give Winfract commands—you can interrupt it at any time.

There are several ways to zoom in on an image in Winfract. Zooming in is a lot like using a microscope to magnify the details of an object. The simplest way to zoom is to use the mouse to make a box framing the area you want to magnify. Pick out an area to zoom in on (the areas near the interior "blue lake" are the most interesting), move your mouse to the center of that area, and press and hold down the left mouse button while you move the mouse pointer away from that spot. As you move the mouse, the zoom box will form and grow. When the zoom box is the right size, let go of the mouse button. If you want to move the zoom box to a different location, just move the mouse pointer to somewhere inside the zoom box and press and hold down the left mouse button again while moving the mouse—the zoom box will follow the movement of the mouse pointer. To recalculate the image using the new magnified dimensions, just double-click on the left mouse button with the mouse pointer somewhere inside the zoom box. To get rid of the zoom box without performing a zoom, double-click on the left mouse button with the mouse pointer somewhere *outside* of the zoom box. Winfract will clear the image area and generate a new image using the area you just selected.

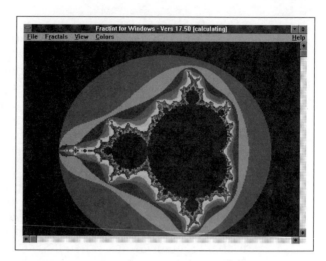

Figure I-1 Winfract starting up.

To select a new fractal type, click on the FRACTALS entry on the main menu, and then the FRACTAL FORMULA submenu item. Try selecting the lambda fractal by double-clicking on LAMBDA on the fractal formula list. Winfract will bring up a dialog box of fractal-dependent parameters and screen corners—just accept the default values (chosen to show a reasonably interesting image) and click on the OK button. Winfract will clear the image and generate a Lambda fractal using the parameters you just accepted.

If you are using a 256-color Windows video driver that supports color cycling, now would be a good time to try this feature (if you're not sure if your Windows video driver supports color cycling, try this feature anyway—Winfract will display an I'M SORRY messagebox if your video driver doesn't support color cycling). Press (SPACEBAR) to begin rotating (cycling) the image's color palette. Pressing the (SPACEBAR) again stops the color cycling. Pressing the (ENTER) key randomly chooses a new palette and switches to a random, color-generation version of color cycling. Pressing (ENTER) again chooses another new palette. You can repeatedly press (ENTER) to see an unending variety of color schemes. The (→) and and (←) keys change the direction of the cycling. The (↑) and (↓) keys speed it up and slow it down.

To exit Winfract at any time, either select FILES from the main menu, and then click on EXIT, or press (ALT)-(F4).

Now that you've gotten an overview of Winfract, you can turn to Chapter 1 to learn what fractals are, and to Chapters 2 and 3 to learn how to manipulate the beautiful fractals you've seen as well as how to create others.

DE-INSTALLING WINFRACT

De-installing Winfract is easily accomplished using the FILE / DELETE entry of Windows' Program Manager to delete first the Winfract Program Item and then its Program Group, and then deleting and removing the files in the WINFRACT directory. Winfract's installation process did not modify any of Windows' various INI files other than to have Windows itself add its program item and group. All of the files placed on your hard disk by the installation process are in the directory where you installed Winfract and can easily be deleted using the File Manager.

COPYING SINGLE FILES FROM THE WINFRACT DISK

All of the Winfract files on the distribution floppy are stored in compressed format using Microsoft's COMPRESS utility. They can be expanded again using Microsoft's EXPAND utility, distributed with Windows 3.1 and a number of other products. Microsoft's COMPRESS utility replaces the last character of the original file with an underscore, so WINFRACT.EXE, for example, is stored on your distribution floppy in compressed form as WINFRACT.EX_ and can be expanded from the MS-DOS prompt with the command:

```
C:>EXPAND A:WINFRACT.EX_ WINFRACT.EXE ENTER
```

You can use this procedure to replace individual files that you might have accidently deleted without having to repeat the whole install procedure.

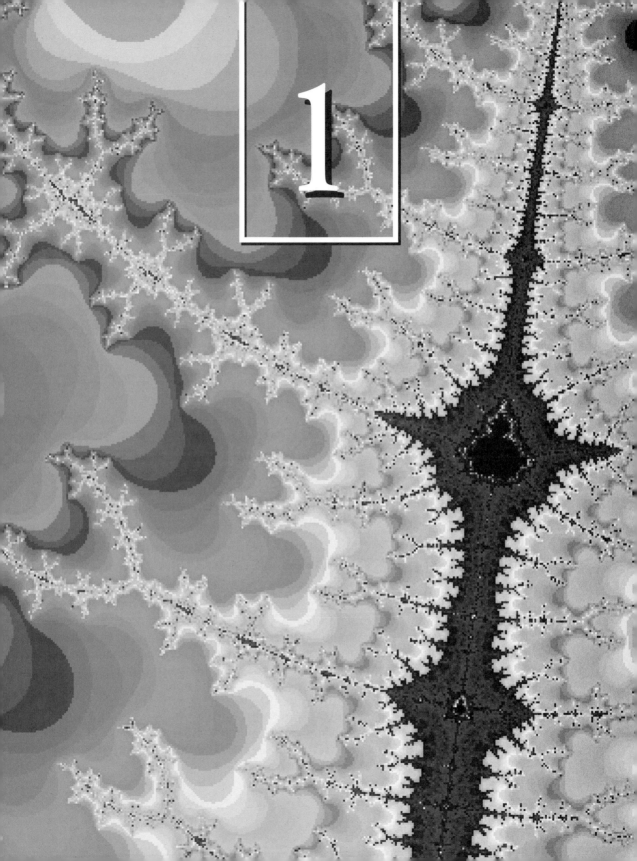

1

Fractals: A Primer

This chapter will teach you what fractals are, where they came from, what can be done with them, and how they are created on a computer. After reading this chapter, you'll be in an excellent position to appreciate the power of the Winfract program that comes with this book. Winfract is described in the next chapter.

WHAT ARE FRACTALS?

Fractals are beautiful, fascinating designs of infinite structure and complexity—the sort of intricate patterns that capture attention and evoke a sense of childlike wonder. A fractal is a mathematical object that has detailed structure no matter how closely you look at it, no matter how great the magnification. Look at Figure 1-1, which is a famous fractal called a Julia set. This fractal was generated on a computer with the software enclosed with this book and then printed. If you hold the page at arm's length, you see spirals within spirals in repeating patterns, sequences of ever-shrinking structures vanishing into nothing. If you hold the page close, your eyes will discover more detail right down to the limit of what the printer could record. What you see here is an infinite pattern somehow compressed into a finite space.

Figure 1-1 A computer-generated fractal

So what are fractals? As you make your way through this book, we will present ample evidence of the diversity of the universe of fractals and the multiplicity of ways of answering that simple question.

THE TRUTH ABOUT FRACTALS

We could go on and on about beauty and complexity, but let's begin this discussion with a healthy dose of reality. Far from being esoteric abstractions, fractals are much closer to home than you realize. In fact, it is the *nonfractal* objects that are unreal, abstract, and removed from our experience. Let's see why that is true.

From the beginnings of our education, formal and informal, we have been given simplified categories for organizing the world. The world is a sphere. Throw a baseball in the air, and its trajectory is a parabola. Nations are divided into the First World, the Second World, and the Third World. All of these statements have a strong element of truth, but none of them turns out to be accurate when you look closely. We have known since the Apollo days that the earth is really pear-shaped. After allowing for air resistance, the pear-shape of the earth, and even the gravitational field of the moon, the path of a baseball is *not exactly* a parabola. As is increasingly evident today, the elements of the First, Second, and Third Worlds are intertwined in a complex way in the economies and societies of every country.

This may sound like splitting hairs, but our everyday lives are full of clothes that don't exactly fit, lawns that are not all grass, and new cars

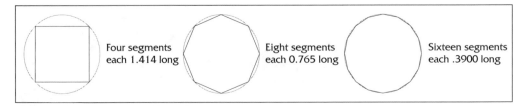

Four segments each 1.414 long

Eight segments each 0.765 long

Sixteen segments each .3900 long

Figure 1-2 Approximating a circle with polygons

with dents in their fenders. Yet we cannot do without our approximations and generalizations; we wouldn't make it through the day without simplifying assumptions. We say, "I'll meet you around 3:00," "enough to feed thirteen," or "about five people per car," instead of "meet me at 3:12:26," "enough food to feed five adults, two children, and six elderlies," or "exactly 4.67359 people per car." There is too much detail in the world to fully grasp. Indeed, there is too much detail in a single leaf for the mind to absorb.

It is irritating in the extreme to have one's simplified picture of the world shown to be inaccurate, but it happens to us all the time. It was Columbus who showed that the world was not flat, and Einstein (as an employee of the Trademark office) who showed that matter and energy are the same thing. The history of the investigation of fractals contains many stories of discoveries made by outsiders who collected up the forgotten crumbs of different disciplines and prepared a feast of chaotic structures and theories. Many scientists are finding that "curious counterexamples" turn out to be the basis of a whole new field of inquiry, and worse yet, a field developed by others! But we are getting ahead of ourselves.

Fractals are about looking closely and seeing more. Fractals have to do with bumps that have bumps, cracks that have crookednesses within crookednesses, and atoms that turn out to be universes. Fractals have to do with the rich structure of our universe that spans all scales from the uncountable galaxies at unthinkable distances to the mysterious inner electric flashes and vibrations of the subatomic realm. Let's see how looking closer results in fractals.

HOW LONG IS THE COASTLINE OF BRITAIN?

Benoit Mandelbrot, of IBM's Thomas J. Watson Research Center, did ground-breaking work in the theory of fractals and coined the word "fractal." He poses a simple question to introduce the notion of a fractal in his book *The Fractal Geometry of Nature*: How long is the coastline of Britain? This deceptively simple question exposes a deep problem and gives us insight into the question "What is a fractal?"

Sides	Length of One Side	Circumference
3	1.732	5.20
4	1.414	5.66
8	0.765	6.12
16	0.390	6.24
32	0.196	6.27
64	0.098	6.28

Table 1-1 The circumference of polygons inscribed in a unit circle

Consider how to approximate the length of the "coastline" of a circle of radius 1. Of course you know the answer in advance from high school geometry, using the formula for the circumference of a circle, 2 r; it is 2 where = 3.14159..., or approximately 6.28. As a way of arriving at a similar result, you could inscribe a square inside the circle, and estimate that the circumference of the circle is the sum of the sides of the square, as shown in Figure 1-2. Notice that if the results are not accurate enough, all you have to do is make a polygon with more sides. Table 1-1 shows how the circumference of an inscribed polygon gets closer and closer to a limiting value, which is the "real" circumference.

This procedure is both mathematically correct and intuitively clear, and it works in much more general settings than this example. Estimating distances of curves by approximating them with a series of straight segments is a tried-and-true procedure that surveyors use when mapping terrain. Think of the side of the polygon (or the length of a sighting with a surveyor's scope) as a giant measuring stick. If the curve being measured is "well behaved"—which is to say, continuous and smooth—the answer can be made as accurate as desired by making the approximating measuring sticks smaller and smaller. Presumably this same logic can be used to find the length of the coastline of Britain. *Or can it?*

Let's try the same trick on a map of Britain, using measuring sticks 200 and 25 miles long. Figure 1-3 shows the measuring stick approximations overlaid on a map of Britain, and Table 1-2 shows the numerical results.

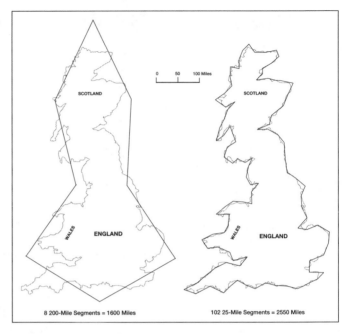

Figure 1-3 Approximating the length of the coastline of Britain

What is strange is that as the measuring stick gets smaller, the coastline estimation seems to grow larger—much larger than we would expect from the way the circumference approximation went! What is happening?

The difficulty is not too hard to see. The coastline of Britain is very, very irregular, full of large and small bays, inlets, tiny rivers, and complex, rocky shores. A long measuring stick does not bend with these many twists and turns, but cuts directly over them. A shorter measuring stick fits snugly inside these nooks and bays, thereby increasing the length estimate. Imagine doing this exercise crawling on your hands and knees, measuring the coastline of Britain with a measuring stick an inch long. Every small rock that you traversed around would increase your coastline estimate. Your answer for estimating the coastline would be astronomical!

Length of Measuring Stick	Coastline
200 miles	1,600 miles
25 miles	2,550 miles

Table 1-2 Estimation of the length of the coastline of Britain

There is a fundamental difference between a curve like a circle and a curve like the coastline of Britain. This difference separates the shapes of classical geometry from the shapes of fractal geometry. So here's your first definition: the coastline of Britain is a fractal, and our difficulty in measuring its length suggests a definition of fractal. For present purposes, we will use informal intuitive definitions, since the formal definitions are beyond the scope of this book.

> **Definition:** If the estimated length of a curve becomes arbitrarily large as the measuring stick becomes smaller and smaller, then the curve is called a *fractal* curve.

While you might not be impressed by this observation of increasing distances measured as we go from circles to coastlines, what is magic is that the idea behind the fractal definition can be generalized to cover many other kinds of shapes besides curves. In all cases the basic idea is the same—the difficulty of measuring is due to the irregularity of the object being measured, and it is an irregularity that continues to the most microscopic level. This difficulty of measuring is related to the idea of dimension. Lines and curves are one-dimensional, planes and surfaces two-dimensional. It turns out that the idea of "dimension" can be broadened in such a way that these unusual curves have a dimension greater than 1. This leads us directly to an alternative way to define a fractal.

> **Definition:** The *fractal dimension* of an object is a measure of its degree of irregularity considered at all scales, and it can be a fractional amount greater than the classical geometrical dimension of the object. The fractal dimension is related to how fast the estimated measurement of the object increases as the measurement device becomes smaller. A higher fractal dimension means the fractal is more irregular, and the estimated measurement increases more rapidly. For objects of classical geometry (lines, curves), the dimension of the object and its fractal dimension are the same. A *fractal* is an object that has a fractal dimension that is greater than its classical dimension.

Because the British coastline is, after all, a curved line, which is a one-dimensional geometric object, the fractal dimension of the coastline must be a little greater than 1. According to Mandelbrot, the mathematician Lewis Fry Richardson estimated it to be approximately 1.2. Indeed, mathematical "one-dimensional" curves can be defined which are so irregular that their fractal dimension approaches 2.0. These are called "space-filling" curves. In the discussion that follows, we will use the term "fractal geometry" to refer loosely to the theory of these bumpy shapes, just as classical geometry is the theory about regular "well-behaved" shapes.

Figure 1-4 Snow-capped mountains from space are fractals

Examples of Fractals Occurring in Nature

Now that we know that the coastline of Britain is a fractal, where else are these fractals lurking? If you have begun to catch the gist of where this discussion is heading, you have probably already guessed the answer: nearly everywhere!

Mountains as Fractals

Have you ever noticed how difficult it is to estimate the distance to a far-off mountain? Nearby foothills and distant mountains have a very similar appearance. A mountain is thus a fractal; its roughness is the same at different scales. Indeed, the fractal characteristic of hills and mountains quickly becomes a practical matter for a hiker; a mild two-hour dash to the top can turn out to be a full day of traversing up and down through ravines and canyons that were invisible from a distance. The fun of scrambling up rocky hillsides is in part due to the fact that the fractal dimension of a mountain applies at all scales, including the scale of a human being. Figure 1-4 shows a range of snow-capped mountains as seen from a space shuttle. The snow line traces the fractured boundaries of ravines,

Figure 1-5 Footprint on the moon

forming a fractal dimension and a pattern amazingly similar to some computer-generated fractals we will be discussing a bit later in the book.

A good example of a fractal is found in the famous picture of a footprint on the moon (see Figure 1-5). Near the footprint is the gravelly crust of the moon's surface. Consider now the "earthrise" view of the earth and moon (see Figure 1-6). This picture is most famous for the beautiful view of the earth, but look at the lunar landscape and compare it with the lunar surface in the footprint picture. Take the footprint out of the picture, and the surface of the moon seen from two feet away looks somewhat like the moonscape viewed from two hundred miles away. When a tiny piece of a fractal is similar to the whole, we say that the fractal is *self-similar*. Understand that a self-similar object is generally a fractal, but not all fractals are self-similar. A fractal is defined by the irregularity that must exist at all scales, but this irregularity need not look the same. Both views of the moon's surface show fractal irregularities, but the fractal dimension appears to be higher in the footprint picture than in the more distant moon surface.

Clouds

Clouds are wonderful examples of fractals. Sophisticated travelers are supposed to prefer aisle seats on airplanes, but real fractal lovers choose window seats so they can watch clouds. You may wonder how something as soft and fluffy as a cloud can be a fractal, which we have defined in terms

Figure 1-6 Earthrise

of jagged but measurable bumps and rough irregularities. Clouds are indeed roughly irregular and jagged; it's just that the colors reflected by the cloud blend smoothly into one another, giving the impression of smoothness. A little later in the book we will try to convince you that clouds and mountains from a fractal perspective are virtually the same thing.

Waves as Fractals

Not too long ago, before the study of turbulence (the complex movements of air or fluids) had advanced, it was believed that ripples on the surface of a lake were uniformly distributed. You can verify for yourself that this is not true, and that the pattern of ripples is very nonuniform, by simply taking a closer look at a body of water on a windy day. Every lake surface has smooth patches. On a windy day they might be small, and on a calmer day larger, but they are always there. But if you look closely at the rough areas of the surface—the areas full of wavelets—you will see that the "rough" areas are not completely rough, but themselves contain little glassy smooth areas. The surface of a lake is complex in the extreme, consisting of a nested pattern of smooth and rough areas that continues as you look closer and closer. This kind of nested mixture of the smooth and rough is a trademark of fractals. We can say that the lake's surface has a fractal dimension.

The Human Circulatory System

Blood flows from the heart in arteries and back to the heart in veins, but what happens in between? The arteries and veins are connected by a network of smaller and smaller vessels successively branching and re-branching until they finally meet in microscopic capillaries. A wonderful article in the February 1990 *Scientific American* entitled "Chaos and Fractals in Human Physiology" describes and vividly pictures this phenomenon. Branching patterns are a characteristic quality of certain classes of fractals.

Fractal Ferns

A more common example of fractal branching can be found in the plant kingdom. Trees, shrubs, and flowers all develop with a branching growth pattern that has a fractal character. Figure 1-7 shows a computer-generated fractal fern based on a deceptively simple scheme of symmetry and self-similarity. (The fern was made using Winfract.) Each frond of the fern is a miniature of the whole. A real fern is not self-similar to the same degree, yet it is amazing how realistic this idealized fern looks.

Weather: Chaotic Fractals

Some of the most powerful supercomputers run complex mathematical models in an attempt to improve weather forecasts, yet the success of this effort has been moderate. A large investment in computational power purchases the ability to predict only a short time further ahead. The reason for this is not that the computers don't work or that the mathematical modelers are inept, but rather that the dynamics underlying the weather are chaotic. Weather is like the flow of water over Niagara Falls. If you launch a small leaf above the falls, where will it be a few minutes later after going over the falls? While a personal computer can easily project the orbit of the Voyager spacecraft far beyond the solar system, the largest supercomputer cannot with any accuracy predict the path of our ill-fated leaf. This is the difference between well-behaved and chaotic dynamic systems.

Figure 1-7 A fractal fern

> **Definition:** A *dynamic system* is a collection of parts that interact with each other and change each other over time. A dynamic system is *chaotic* if small changes in the initial conditions of the system make large changes in the system at later times.

The weather is a great example of a dynamic system. There are periods of relative calm and predictability, like the calm patches on a disturbed lake. But as anyone who has watched the weather report on TV knows, there are always fronts on the way, low pressure areas with huge spiral arms slowly moving to the east, and hurricanes brewing in the Gulf.

Satellite pictures of weather patterns have become a part of our cultural memory. They have a certain beauty to them and, from our present perspective, a definite fractal character. If the weather forecaster could zoom the satellite picture, the audience would be treated to a succession of equally detailed pictures as the nation-sized low pressure areas would give way to a picture of the wind eddies around their city. These satellite pictures can be thought of as a graphical representation of the chaotic weather dynamics. So now we have another route to fractals—pictures of chaos.

Qualities of a Fractal

The different qualities of fractals that have come up in the discussion of these examples are summarized below. Note that not all of these qualities apply to every fractal.

Qualities Of Fractals

Fractional Dimension

Complex Structure at All Scales

Infinite Branching

Self-Similarity

Chaotic Dynamics

OF WHAT PRACTICAL USE ARE FRACTALS?

The second most common question about fractals after the question "What are they?" is some variation of "What earthly use do they have?" This is really a very reasonable question, but somehow we fractal fanatics are irritated by it. Imagine going to Paris to see the Mona Lisa in the Louvre and having someone ask you, "Fine, but what is it good for?" Let's see.

Mathematics Education

Fractals are educational because they visually illustrate many basic mathematical concepts and make an ideal vehicle for challenging visually oriented people with those concepts. While appreciation for graphic images is not a substitute for learning the abstract foundations of mathematics, intrigue with dazzling fractal images can motivate a student to dig through math texts looking for abstract concepts that made possible the visual feast.

Understanding Chaotic Dynamic Systems with Fractals

While we rarely think this way, the life of a person in our complex society is utterly dependent on both artificial and natural dynamic systems. As stated earlier, a dynamic system is a collection of parts that interact with each other and change each other over time. A few examples are power systems, the weather system, computer systems, or even the planetary ecosystem. We say that dynamic systems can exhibit behavior that is stable or chaotic. You may feel the word "chaotic" has negative connotations, but it is not necessarily a bad thing. When you are roasting marshmallows in front of a campfire, eyes transfixed on the swirls of smoke twisting up to the sky, you are observing a chaotic dynamic system made up of the air, the fire, and the wood. That kind of chaos is a pleasure, not a problem. But when chaotic interactions in power systems cause blackouts, that is usually a bad thing (although certain criminals would disagree). Useful computer algorithms (equations) are sometimes stable for some numeric inputs but exhibit chaotic behavior for others. This is an important concept to understand—certain formulas "blow up" and act unpredictably at certain times. If such an algorithm is used to calculate the position of a spacecraft just before reentry, the experience of the chaotic region of the algorithm could have serious consequences.

As we have already seen in connection with our example of the weather system, fractals are intimately connected with chaos. In fact, many computer-generated fractals are created precisely by operating otherwise well-behaved algorithms in regions where they exhibit chaotic behavior. The study of fractals cannot help but increase our knowledge of the chaotic behavior of dynamic systems. Indeed, fractal theory may not only help us predict the weather, but it can also help us understand the limits of our ability to predict it.

Image Compression

Now let's move from chaos and weather to discuss an application of fractals for computers.

Most MS-DOS personal computer users have encountered compression utility programs like ARC and PKZIP that allow computer files to be stored in a very compact form. These compression programs take advantage of the redundancy in the pattern of bits that make up your file. Because graphic images consume so much disk space, the need for this kind of file compression becomes even more critical. For example, one of the typical new "super" VGA graphics adaptors can display an image 640 pixels wide and 480 pixels high (*pixels* are the small dots that make up a computer screen image). Since each of these pixels can be any of 256 colors, it takes 8 bits (or 1 byte) of storage to store the color of each pixel. Multiply that out, and you discover that storing one graphics image from your screen at that resolution on your disk takes 307,200 bytes. That is as large as any major application you can buy for DOS. After compressing—with PKZIP, for example—the same image can be stored in less than half the space.

Fractals are complex images, but what is amazing is that in many cases they can be represented by simple equations that consume little space. In some cases, it is possible to identify patterns of self-similarity in a graphics image and compress the image storage by describing the self-similarity rather than drawing the image. Taking this concept one step further, consider attempting to identify fractal patterns in any graphics image, and compress storage by representing the images with the rules generating the fractals. Imagine how powerful a technique this could be, as it might allow huge amounts of information to be reduced to a simple formula made of five or six characters! Michael Barnsley, one of the originators of the Iterated Function Systems approach to generating fractals which we will discuss shortly, has started a company that is building a commercial venture on this idea of graphics image compression. If Mr. Barnsley could find a way of determining the fractal formula for an arbitrary text file, a disk that holds 20 megabytes might hold 2,000 megabytes!

Computer-Generated Simulation

Last but not the least of practical fractal applications, we come to computer-generated simulations. Movie special effects is a whole industry that uses many different technologies, ranging from animated artwork to miniature models. We have discussed how many natural objects from mountains to plants have a fractal nature. With the advent of high-resolution graphics workstations, it is possible with fractal formulas to generate realistic-looking computer images of mountains, trees, forests, and flowers. In the movie *Star Trek: The Wrath of Khan* the entire Genesis planet was a computer-generated fractal landscape. In the popular mind, computer-generated images have a mechanistic quality, perhaps due to the fact that popular computer drawing and paint tools come equipped with a repertoire of regular shapes such as lines, circles, and squares. But if the computer artist can supplement those with tools that create fractal

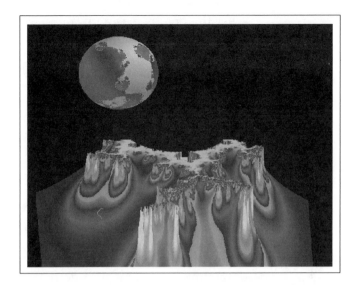

Figure 1-8 View of a fractal planet from a fractal landscape

shapes, with roughness, texture, branching, and cloudiness, then the mechanistic feel will be replaced by the earthiness of the natural world. Figure 1-8 shows a scene of a fractal planet as viewed from a fractal land-scape. This example was generated with Winfract.

AN EMERGING VIEW OF NATURE

If you have begun to feel that more is at stake with fractals than beautiful pictures, education, or image compression, you are on the right track. The universe of fractals is part of a larger issue of understanding the relationship between humanity and the natural world.

Ever since the Greek philosophers, our Western civilization has operated out of the idea that lines, circles, squares, and the other objects of classical geometry were somehow "more real" than nature itself, which contains few pure examples of these shapes. Plato postulated a world of ideal forms, where these perfect shapes resided unblemished. The world of human experience to Plato was but an imperfect and dim image of this ideal world. So, unable to live in this perfect world, people remake the natural world into a vision of imaginary perfection. Buildings must be square, shelves straight, and wheels round. Could it be that this deeply held world view is behind our impulse to bulldoze forests and build cities of rectangular skyscrapers laced with a gridwork of roads? Whatever the case, the irony is that classical geometry is used to model nature, and when the model doesn't fit, we blame nature rather than the model. What's worse, we then try to change nature to fit our preconceptions!

While this doesn't necessarily mean we should make buildings shaped like fractals, it does mean fractal geometry can often provide a much better "fit" for nature, and it can describe with great accuracy the structure of clouds, mountains, rivers, ferns, waterfalls, sunflower fields, and even weather. It may also tell us more about how the weather works, secrets of biochemistry, or insights about how people think. What is of critical importance is not the success of the theory but the reorientation of fundamental thinking. This emerging view of nature is more humble, less arrogant. The deepest wonder is for nature itself, not our attempts to model it and understand it.

THE COMPUTER AS A WINDOW TO CHAOS

Examples of chaotic phenomena occur in many disciplines, often as anomalous special cases. In many fields you will find the term "ill-behaved" used to describe chaotic phenomena. This is a very curious term indeed, reminiscent of the attitude that children are meant to be seen and not heard, and when they are heard, they are bad! But can the notion of "badness" be extended to a mathematical algorithm? That question will remain unanswered here, and this observation will have to suffice: where fractals are concerned, what is "bad" often turns out to be "good"!

For years, algorithms that exhibited chaotic behavior were ignored. Chaotic behavior represented as numbers is very hard to understand. But make this chaotic behavior visual and it can be directly grasped. With the advent of low-cost video adaptors, a personal computer can now be used as a tool to visualize such chaotic dynamics—a kind of window to chaos.

We've spent a good deal of time drawing parallels between nature and fractals and revealing ways in which fractals play a role in science. Now we are going to go into more depth and explain how a simple fractal is generated on a computer. You don't need to understand this to run the Winfract program that comes with this book, but knowing how the fractal is made can enhance your appreciation of its physical beauty. This section explores a whole category of fractals created by what are known as *escape-time* algorithms. The term *escape time* comes from the fact that the algorithm works by determining when an orbit "escapes" a circle, as will be explained shortly. The most famous fractal of them all, the Mandelbrot set, is an example of this kind of fractal. Let's have a look at how pictures of this fractal are created.

How the Escape-Time Mandelbrot Set Is Generated

To appreciate the Mandelbrot fractal, a few mathematical preliminaries are needed. We will be using these rules later, so it is important to understand them. A *set* is simply a collection of objects of some kind. In the case of the Mandelbrot set, those objects are the coordinates of locations on a mathematical map called a complex plane. These particular locations are unique because they are made up not of regular numbers we are used to but what are called complex numbers. You might think of this plane as being like the map of a city with rectangular streets and avenues. The horizontal *x*-axis might be considered a collection of avenues numbered from some large negative number to some large positive number. The vertical *y*-axis would be unusual in that it corresponded to complex numbers (from negative large to positive large) with names such as $2i$, $6.529i$, and so on.

Complex Numbers and the Complex Plane

What's so special about complex numbers? First, they are unusual in that they are composed of two parts, one a familiar real number, the other an imaginary number. The imaginary part is most interesting. With real numbers, you are not allowed to take the square root of a negative number, and this operation is not defined. With complex numbers this is allowed, and the result is a special number designated "*i*." Looking at this another way, the number *i* is defined to be the complex number such that $i^2 = -1$, which is another way of saying that $i = \sqrt{-1}$. Every complex number is written as the sum of a real number and another real number times *i*, or $a + bi$, where *a* and *b* are real numbers.

Complex numbers can be graphed using a "real" axis (for the "*a*" part), and an "imaginary" axis (for the "*bi*" part). Figure 1-9 shows how the complex number $a + bi$ can be graphed using the two axes on the complex plane. The place where the two axes meet is called the *origin*, and it is the graph of the complex number $0 + 0i$, which is the familiar zero from ordinary arithmetic.

Using the fact that $i^2 = -1$, and the ordinary rules of arithmetic, you can do arithmetic using complex numbers. For example, $(2 + 3i) + (-3 + 2i)$ is calculated by adding the real parts together and the imaginary parts together, so the answer is $[(2 - 3) + (3 + 2)i]$, or $-1 + 5i$.

Multiplying is a little more complicated. The expression $(2 + 3i) \times (-3 + 2i)$ is multiplied out exactly as it would be in algebra if "*i*" were a variable, and then simplified using $i^2 = -1$.

Distance Between Complex Numbers

The next concept we need to grasp is how to calculate the distance between complex numbers. Imagine our map is Manhattan, New York City, U.S.A, where the *x*-axis is avenue numbers and the *y*-axis is street numbers. Suppose you live in a high-rise apartment at 3rd Street and 4th Avenue, and a friend of yours lives in another high-rise apartment at 6th Street and 8th Avenue. You are peeking at your friend's apartment through

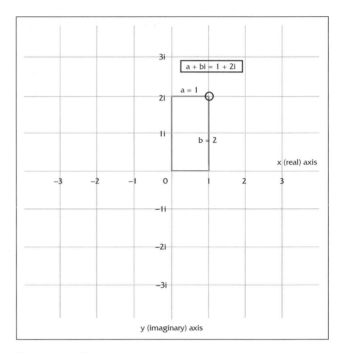

Figure 1-9 The complex plane

a telescope, and you are curious about how far away it is. For the sake of this discussion let's say that New York blocks are perfectly square, so a block along the avenues is the same distance as a block along the streets. Figure 1-10 shows the section of Manhattan where these two apartments are located.

You can see that the apartments are on the ends of the hypotenuse of a right triangle. One leg of the triangle, the leg that runs in the avenue direction, is three blocks long. The other leg is four blocks long. Using the Pythagorean theorem, we see that the distance is five blocks, because $5 = (3^2 + 4^2)$. The formula for the distance between two complex numbers is based on the same idea. The avenues are the real part of the complex number, and the streets are the imaginary part. The distance formula is just the Pythagorean theorem applied to the distance between the two complex numbers in the x-axis (real) direction and the y-axis (imaginary) direction.

To make a Mandelbrot set, we need the distance from the complex number $a + bi$ to the origin $0 + 0i$. Again, this distance is the square root of the sum of the squares of the real and imaginary parts, or $(a^2 + b^2)$. A shorthand way of writing the distance of a complex number $a + bi$ to the origin is $|a + bi|$, and when you see this you will know that the real meaning is $(a^2 + b^2)$.

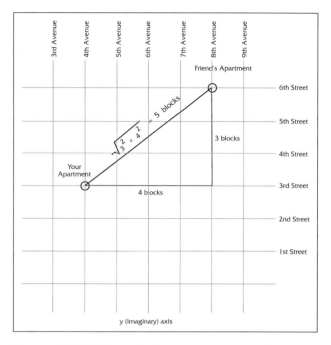

Figure 1-10 Distance between two apartments in Manhattan

The purpose of using this formula in generating a Mandelbrot set is to test whether a point is inside a circle of radius 2 centered on the origin of the complex plane. If $|a + bi|$ is less than 2.0, then the point is inside the circle.

Orbits Escaping

The Mandelbrot set is a collection of points "in" the complex plane. In order to calculate it, each point is tested to determine if it is in the set. Here is how the test works. Each test point determines a sequence of points in the complex plane (you'll see how in a minute). A sequence is just a list of numbers. A subscript is used to show which is the first, the second, and so forth. This sequence is sometimes called the *orbit* of a particular test point, such as the point $37 + .4i$. Think of the sequence of complex numbers as the successive positions of an object flying through space, and you'll see why the term "orbit" is appropriate. Here is how a point passes or fails the test for membership in the Mandelbrot set. If any of the points in the orbit belonging to the test point are outside the circle of radius 2 about the origin, then that test point is *not* in the Mandelbrot set. If all of the orbit positions remain inside the circle of radius 2, then the test point is in the Mandelbrot set. Another way to put this is that the Mandelbrot set consists of all those test points whose orbits never escape the circle of radius 2, but whizz around forever inside it. A radius larger than 2 would work fine for this computation, but a smaller radius would not. A radius of 2 is the smallest radius centered on the origin that contains all of the Mandelbrot set, as you can see in Figure 1-15, on page 27.

The Magic Formula

How are these orbits generated from the test point? Suppose the point to be tested is the one on the origin, $a + bi$, which we will call c. The sequence of points generated by c will be designated $z_0, z_1, z_2, z_3,...,z_n,....$ Here, z_n is the nth member of the sequence, counting up from zero, and the little dots are mathematics-ese for "and so forth." (By the way, mathematicians often use the letter "z" to represent complex numbers.) The first element of the sequence is the origin itself, so $z_0 = 0 + 0i$, that is, $z_0 = 0$. To get the next member of the sequence, the previous member is multiplied times itself and added to c. This sequence-building process is described by the equation:

$$z_0 = 0 + 0i$$
$$z_1 = z_0^2 + c$$
$$...$$
$$z_{n+1} = z_n^2 + c$$

Let's use a real point. Suppose the test point is the complex number $.37 + .4i$. Calculating z_1 is easy, because $z_1 = z_0^2 + (.37 + .4i)$, and $z_0^2 = 0 \times 0 = 0$, so $z_1 = .37 + .4i$. The distance of this point to the origin is $(.37^2 + .4^2)$, or about .545, which is well within the circle of radius 2. The orbit value z_2 is $(.37 + .4i)^2 + (.37 + .4i)$. To simplify all this we used a computer, and Table 1-3 shows the orbit sequence values for the test point $.37 + .4i$, along with the distance from the origin of each sequence member. Figure 1-11 shows a plot for the orbit formed by this table of results.

The orbit starts to swing outward, comes back in to a minimum value at z_5, and swings around outward again. The orbit member z_{12} is the first one to wander outside the circle. Notice that the distance value for z_{12} is 3.950, almost double the test circle radius. Figure 1-11 shows a plot of this escaping orbit in the complex plane.

This calculation shows that the test point $.37 + .4i$ is not in the Mandelbrot set because its orbit escapes the circle.

Nonescaping Orbit

Now, changing this complex number just a little gives a different result. Table 1-4 shows the orbit of the point $.37 + .2i$. One hundred values were calculated, but not all are shown. Figure 1-12 shows a plot of these values. Note how nice and symmetrical this orbit is.

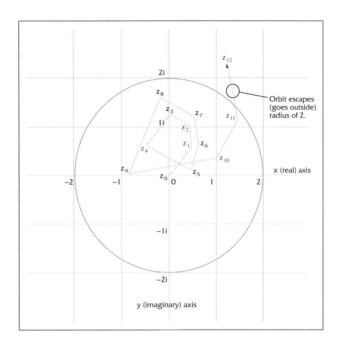

Figure 1-11
The escaping orbit of .37 + .4*i*

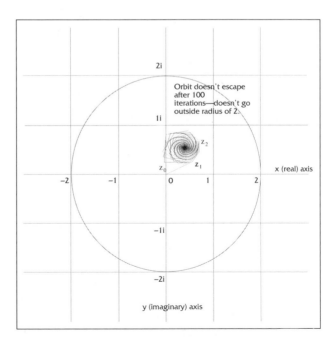

Figure 1-12
The nonescaping orbit of
.37 + .2*i*

		Real		Imaginary	Distance		
z_0	=	0.000	+	0.000i	$\|z_0\|$	=	0.000
z_1	=	0.370	+	0.400i	$\|z_1\|$	=	0.545
z_2	=	0.347	+	0.696i	$\|z_2\|$	=	0.778
z_3	=	0.006	+	0.883i	$\|z_3\|$	=	0.883
z_4	=	−0.409	+	0.410i	$\|z_4\|$	=	0.580
z_5	=	0.369	+	0.064i	$\|z_5\|$	=	0.375
z_6	=	0.502	+	0.447i	$\|z_6\|$	=	0.672
z_7	=	0.422	+	0.849i	$\|z_7\|$	=	0.948
z_8	=	−0.173	+	1.117i	$\|z_8\|$	=	1.130
z_9	=	−0.848	+	0.014i	$\|z_9\|$	=	0.848
z_{10}	=	1.089	+	0.376i	$\|z_{10}\|$	=	1.152
z_{11}	=	1.415	+	1.219i	$\|z_{11}\|$	=	1.868
z_{12}	=	0.885	+	3.8500i	$\|z_{12}\|$	=	3.950

Table 1-3 Test orbit for .37 + .4 i

If we calculate the orbit sequence starting with .37 + .2i, we discover that the orbit values stay well inside the circle for the first 100 orbit calculations. This raises a difficult point. Just because the first 100 orbit values are within the circle doesn't mean some later values might not escape. So how do we ever know a test point is in the Mandelbrot set? The answer is that we don't really know. The Mandelbrot set has to be approximated by setting an arbitrary cutoff point for how many orbit values will be tested. So for practical purposes, we will say that the test value .37 + .2i is in the Mandelbrot set, because for the 100 orbit sequence values that were checked, all were confined to the inside of the test circle. (Winfract will let you control this parameter.)

	Real	Imaginary	Distance
z_0 =	0.000 +	0.000i	$|z_0|$ = 0.000
z_1 =	0.370 +	0.200i	$|z_1|$ = 0.421
z_2 =	0.467 +	0.348i	$|z_2|$ = 0.582
z_3 =	0.467 +	0.525i	$|z_3|$ = 0.703
z_4 =	0.312 +	0.690i	$|z_4|$ = 0.758
z_5 =	−0.009 +	0.631i	$|z_5|$ = 0.631
. . .			
z_{96} =	0.352 +	0.479i	$|z_{96}|$ = 0.594
z_{97} =	0.264 +	0.537i	$|z_{97}|$ = 0.598
z_{98} =	0.152 +	0.484i	$|z_{98}|$ = 0.507
z_{99} =	0.159 +	0.347i	$|z_{99}|$ = 0.382
z_{100} =	0.275 +	0.310i	$|z_{100}|$ = 0.415

Table 1-4 Test Orbit for .37 + .2i

Even though only the first 100 values were checked, this orbit looks very convincingly nonescaping. It has a definite, regular inward spiral that appears to converge to a point. Winfract lets you watch these fascinating orbits come and go while fractals are being generated.

Constrict Your Window and Your Pixels

The next problem is how to test all the points of a given set in the complex plane. This is impossible because there are an infinite number of points to test. But it isn't really necessary to test all the points. The end objective is to make a picture of the Mandelbrot set on a computer screen. The solution is to map the pixels (small dots) on the computer screen to the complex plane, and just test those complex points that correspond to a pixel. This is analogous to coloring just the street/avenue intersections of our Manhattan map.

When this is accomplished, the pixels are colored one color if the test value is in the Mandelbrot set and another color if it isn't.

The Final Black-and-White Mandelbrot Algorithm

Let's summarize what has been said so far, and use a little different notation. For each pixel on the computer screen, the complex number z_{pixel} mapped to that pixel will be tested to see if it is in the Mandelbrot set or not. z_{pixel} is the test point we discussed in the above examples and, therefore, it is the variable "c" in the Mandelbrot orbit formula $z_{n+1} = z_n^2 + c$, so $c = z_{pixel}$. We will define the sequence of complex numbers (called the "orbit sequence") $z_0, z_1, z_2,..., z_n,....$ The first member of the orbit sequence is the origin, so $z_0 = 0 + 0i$. The second member of the sequence, z_1, is $z_0^2 + c$, or c itself, since z_0 is zero. If c is already outside the circle, we are done; we'll color the pixel white.

The next member of the sequence, z_2, is the first member squared plus c, so $z_2 = z_1^2 + c$. We must plug values into z and then, after checking to see if the new value is outside the circle, the process is continued. In general, each orbit value z_{n+1} is obtained from the previous orbit value z_n by the formula $z_{n+1} = z_n^2 + c$. Each time a new z_{n+1} is calculated, it is tested to see if it has gone outside the circle. The notation for the "in the circle test" for our Mandelbrot set is whether $|z_{n+1}| < 2$, where $|z_{n+1}|$ is the distance of z_{n+1} to the center point. If $|z_{n+1}| < 2$ is true, we calculate another iteration; otherwise, the orbit value has escaped, and it is colored white. Since we do not want the computer to calculate forever, we have a maximum iteration cutoff, and if the orbit has not escaped by the time we reach the cutoff, we quit and declare the point to be colored black.

Figure 1-13 shows the result of this little exercise after all the points are colored. The Mandelbrot set consists of all those points we colored black—points whose orbits always stayed inside the circle (or at least, stayed inside for as long as the computer had the patience to wait). The actual edge of what appears as a lake in the figure is a fractal in the sense of the definitions earlier in this chapter. Measured with a small enough "inchstick," the coastline of "Mandelbrot Lake" can be made as long as you want, and it has a fractal dimension greater than one. The exact fractal dimension of the Mandelbrot set coastline was until recently an unsolved problem, but is now known to be 2.

Where Did the Mandelbrot Fractal REALLY Come From?

In Figure 1-13, there are two big "bays" in the giant lake, with smaller baylets at the top and bottom. The whole "coastline" is an impossibly detailed nesting of bay within bay within bay, resulting in thin, jagged filaments shooting out like static electricity. This is a picture of a set that James Gleick called "the most complex object of mathematics."

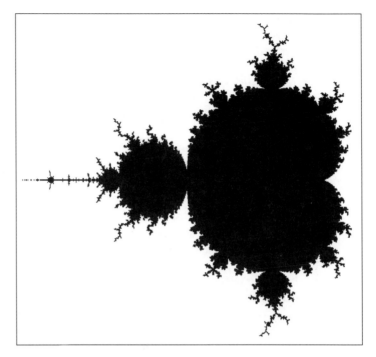

Figure 1-13 The Mandelbrot set

By contrast, look at this formula, placed in a box in big, bold type, so you can soak it in, meditate on it, and wonder about it.

$$Z_{n+1} = Z_n^2 + c$$

Appearances of simplicity CAN be deceiving. The innocent-looking formula $E = MC^2$ somehow encapsulates the whole theory of relativity. Not so here! The formula $z_{n+1} = z_n^2 + c$ is no more, and no less, than what it appears to be. Take a number, square it, and add a number. Nothing fancy, nothing tricky, nothing profound. No energy, no mass, no real-world stuff. Yet this is the formula which, given a few more details about repeating and checking for escaping orbits, generates the beautiful Mandelbrot set. How can such a wondrous and complex shape come from the absurdly simple formula $z_{n+1} = z_n^2 + c$?

Here is a hint of where to look for the mysterious source of fractals. The formula $z_{n+1} = z_n^2 + c$ may be simple, but it is repeated over and over a very large number of times. At the very beginning of this chapter, a fractal was described as an infinite pattern somehow compressed into a finite space. There are many different kinds of fractals, but however different they are, and however diverse their methods of generation, all of them have some kind of iterative scheme at their heart. The possible secret: formulas play a more minor role in a fractal compared to the iterative powers at work. Yet this is not enough to explain fractals completely. And while the mathematics and iterative method are logical, perhaps limitations of the human mind will never allow us to fully understand fractals. For some of us, therein lies their appeal!

Fractals Come Alive: Escape-Time Colors

Our black-and-white coloring scheme for each test point works well and provides a beautiful picture. But there is one more refinement we can make to an escape-time fractal that gives an additional and wonderous level of beauty: color.

As we have seen, the Mandelbrot set is defined as the set of points that do not escape a circle of radius 2 under iteration of the formula $z_{n+1} = z_n^2 + c$. And we have seen that a picture of the Mandelbrot set can be made with two colors, one for the points in the set, one for the points out of the set.

A brightly colored variation of this picture can be created by coloring the points *not* in the Mandelbrot set—the ones that escaped the circle—according to how long it takes for the orbit to escape, where "how long" means "how many orbits." We can use the number of iterations to control the final color of the test-point pixel. So if the test point escapes in a few iterations, the color might be red, but if it takes many iterations it might be colored blue.

Figure 1-14 shows a more graphic view of how escape-time coloring works. The bottom of the diagram shows the familiar two dimensions of the complex plane, with two points, *a* and *b*, selected for testing and coloring. The vertical axis represents the number of times the formula is iterated. You can imagine the 2-inch radius escape circle as a cylinder that is stretched into the third dimension, with the iteration values on the vertical scale color-coded. Therefore, the vertical level reached when the orbit escapes the cylinder is used to color the test pixel according to the color for that level. In our figure, we show that test-point *a* forms a spiral that never escapes, so it is colored the "inside color" (blue in Winfract). Test-point *b* forms an orbit that escapes on the seventh iteration, so it is made of color number 7. The overall effect of this coloring scheme divides the Mandelbrot fractal into bands reminiscent of terraced rice paddies on a Chinese mountainside. Each band represents an area where the orbits begun with points in these bands escape at the same iteration. Near the "lake edge" of the Mandelbrot set, these bands become more and more irregular and bent. You can see these bands in full color on the front cover of this book and on the color plate. See also Figure 1-15.

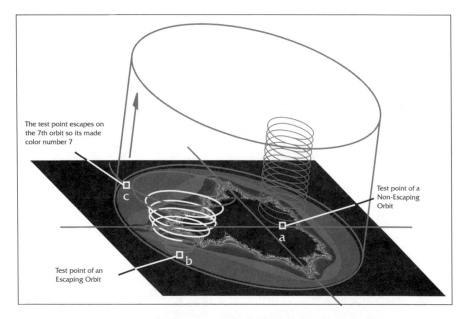

The test point escapes on the 7th orbit so its made color number 7

c

Test point of a Non-Escaping Orbit

a

Test point of an Escaping Orbit

b

Figure 1-14 Escape-time coloring of the Mandelbrot set

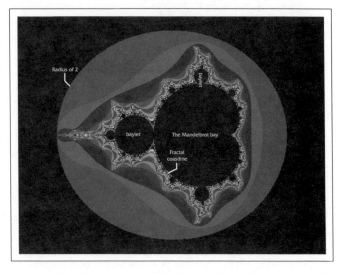

Radius of 2

baylet

baylet

The Mandelbrot bay

Fractal coastline

Figure 1-15 Colorized mandelbrot set (in grayscale with the parts identified)

The spectacular stripes of the Mandelbrot set rendered with escape-time coloring should not be confused with the set itself. Mathematically, the Mandelbrot set consists of the solidly colored lake area. The colorful stripes are points *near* the Mandelbrot set. However, this distinction is not always made, and in popular fractal parlance the Mandelbrot set often refers to the whole colorful image—lake, stripes, and all.

Zooming In, or How Big Is a Fractal?

Since there are too many possible points to calculate—infinitely many, to be exact—the complete Mandelbrot set cannot be rendered in a picture. In common computer practice, a rectangular grid of numbers is used for the values of *c*, using as fine a mesh as can be resolved by the particular graphics hardware. To show the complete Mandelbrot set, these numbers must span a range of approximately –2 to 2 in the *x* and *y* dimensions. However, there is no law that says that the entire Mandelbrot set from –2 to 2 must be included in the view. By picking a very small piece of the complex plane as the corners for the calculation grid, a small area of the fractal can be blown up with a zoom effect. For example, you can look at the fractal between –.2 and +.2 or –.02 and +.02. From what we have said so far, you are undoubtedly prepared for the fact that the Mandelbrot set, being a fractal, is just as interesting in these microscopic views as it is in the large view. That is indeed the case. Even a modestly powered personal computer can reveal staggering patterns in the Mandelbrot set. Let us do a quick calculation to see just how staggering.

Winfract allows zooming in successively on a fractal ten times, magnifying the image a maximum of about twenty-five times for each zoom. The limit of ten zooms is not mathematical but is due to the computer's representation of numbers. At the most extreme magnification, a small patch of the complex plane about .000000000001 (1.0×10^{-12}) units wide fills the screen. Using the width of the Mandelbrot set of 4.0, and the width of the physical screen of about a foot, we can calculate how big the complete Mandelbrot set would be at the same scale.

Don't peek at the answer—guess! You're probably thinking that the giant Mandelbrot set would be pretty big, or we wouldn't be making much of a fuss about it, so maybe the answer is...ahhh...as big as a football field? Maybe a mile or two? Well, that's a brave answer. Indeed, if the giant Mandelbrot set were a mile wide, and because there are about twenty-five *million* different one-foot-wide patches in a square mile, you could be pretty busy charting them all.

But a mile wide is the wrong answer. A Mandelbrot set blown up to the scale of the most extreme zoomed view you can see on your PC screen with Winfract would be *one billion miles wide*. That is *ten times* the distance from the earth to the sun; almost the distance to Jupiter. Figure 1-16 shows the relative sizes of this giant Mandelbrot set and the solar system.

What are the chances, then, that in your fractal explorations you will find a piece of the Mandelbrot set never before seen with human

Figure 1-16 A giant Mandelbrot set swallows the orbit of Mars

eyes? Not only pretty good, but virtually certain, as a matter of fact. You may have heard of a company that for a fee will name a star after you and record it in a book. Maybe the same thing will soon be done with the Mandelbrot set!

Mandelbrot and Julia Sets

Although the magnitude of exploration possibilities so far discussed is already of an astronomical size, you should be warned that the parade of endless fractal vistas has not even begun! The Mandelbrot set can be viewed not only as a fascinating fractal in its own right, but as an infinite "catalog" of a related class of fractals, called Julia sets. Each *point* of the Mandelbrot set may be considered an index pointing to a specific Julia set. These Julia sets are named after the French mathematician Gaston Julia, who discovered them.

Here is how Julias are formed. Consider a point c in a picture of the Mandelbrot set, and let it be inside or outside the "lake" that is the Mandelbrot set proper. Given this fixed point c, let's apply a slight modification of the escape-time algorithm for calculating the Mandelbrot set. In the calculation of the Mandelbrot set, the c in the formula $z^2 + c$ was set to the value z_{pixel}, which changes for each pixel being colored. In the Julia set calculation, by way of contrast, the value of c is kept *fixed* for the entire image and just z changes. This little trick results in a new type of fractal. Changing the value of c changes the entire Julia set to another Julia set. Thus there is no one Julia set, but rather an infinity of them, one for each value of c. That same number c corresponds to *one point* of the Mandelbrot set, so that one point may be considered as the index of the Julia set.

Figure 1-17 shows a picture of the Mandelbrot set surrounded by smaller pictures of Julia sets, with numbers connecting the Julia sets with the corresponding index points on the Mandelbrot set.

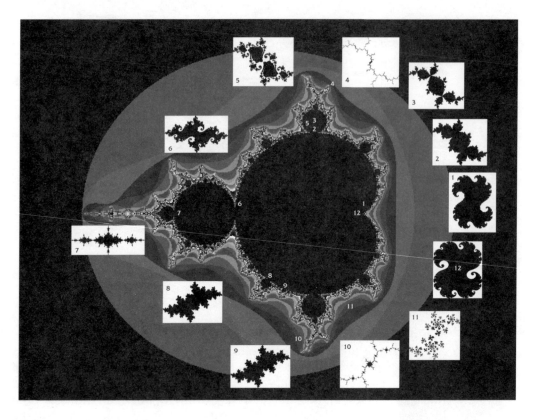

Figure 1-17 Julia family

Note that Julia sets whose Mandelbrot index is inside the Mandelbrot lake have a lake themselves, whereas index points well outside the Mandelbrot lake do not have a lake. Some of the most interesting Julia sets have an index near the shore of Mandelbrot lake. As the index approaches the shore from within the Mandelbrot lake, the Julia set lake's shoreline becomes more and more convoluted, until it explodes into fragments just as the index "hits the shore." In fact, this phenomenon can be used as the definition of the Mandelbrot set (which is, you recall, just the lake part of the escape-time picture of the Mandelbrot set). The Mandelbrot set consists of exactly those Julia indices of Julia sets with lakes in one connected piece.

This idea of one fractal being a catalog for a whole family of other fractals is a quite general idea. Later on in the book, when we are discussing other kinds of fractals, we will refer to the catalog fractal as the Mandelbrot form, and the family of fractals that correspond to the indices as the Julia form. This relationship makes sense even though the iterated formulas used to calculate the fractals are very different than the familiar $z^2 + c$ formula. When we want to make it clear that we mean the original Mandelbrot or Julias, we will speak of the "classic" Mandelbrot/Julia.

The Ubiquitous Mandelbrot Set

In physics and mathematics, there are certain numbers that appear over and over again, sometimes in completely different contexts. A good example is the number . The definition of   comes from geometry; it is simply the ratio between the circumference and diameter of a circle. But   is ubiquitous: it pops up again and again in connection with waves, power systems, complex numbers, exponentials, and logarithms.

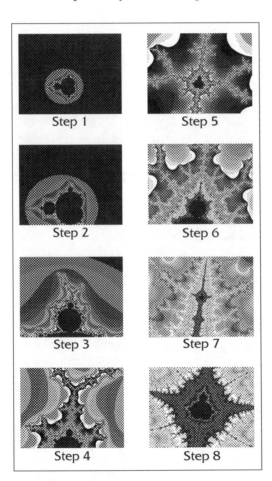

Step 1

Step 2

Step 3

Step 4

Step 5

Step 6

Step 7

Step 8

Figure 1-18 Fractal zoom in steps

In a similar way, you will find the familiar bulging shape of the Mandelbrot set reappearing over and over in miniature form, both within itself and as a detail within totally different fractals. Figure 1-18 shows several "baby Mandelbrots" within a sequence of successively greater magnification zooms.

Given the fundamental nature of fractals, which has to do with the existence of infinite detail, at greater and greater magnification, it is not too surprising to find baby Mandelbrots inside the original Mandelbrot fractal. But suppose we use the same approach to fractal generation (coloring pixels by iterating a formula), but change the formula to something completely different, say, $z_{n+1} = c \times \text{cosine}(z_n)$. This formula doesn't look anything like the Mandelbrot formula, and neither does the generated fractal. Yet buried within the fractal is the shape shown in Figure 1-13. Another baby Mandelbrot! This is not an isolated example—it happens again and again. The ubiquitous Mandelbrot set shape is to fractal theory what the number is to mathematics and engineering. Indeed, the plaque on the Pioneer spacecraft should have contained a Mandelbrot set engraving!

Now that we've covered the Mandelbrot in great detail, let's take a look at some other kinds of fractals.

Newton's Method-Escape to Finite Attractor

The escape-time method of generating fractals we have discussed so far might be called "escape to infinity." The test for when an orbit has escaped (strayed outside a circle of radius 2) is really a test for escaping to infinity. In the case of the Mandelbrot and Julia orbit formulas, once the orbit value gets outside that circle, if you were to continue to calculate the orbit it would spiral outward forever. In this case, we say that "infinity is an attractor" for the orbit. It is as if infinity were a magnet trying to attract the Mandelbrot orbit values to itself. And we can imagine that the orbit test point is trying to keep the orbit values in check.

A similar kind of fractal image is generated by measuring the escape time to a finite value rather than infinity. One example of this creates fractals using what is called Newton's method. (Newton, as you probably recall, was a famous physicist who invented—that is, discovered—a great many truths about moving objects and gravity. He also discovered some clever math techniques.) For example, every time you press the square root button on a calculator, you are using Newton's method. Newton's method is a way of doing a calculation by beginning with a guess for the answer, and repeatedly applying a formula that transforms the guess into a better guess. The series of answers so generated converges rapidly to the correct answer.

Consider the problem of finding the cube root of 1. This is the same problem as finding the solution to the equation $z^3 - 1 = 0$. The solutions to this equation are the numbers that when multiplied by themselves two times ($z \times z \times z$) give 1 as an answer. You might think that this is a silly problem, because the answer is clearly the number 1, since $1^3 = 1$. What makes the problem interesting is that when complex numbers are considered (the same kind of numbers we just discussed in connection with the Mandelbrot calculation), there are actually *three* solutions to the equation. These three answers are three equally spaced points on a circle of radius 1. They are the complex numbers $1 + 0i$, $-1/2 + i\sqrt{3}/2$, and $-1/2 - i\sqrt{3}/2$. Figure 1-19 shows the three cube roots of 1 distributed on the unit circle in the complex plane, and what happens to several initial guesses when fed into the Newton's method formula.

The Newton's method approach is very similar to the Mandelbrot set calculation. The pixels on the screen are mapped to complex numbers in the same way. For each complex number z_{pixel} corresponding to a pixel, an orbit sequence $z_0, z_1, z_2,...,z_n,...$ is generated. This time the orbit sequence is generated by a slightly more complicated formula, $z_{n+1} = (2z^3 + 1) / 3z^3$. But the main difference is that with Newton's method the

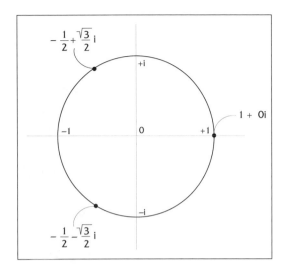

Figure 1-19
The three complex cube
roots of 1

criterion for "escape" is different. For the Mandelbrot set, escaping meant that the orbit got outside of a circle of radius 2 centered on the origin. The orbits that got too close to the "magnet" at infinity were attracted to it. But in the case of Newton's method, there are three magnets, one located at each of the cube roots of 1 around the unit circle. Orbits escape (or perhaps we should say they die) when they are irreversibly attracted to these magnets. Each test-point pixel is colored according to the magnet that captures its orbit.

But what happens when the test-point guess is *between* two of the three possible attracting values? The answer is chaos! Areas colored according to the ultimate destination of the orbit become intertwined in an infinitely complex pattern, as Figure 1-20 reveals.

Newton's method is an example of where fractals turn up in situations that engineers want to avoid. That square root button on your calculator has a purpose—to find the square root. The first guess your calculator makes before applying Newton's method is designed to be close enough to the final answer so that the algorithm will work effectively to find the square root. If the algorithm doesn't work for bad initial guesses, then it is the job of the calculator designer to avoid those values. The designer will be out of a job if he or she builds a calculator where an "ill-behaved" initial guess is used and the calculator gives the wrong answer.

Generating a Newton Fractal
Here is how to use Newton's method to generate a fractal. Start with a grid of complex numbers that more than covers the unit circle and our three

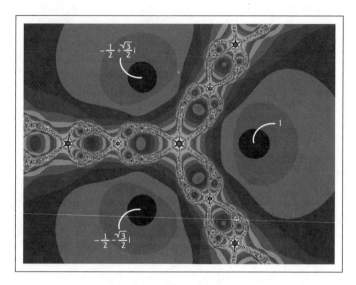

Figure 1-20 Newton's method fractal for the cube root of 1

cube roots of 1. The corner values might extend from −2 to 2 in both the x and y directions. Assign colors to the three answers. Winfract uses dark blue, light blue, and green. For each number, z_{pixel} in the grid is used as an initial guess for the Newton's method calculation. Set $z_0 = z_{pixel}$ and successively apply the Newton formula to get a sequence z_0, z_1, z_2,.... Each time the formula is iterated, the orbit is checked to see if it has come near one of the roots. If it does, the calculation is finished, and z_{pixel} is assigned the color of the root that captured it. The areas near the three roots end up being solidly colored with the color for that root. In between the roots, the three colors twist together in an intricate braided pattern. These solid areas are called *basins of attraction*, because they show all the starting points that end up converging to a particular attractor. Figure 1-20 shows this intriguing fractal, which might be said to be based on the applied mathematician's nightmare—the indecision of Newton's method!

Chaotic Orbits and the Lorenz Attractor

The discussion of escape-time fractals introduced the idea of an orbit as a series of points that can be imagined to be the path of a flying object. The only concern for the orbit was the time required to escape outside some radius, or the time required to be captured by an attractor (that is, the number of iterations required). The orbit itself was not the main concern but was simply a step in the calculation of a color of a single point. However, orbits can be interesting in themselves.

The idea of plotting orbits from the equations describing dynamic systems is as old as physics itself. One of the first triumphs of theoretical physics was the demonstration that the elliptical orbit of a small moon around a large planet is a consequence of the inverse square law of gravitation. The problem of determining the orbits of two objects revolving around each other is known as the "two-body problem." It has a simple and elegant solution. But adding a third body to the dynamic system greatly complicates the orbits. Three-body orbits can be complex beyond imagination.

Why is it, then, that every high school science student has the idea that planetary orbits are ellipses, when there are, to make a slight understatement, more than two objects in the universe? *No* orbit in the physical world is exactly an ellipse. If the three-body problem has a complicated solution, how about the trillion-body problem, the one that exists today in our universe!

There is, of course, a perfectly reasonable answer to this question. An ellipse is a simple geometric shape that has simple mathematical properties that make it very suitable for computational purposes, not to mention educational purposes. In science and engineering, careful simplifications and approximations can make intractable problems manageable, and they are a very important tool in the engineering tool kit.

Yet this eminently reasonable answer is unsatisfying. This propensity to imagine orbits in the simplest possible geometric terms is probably yet another manifestation of a deep cultural bias toward a classically geometric way of imagining the world. What do we find when we abandon the simple beauty of the ellipse and contemplate chaotic orbits—which is to say, virtually every *real* orbit? Fractals, of course!

Before launching into an example of a chaotic orbit, let us review a few properties of the well-behaved orbits of classical mechanics. The elliptical orbit is periodic. That is, the orbiting object describes a single path over and over. Alternatively, under different conditions the orbit might be a parabola or a hyperbola, in which case the orbit is not periodic, but the object traverses the orbit exactly once. In all of these cases, the orbit is a well-defined smooth curve.

In late 1963, Edward Lorenz published a paper on deterministic chaos that included some plots of an unusual orbit. Like the Mandelbrot set, his "monster curve" had a very simple mathematical description. But the behavior of this orbit, which we will refer to as the Lorenz attractor, is far from simple.

The plot of the Lorenz attractor orbit consists of two connected spirals, in two different planes at an angle to each other (see Figure 1-21). The orbit path would swirl around inside one of these spiral areas, and then at random intervals it would switch allegiances to the other, and so

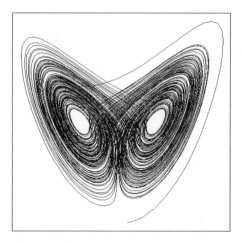

Figure 1-21 The Lorenz attractor

on back and forth. This orbit has some bizarre properties. It is bounded, like the ellipse, and contained forever within a delimited region of space. But unlike the ellipse, the Lorenz orbit is not periodic; in fact, it never crosses itself or repeats. Its path is, therefore, an infinitely long thread wound around in a finite space. The combination of these three factors—bounded, infinitely long, never crossing itself or repeating—implies a complex interweaving of arbitrarily close near misses of different strands of the orbits like an air traffic controller's worst nightmare! From all that we have discussed so far, you will not be surprised to learn that such an orbit is a fractal. Figure 1-21 is a plot of the first few thousand or so turns of this chaotic orbit. You can generate the Lorenz attractor in stereo 3D using Winfract and even have it generate tones as it's being made.

Gaskets and Ferns—Iterated Function Systems

The essence of a fractal is to have detail at all scales, including the most extreme magnifications. One way to achieve this characteristic is through self-similarity. An object is self-similar if small pieces of itself are identically shaped versions of the complete object, only on a smaller scale. One method of generating fractals is to directly exploit this idea. A fractal can be defined by exactly specifying the relationship between itself and its self-similar parts.

Michael Barnsley has developed this approach and named it Iterated Function Systems, or IFS for short. An endless variety of fractals can be created in this way, some of them eerily lifelike. Winfract can create a variety of bushes, trees, and ferns using the IFS fractal type.

The Sierpinski Gasket

The Sierpinski (pronounced "sear-pin-ski") gasket is a fractal that looks as if it is made of Swiss cheese because it has so many holes. It's called a gasket because it seems to offer the structure you might find in a gasket—lots of passages surrounding each other.

The Sierpinski gasket can be exactly specified by stating the rule governing its self-similarity: it's a geometric object built within a triangle, with the property that each of the three subtriangles formed from one of its corners and the midpoints of the adjacent two sides is an exact self-similar replica of the whole triangle.

Another way to define this fractal is to use what are called affine maps. An *affine map* is a transformation of an object that preserves its shape. The transformation can rotate it, move it, enlarge it, or shrink it, but it must not distort the shape of the object. Therefore, you must be sure your transformations do the same operation to each point in the same way. Such a map is said to be contractive if it always shrinks objects. The notion of a contractive affine transformation is a formal way of saying "self-similar." In other words, if there is a contractive affine map between an object and itself, then the object contains a miniature image of itself and is self-similar.

We can easily describe the Sierpinski gasket with three affine maps. Draw the Sierpinski gasket on a graph, so that two of the sides are nestled against the x and y axes. The corners of the triangle are the points (0,0), (1,0), and (0,1). Here are three affine maps defining this Sierpinski gasket:

1.   Map every point (x,y) to the point $(x/2,y/2)$. This maps the whole triangle to the lower left triangle by shrinking the scale by a factor of a half.

2.   Map every point (x,y) to the point $(x/2,y/2 + 1/2)$. This maps the whole triangle to the upper left corner subtriangle by shrinking the scale by a factor of a half and shifting up half a unit.

3.   Map every point (x,y) to the point $(x/2 + 1/2,y/2)$. This maps the whole triangle to the lower right subtriangle by shrinking the scale by a factor of a half and shifting to the right half a unit.

These three affine maps are shown in Figure 1-22.

In this particular example, the transformations are particularly simple because no rotation was involved, only shifting and shrinking. The key insight into the relationship between affine transformations and the Sierpinski gasket is to notice that there are four possible triangles with sides equal to half the sides of the original. The missing triangle is the center one, formed from the midpoints of the three sides. Why is there no transformation mapping the whole triangle to the center? Because there is nothing in the center—that is the "hole"! If the fourth affine transformation were added, mapping the whole triangle to the middle, the result would be rather boring—simply a filled-in triangle! Leaving out the center is what creates the "Swiss cheese" effect with the missing centers of the triangles.

Barnsley suggests a method of generating the fractal from these affine transformations that he calls the "chaos game." Start with any arbitrary point whatsoever. Pick one of the transformations at random and apply it to the point, plotting the result. Continue by applying a new randomly chosen transformation each time to the last point, again

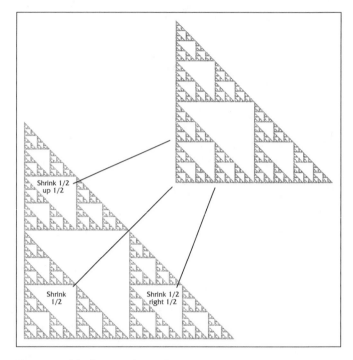

Figure 1-22 Sierpinski gasket

plotting the result. But as the process is repeated, the points generated will produce the shape of the Sierpinski gasket. The name Iterated Function Systems for this kind of fractal comes from the repeated, or iterated, application of these affine maps, or function systems.

The Sierpinski gasket is used here to illustrate IFS fractals, but it can also be generated in two other ways by Winfract: by using lsystems (see Chapter 4) and by using the escape-time methods we have discussed. The Sierpinski gasket holds the record for the number of ways that Winfract can create it.

A Fractal Fern

The Sierpinski gasket is a very unnatural-looking object, but it is just one of an endless variety of images possible with the IFS approach. Another fractal that has become almost a trademark of Barnsley's work is the fractal fern.

Many plants have several levels of self-similarity because of their branching structure. Some kinds of ferns have wide fronds at the base and narrower fronds in the center, tapering to a pointed tip. If you broke off the very bottom fronds, you would end up with a smaller but still similar fern. Four iterated functions can be used to define a very natural-looking fern. Two functions define the self-similarity between the left and right fronds

Figure 1-23
The self-similarity of a fractal fern

with the whole. One function defines the stem. Finally, another function defines the relationship between the whole fern and the fern less the bottom fronds. Figure 1-23 shows these self-similarities. As with the Sierpinski gasket, probabilities are assigned to these functions, and their repeated application seeded with an arbitrary starting point generates the image, just as we described earlier for the Sierpinski gasket.

THERE'S MUCH MORE...

No introduction to fractals can completely cover the subject. This fractal primer was designed to give you a taste and feel of what fractals are all about, as well as a slight touch of the mathematics behind them. But since this is really more a book about exploring and creating fractals, the next chapter begins that exploration with a guided tour of the Winfract program that comes with this book.

Winfract Tutorial

Are you ready for a wild ride into the mysterious world of fractals? You have come to the right place. This chapter is a guided tour of the program Fractint for Windows, or Winfract for short, that comes with this book. See Chapter 4 for a complete reference to all the Winfract commands and functions.

Winfract generates fractals based on any of its 78 different built-in formulas. It can save and retrieve fractals in CompuServe's Graphics Interchange Format (GIF). You can copy fractals to the clipboard for pasting into other applications, and you can save them in Windows' BMP format and use them for your desktop wallpaper. Winfract has additional capabilities for generating 3-D transformations of fractals, making stereo funnyglasses images, doing color-cycle animation, changing color palettes, letting you experiment with your own fractal formulas (with no programming needed), and much more. In this chapter, you will learn how to access some of these features and how to fine-tune the way the program operates.

This chapter will take you through a hands-on demo of Winfract's most basic functions. It is for readers who have never used Winfract before, but it will also show you nooks and crannies of the program that even experienced users may not have discovered. Don't feel restricted by

Figure 2-1 The Winfract Icon

our tour, however. You may want to explore on your own at various points along the way. But do come back. Winfract is the kind of program that grows on you because it has more possibilities than you can absorb all at once.

UP AND RUNNING

We assume you have read the Installation instructions and that Winfract is installed. The Winfract fractal icon should be available in one of the Windows Program Manager groups. If not, go back and read the Installation section, make sure you have the correct files in your Winfract directory, and come back here as soon as you have Winfract running. The friendly Winfract icon is shown in Figure 2-1. The icon is itself a fractal image, none other than the famous Mandelbrot set.

A WINFRACT GUIDED TOUR

Before we start, here are a few conventions we will use to describe how to invoke commands.

When we want you to select a menu item with the mouse, we'll say:

Click on the FILE menu item.

Sometimes when we want you to click on a menu item that is under another menu item, we'll use a little shorthand and say:

Select FILE / SAVE AS

when we mean:

Click on the FILE menu item, and then click on the SAVE AS menu item.

When we want you to type in something literally, we'll show it in monospace. We'll say:

Type in the filename `altern.map`.

Then you type in ALTERN.MAP.

> **Note about Winfract Hotkeys:** Winfract has two completely different hotkey user interfaces. (Hotkeys are shortcuts that work with the keyboard rather than the mouse.) One is a Windows-style interface, and the other is identical to the interface of the DOS-based parent program Fractint. You can set which user interface is operating by clicking on VIEW and then HOTKEY ACTIONS, and checking either Fractint-style prompts or Windows-style menus. The HOTKEY ACTIONS setting does not affect what screens you see when you use the menu system, but only the effect of the hotkeys. This tutorial assumes that you have set Windows-style menus. If you have set Fractint-style prompts, you can still follow the tutorial, as long as you are aware that the detailed instructions will not exactly match the screens you will see when you use hotkeys.

Now on with the tutorial!

Your First Fractal!

To generate your first fractal, just double-click on the Winfract icon. The Winfract window will appear on your desktop, and after a few seconds you will hear a beep. A fractal will appear in the Window, none other than the world-famous Mandelbrot set! (For a discussion of the Mandelbrot set and how it is computed, see Chapter 1.) This fractal alone provides enough variety to give you many hours of exploring pleasure, as you'll see in a moment. Yet it is just one of many fractal types you can explore with Winfract.

The Winfract Screen

Your screen should look like the Winfract window shown in Figure 2-2. The various window manipulation features are labeled in the figure. Click on the MAXIMIZE button to make the Winfract window fill the whole screen. Use the MINIMIZE button to reduce the window to a desktop icon. This is handy when you are generating a very slow fractal and want to do other work in the foreground while the fractal is generating. Winfract's fractal-generating resolution is not limited to your screen resolution. If, for example, you are using a 640 x 480 windows driver but are generating a 1,024 x 768 fractal, you can use the scrollbars to pan around the fractal so you can see the whole image, since the fractal is too large to show completely on the screen at once. (These scrollbars don't do anything at first because the fractal is smaller than the window, so no scrolling is needed.) Finally, double-clicking the mouse on the Menu-Control Box in the upper left corner of the Winfract window is one of the ways of exiting from a Winfract session.

Winfract Menus

The menu bar contains the main menu items FILE, FRACTALS, VIEW, COL-ORS, and HELP. These menus are your keys to accessing Winfract's power. They are standard Windows drop-down menus. You select items by click-ing on the menu items. Try clicking on each of the main menu items in turn to see what submenu items are available. We'll just touch briefly on what the menu items do here; the guided tour will go into greater detail.

File

The FILE menu allows you to save and restore fractals, make hard copies of fractals on your printer, run parameter files, transform 2-D fractals into 3-D, and copy fractals to the clipboard for pasting into other applica-tions. The FILE submenu also contains the all-important EXIT command. Figure 2-3 shows the FILE submenus.

Fractals

The FRACTALS menu lets you select from the 78 different, built-in fractal types. You can set the many fractal-generating options that allow you to

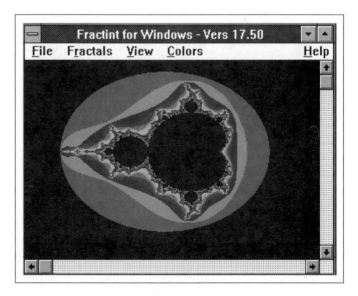

Figure 2-2 The Winfract window

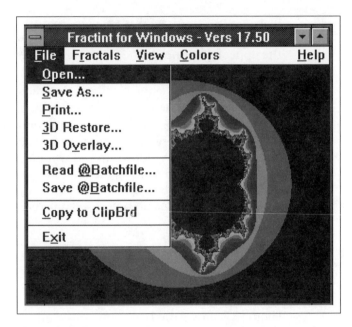

Figure 2-3 The FILES submenu

create dazzling effects in endless variety. The options are divided into the BASIC OPTIONS and EXTENDED OPTIONS submenus. The FRACTAL PARAMS submenu allows you to tune the parameters that affect the current fractal. The 3D PARAMS submenu lets you rotate, translate, and control Winfract's 3-D fractals. The STARFIELD option transforms the current fractal image into a realistic starry sky. The FRACTALS submenu items are shown in Figure 2-4.

View

The main function of the VIEW menu is to allow you to set the image dimensions of the generated fractals. This is done using the IMAGE SETTINGS menu item. The other submenu items let you control the zooming action and set options that determine how the pixels are updated. Users of the DOS program Fractint can select Fractint-style input screens by setting the HOTKEY ACTIONS toggle. STATUS! gives you information about the current fractal calculation, including what the type is, what the coordinates and parameters are, and whether it is finished. The VIEW submenu items are shown in Figure 2-5.

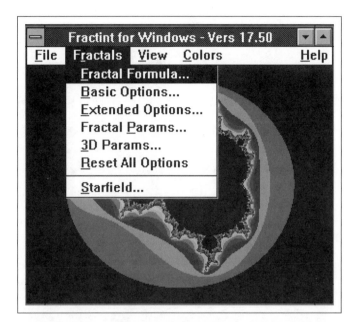

Figure 2-4
The FRACTALS submenu

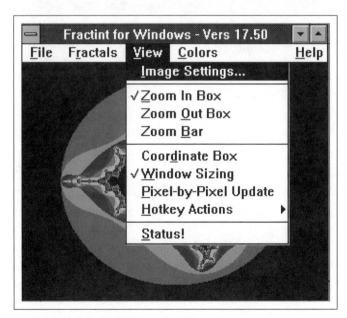

Figure 2-5
The VIEW submenu

Colors

Here is where you can load and restore color maps that assign different colors to different parts of fractal images. Winfract's all-time most popular

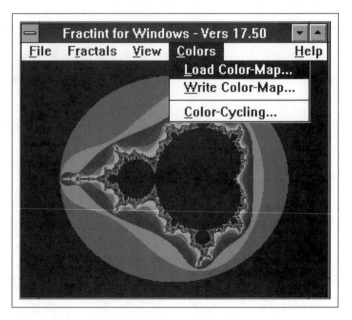

Figure 2-6 The COLORS submenu

feature, color cycling, is controlled with the COLOR-CYCLING menu item. The COLORS submenu is shown in Figure 2-6.

Help

Last but definitely not least is HELP. You can access the standard Windows help program using the INDEX and USING HELP items. The Fractint Help accesses the DOS Fractint program hypertext system for the benefit of those familiar with the Fractint program. Because some of that information applies to the DOS version only, new Winfract users should restrict themselves to the Windows-style help until you are familiar with the program. The HELP submenu items are shown in Figure 2-7.

Zooming In

Now that you have a Mandelbrot image displayed on your screen, what can you do with it? Fractals are full of interesting details that unfold as you expand them. The "zoom" function of Winfract lets you dive inside a fractal on the screen and behold its inner beauty.

To zoom in, point the mouse arrow at an interesting detail, hold down the left mouse button and drag the mouse. As you drag the mouse, a zoom box will appear which gets larger as you drag the mouse farther from the original point. If you want to make the box smaller, and you are

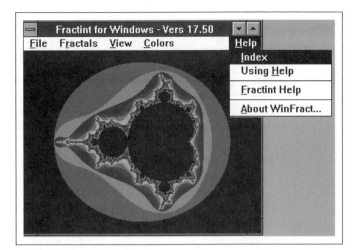

Figure 2-7 The HELP submenu

still holding down the left mouse button, just move the mouse cursor back toward the center of the box. When you release the left mouse button, the size of the box is fixed. You can move the box by pressing the left mouse button again while the mouse cursor is inside the box and dragging the zoom box to the desired position. Once the zoom box is framing the desired piece of the fractal, double-click inside the zoom box, and the fractal will be recalculated with the area framed in the zoom box now filling the screen. If you double-click outside the zoom box, the zoom box disappears.

This action of zooming in assumes that ZOOM IN box is checked under the VIEW menu. If ZOOM OUT box is checked instead, then the action of creating and double-clicking inside a zoom box results in zooming out so that the previous image is reduced to the size of the zoom box.

Finding Baby Mandelbrots

In order to try out the zooming facility, try to locate some baby Mandelbrot sets in the left-hand spike of the Mandelbrot set. Figure 2-8 shows the results of two zooms which you can duplicate. The image on the left shows the full Mandelbrot set with a zoom box centered on a bulge in the left-hand spike of the Mandelbrot. The second image shows the resulting zoomed image, which contains a miniature copy of the whole Mandelbrot set, and another small zoom box centered on another small bulge in the fractal image. The third image shows the result of this deeper zoom, revealing yet another small Mandelbrot shape. Even a short investigation of the Mandelbrot spike should convince you that there are an infinite number of such baby Mandelbrots.

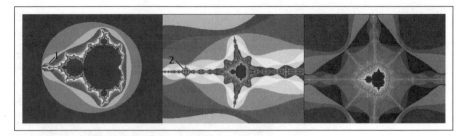

Figure 2-8 Zooming in on baby Mandelbrots

Starting with the full Mandelbrot set, move the mouse cursor to the spot where the zoom box shows in Figure 2-8, hold down the left mouse button, dragging the mouse until the zoom box is the desired size. Release the mouse button, and double-click inside the zoom box. Your image should look something like the middle image in Figure 2-8. Repeat this process, trying to duplicate the zoom box in the middle image to generate the third image.

Increasing the Maximum Iterations

Try zooming in several more times, finding still smaller baby Mandelbrot sets. If you zoom far enough, you will find that the Mandelbrot shape degrades. The Mandelbrot set is defined to be the set of points c whose orbits generated by iterating the formula $z_{n+1} = z_n^2 + c$ *never* escape a circle of radius 2 no matter how many iterations are calculated. (See Chapter 1 for a discussion of escape-time fractals.) Winfract approximates "never" by waiting until some maximum number of iterations is reached, and then assuming that if the orbit hasn't escaped yet, it will never escape. This assumption is not completely accurate, but it is better if a higher maximum iteration cutoff is used. The default value in Winfract is 150 iterations, but you can set it as high as 32,768. The price you pay for accuracy is that the calculations will take longer. You can set the maximum iterations by clicking on BASIC OPTIONS under the FILE menu, and filling in a value for Maximum Iterations. Figure 2-9 shows four versions of a baby Mandelbrot found after a number of zooms. The Maximum Iterations values used for the four images were 150, 250, 350, and 1,000. You can see that the first image has lost the characteristic Mandelbrot shape, but that as the Maximum Iterations value is increased, the shape gets more accurate. For moderate depth zooms, the default maximum iterations value of 150 works very well.

Color Cycling

One of the really fun features of Fractint is the color-cycling mode. In this mode, Winfract rapidly alters displayed colors of an image, giving

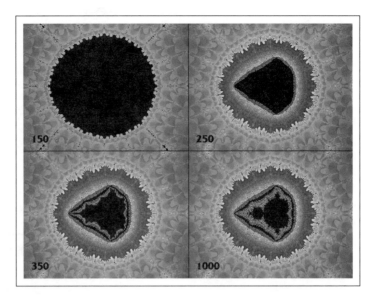

Figure 2-9 Effect of increasing Maximum Iterations

an effect of animation. This works because most graphics adaptors create colors by using color palettes. There are as many palette entries as the number of colors your computer's hardware video adaptor can display at one time. So, a palette for an EGA has 16 entries, and a VGA has as many as 256. But—and this is a big "but"—the colors assigned to the palette entries are drawn from a much larger selection. For example, the VGA 320 x 200 mode can display 256 colors on the screen at one time, but these 256 can be selected from 262 thousand possible colors! (Understand that in Winfract, different shades of the same color are considered different colors. Some fractals, for example, may have only two colors with 128 shades.) What Winfract can do is rapidly change which colors are assigned to which palette numbers. As you'll see, this simple technique creates a magical effect.

Most fractal images have more information in them than the mind can comprehend. By assigning colors differently, you can make different details visible in the same image. By cycling the colors, areas that make up the fractal are revealed by color moving between them. Since the areas are connected in a highly organized fashion, there is a high degree of animation potential. Playing with the colors is at least half the fun of Winfract. Alas, this feature only works with paletted Windows drivers that support 256 colors. Windows drivers for most super VGA graphics adaptors should work fine. (For more information, see Appendix A.)

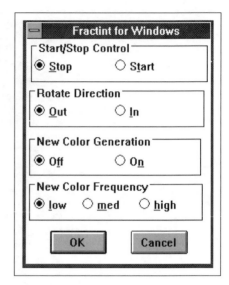

Figure 2-10
COLOR-CYCLING menu

Press the ⊙ key to see your fractal color cycle. Showtime! The colors of your fractal will now start wildly gyrating! (If the cycling is too fast on your machine, you can slow it down with the ⊙ key.)

Controlling Color Cycling and Experimenting

You start and stop the color-cycling mode using the COLOR-CYCLING menu under COLORS. Figure 2-10 shows this menu. This menu also lets you determine the direction of the cycling, whether to just rotate the existing colors or generate new ones randomly, and (for random color-generation) whether the new colors are added with a low, medium, or high frequency.

You can also use the following "Hotkeys" for color cycling. "In" and "out" in the hotkey action descriptions below refer to the apparent direction of the color motion when used with the default Mandelbrot fractal.

Key	Action
(SPACEBAR)	Toggles color cycling on and off
⟨,⟩ (comma)	Shifts the palette in one color
⟨.⟩ (period)	Shifts the palette out one color
⟨←⟩	Turn on color cycling and set the direction in
⟨→⟩	Turn on color cycling and set the direction out
⟨↑⟩	Speed up color cycling
⟨↓⟩	Slow down color cycling
(ENTER)	Random color cycling with all new colors

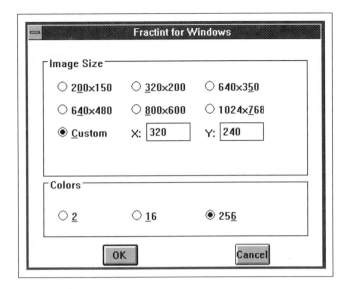

Figure 2-11 IMAGE SETTINGS dialog box

Suppose you have a markedly striped fractal, and you want to see more smoothly changing colors. You would select a low New Color Frequency on the COLOR-CYCLING menu. The new colors will be added to the end of the 256-color palette, and they will take a little time to "flush out" the old colors.

Controlling Image Size

Winfract defaults to a small image size of 200 x 150. This is a great size for exploring because the time it takes to generate a fractal is proportional to the number of pixels. A 200 x 150 image has 30,000 pixels, whereas a 1,024 x 768 image has 786,432 pixels, or 26 times more! However, once you have found an image you like and want to save it, you'll want to redo the image at a higher resolution. Good values for most purposes are 640 x 480 or 1,024 x 768. You can set the image size using the IMAGE SETTINGS dialog box under VIEW. Figure 2-11 shows what this dialog box looks like. You can select one of the preset sizes, or enter a custom size with any dimensions you want up to Winfract's limit of 2,048 x 2,048. You may also find out that your system does not have enough memory for really high resolutions; if so, Windows will give you an error message.

Saving a File

Between creative zooming and color cycling, by now you should have created a few beautiful fractals. Chances are very good that your creation

Figure 2-12 Fractal SAVE dialog box

is unlike any other. If you save it as a GIF, it can be opened again and experimented with, or uploaded to CompuServe. You can save a fractal by clicking on SAVE AS under FILE, or alternatively using the Ⓢ hotkey. Winfract can save images as GIF89a files, GIF87a files, and as Windows BMP files. Figure 2-12 shows the fractal saving dialog box.

Saving as a GIF file

The GIF stands for Graphics Interchange Format, which is a device-independent way of representing images developed by CompuServe Information Service. GIF has the advantage that software to view images in this format is widely available on many different kinds of computers. The GIF89a has an additional advantage that makes it the format of choice for saving Winfract fractals. Winfract uses special areas in the GIF89a format to store all the fractal information needed to reproduce the file. If you open a GIF89a format file created by Winfract or Fractint, Winfract can extract from the file not only the image but all the Winfract settings that were used to generate the file. Better yet, if the image was saved before the fractal calculation was completed, Winfract can open the partially completed GIF file, load the parameters, and resume the calculation. GIF87a files are an earlier version of GIF. This file format is provided only for compatibility with older software that cannot handle GIF89a. Fractal information is not stored with GIF87a files.

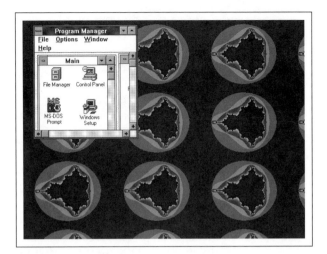

Figure 2-13 A Windows desktop wallpapered with Mandelbrots

Saving as a BMP file

You can also select the Windows BMP, short for Bitmapped, file type. The BMP type can be read by many other Windows applications. But the most enjoyable use of BMP is for making Windows wallpaper.

Making Mandelbrot Wallpaper

To cover your Windows desktop with many small Mandelbrot sets, select fractal type mandel from the fractal type pick list (click on FRACTALS and then FRACTAL FORMULA). Generate a small 200 x 150 fractal. If the image size is set differently, you can change it by clicking on VIEW and IMAGE SETTINGS. Save the image using the (S) hotkey or FILE and SAVE AS menus, making sure that you select the .BMP file type. Save the file in the directory where your Windows files are located. For example, if your Windows directory is C:\WIN, and you want to save the image using the name MANDEL.BMP, then just type `C:\WIN\MANDEL.BMP`.

Exit Winfract, double-click on the CONTROL PANEL icon, and then double-click on the DESKTOP icon. If you have successfully saved MANDEL.BMP to the correct directory, you will see it listed as one of the possible BMP files to use for your desktop under the WALLPAPER section. Select MANDEL.BMP, press the TILE radio button, and click on OK. Voila! Your desktop will now be tiled with fractals! Figure 2-13 shows how this looks. You can see the desktop when the Program Manager and all your applications are minimized.

You can also fill your whole desktop with one fractal rather than tiling the screen. To do this, click on VIEW and then IMAGE SETTINGS, and set the image size the same as the dimensions of your Windows video driver. For example, if you are using a 640 x 480 256-color Windows driver, then set the image size to 640 x 480, and the number of colors to 256 in the IMAGE SIZE dialog box. Save the image in your Windows directory as before. When you select the new BMP file, click on the CENTER radio button.

A 3-D Mandelbrot Set

Let's continue the Winfract tour. What we are going to do next is perform some 3-D transformations on the Mandelbrot fractal you last created. For the mathematically curious, the result will be a 3-D plot of the escape times of the Mandelbrot formula. Also, note that the zooming feature does not work in the 3-D mode.

If you have made many changes to Winfract settings, reset Winfract so all the fractal settings are returned to the default values. To do this, click on RESET ALL OPTIONS under the FILES menu.

Press the (X) hotkey, or click on BASIC OPTIONS under FRACTALS and set INSIDE COLOR to MAXIT. The second line of the dialog box contains a set of radio buttons with various values for inside. (Radio buttons work like a 60s car radio with buttons to select stations—only one button can be pushed at a time, because when you push another button the previously pushed button pops out.) Click on the MAXIT radio button. Figure 2-14 shows the BASIC OPTIONS dialog box with the MAXIT radio button pushed. While you're at it, look at the odd assortment of things that you can set using the BASIC OPTIONS dialog box. Don't worry—you don't have to understand them all at once. In fact, you never need to touch most of these settings to get a tremendous amount of enjoyment out of Winfract.

Moving the Lake

The inside color represents the palette number of the color used to color the lake areas of fractals—locations where the orbit never escapes and the Maximum Iterations limit is reached. This inside color value defaults to 1, which is the color blue in the standard IBM color palette on both EGA and VGA adaptors. This setting is a Winfract tradition begun by the original author, Bert Tyler. Many other fractal programs favor the color 0, which is black, but Bert preferred to see a blue "lake." Setting the inside color to MAXIT has the effect of setting the inside color to the maximum iteration value, which defaults to 150.

Normally, the choice of inside color is purely aesthetic, but not for what we are about to do. The reason is that for interpreting fractals for 3-D purposes, Winfract treats the color as a number, and the color number is interpreted as the height above the plane. A color number of 2

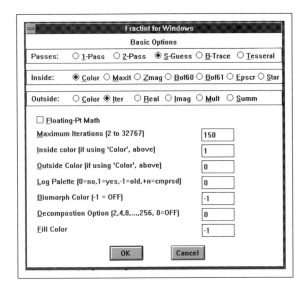

Figure 2-14 The BASIC OPTIONS dialog box

means a low point, while a high color number means a mountain or high place. The setting of the INSIDE COLOR to MAXIT has the effect of making the lake float at the top of the 3-D surface. This makes mathematical sense because the resulting image is a graph of the iteration count of the escape-time calculation, and when the lake occurs the iteration value is at the maximum, or 150. (You can change the maximum number of iterations using the (X) command.) The important point is that setting the inside color affects the height of the lake when you are doing a 3-D transformation, and we have jammed it to the maximum height so it hangs above the plane of our fractal. Set the INSIDE COLOR to MAXIT now.

When you are done with the BASIC OPTIONS screen, click on OK to accept the values and return to the screen where you'll generate the fractal image. Now click on VIEW and then IMAGE SETTINGS, and set the IMAGE SIZE to 320 x 240 using the CUSTOM X AND Y boxes. After you click on OK in the IMAGE SIZE dialog box and the image recalculates, note that the lake area is no longer blue but rather green.

When the image is complete (you'll hear a little whistle), save the image by clicking on FILE and then SAVE AS (or use the (S) key) and fill in a filename. Make a mental note of the filename if you used the one Fractint suggested—it was probably something like FRACT003.GIF, depending on how many images you have already saved. Now click on FILE and 3D RESTORE and select the file you just saved. (You might need to change directories to the directory where your image was saved.)

Setting the 3-D Parameters

Winfract is now going to lead you through some screens that allow setting all manner of parameters and effects for 3-D. The good news is that the default values almost always make sense—you do not have to understand what all of them mean. The screens are documented in detail in Chapter 4.

The first screen is entitled 3D OPTIONS. Here is where you can turn on what's known as funny-glasses stereo (stereo using red/blue glasses), set the light source options, or use the sphere mode to create a fractal planet. But not yet! This time around all the default values will be just fine, except one. Click on the JUST DRAW THE POINTS radio button, then click on OK to accept all the values.

The next somewhat imposing screen, entitled PLANAR 3D PARAMETERS, presents numerous options for these three-dimensional rotations and scale factors. You can view your fractal from different angles, spin it in space, stretch it, shrink it, and move the viewer's perspective right into the middle of it! When making fractal landscapes, you can control the roughness of mountain ranges and the height of floods in the valleys. For this tour, the default values are all okay, so click on OK to accept them. After the tour, you can come back and experiment.

If you have a slower XT- or AT-compatible PC, you may want to get up from your chair, stretch your legs, and grab a quick cup of coffee or beverage of choice. The 3-D transformation takes a few minutes. You will see the blue background of the Mandelbrot image appear just as you saw it on the screen a few moments before, but laid at an angle like a piece of paper on a desk. As the image develops, you will see that the colored stripes of the Mandelbrot image are raised like Chinese terraces on a mountainside. Floating above everything is the green Mandelbrot lake, raining a sparkling mist down to the terrain below. You should now understand why we set inside=maxit. If we had left the default inside=2, the lake would have been at the same level as the blue background, instead of floating mysteriously above it.

Figure 2-15 shows what your 3-D fractal should look like. For the final touch, press ⊙ to launch color cycling. When you are done playing with the colors, stop the color cycling with (SPACEBAR).

Variations on a Theme

Let's try a few variations. For each variation, start with the FILES/3D RESTORE menu item, or use the ③ hotkey. Winfract will remember your previous settings, and you can move from screen to screen by clicking on OK, pausing only to make the indicated changes.

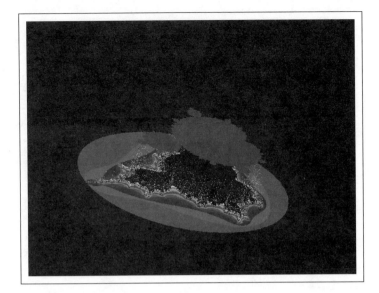

Figure 2-15 Mandelbrot lake floating in space

Variation #1: Make Solid Cliffs

Start with the ③ hotkey, select the file, and when you come to the 3D OPTIONS screen, click on the SURFACE FILL (COLORS INTERPOLATED) radio button, but otherwise leave the settings unchanged, clicking on OK until the image regenerates. This option definitely slows things up, so take another break! This time the floating Mandelbrot image will become the top of a mountain with precipitous cliffs hanging under it.

Variation #2: Add a Perspective Viewpoint

Start with the ③ hotkey, and move through the screens. When you come to the PLANAR 3D PARAMETERS screen, look for PERSPECTIVE DISTANCE [1–999, 0 FOR NO PERSP] about halfway down. Type in 150. Smaller numbers provide the more extreme perspective of a closer viewpoint, while higher numbers create a flatter perspective like photographers obtain through a telephoto lens. Click on OK to regenerate the image. As a side effect the image edges will look a little bit rougher. But you are now closer to the scene, with closer features expanded! Figure 2-16 shows the "Mandelbrot cliffs" in perspective.

Variation #3: Make the Mountain into a Lake

Throughout this book we have referred to the classic Mandelbrot shape in the center of the Mandelbrot fractal as a lake, but then we turned around

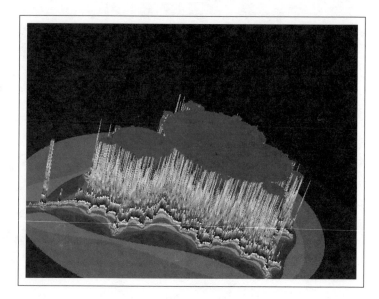

Figure 2-16 Mandelbrot cliffs in perspective

and made it into a mountaintop in 3-D. We'll show you how to remedy that. Start with ③, and move through the screens by clicking on OK. When you come to the PLANAR 3D PARAMETERS screen, look for SURFACE SCALING FACTOR IN PCT, which should have the default value of 30. We want you to depress the mountaintop and make it a lake, so change the SURFACE ROUGHNESS value to –5. That's right, the new value is negative 5, which means that the z-coordinate will be scaled by negative 5 percent—depressing the mountaintop below the surrounding plain. Click on OK to regenerate the image. You have turned the mountain into a lake-bottomed canyon!

Variation #4: Zoom the Viewpoint into the Canyon

Try repeating Variation #3 with different values of PERSPECTIVE DISTANCE [1–999, 0 FOR NO PERSP]. Try 120, 100, 80, and 60. The values less than 100 place the viewer's perspective over the fractal landscape. The sequence of images created in this way looks like photographs that might be taken by a landing spacecraft. The last image places you inside the canyon (see Figure 2-17).

And Now, Images in Stereo!

Let's try one more bit of magic and plot this Mandelbrot image in red/blue stereoscopic 3D. For this you'll need your trusty red-and-blue glasses—the

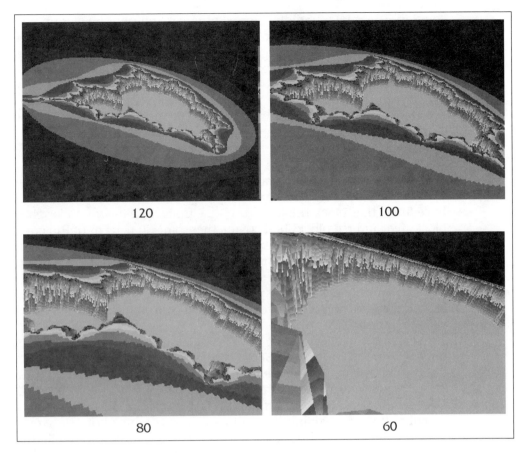

120

100

80

60

Figure 2-17 Zooming into the canyon

ones that came with this book. Here's how these images work: A number of different cues tell you that a scene has depth. Distant objects appear smaller than nearer objects. As you move your head, nearer objects get in the way of farther objects. Mist obscures distant objects. Because of these cues, a person with one eye can still perceive depth. Those of us with two good eyes have another depth cue: binocular vision. Our brain fuses the images coming from our two eyes and gives a sense of depth.

Red/Blue Glasses
Winfract is capable of performing the perspective transformations necessary to simulate the viewpoints of two eyes. The problem is how to get the left image to the left eye and the right image to the right eye. One

solution would be to rapidly alternate the left and right images on your screen and have the user wear special glasses with liquid crystal shutters synchronized to the monitor. High-end workstations can be purchased with this capability, but it is expensive, costing thousands of dollars. Recently game manufacturers have made inexpensive versions of these glasses, so soon this may be a reasonable option. For Winfract, we have opted for a simpler approach that has cost you just the price of this book: red/blue glasses. These are the very same kind of glasses that kids of a bygone era eagerly retrieved from cereal packages in order to view stereo scenes on the box.

The idea is simple. Winfract puts a left view of a fractal on the screen in red and a right view of the image in blue. You put on the glasses, which have filters that block the incorrect view from reaching your eyes: blue blocks red, and red blocks blue. (Note that some 30 percent of the population cannot see these binocular effects for one reason or another, and we hope that you will be able to enjoy the effects.) And alas, even if your eyes are perfect, you are still going to need a color monitor that can display red and blue. That rules out all monochrome VGA setups which cannot show red and blue. If you have a 256-color Windows video driver, you are in business.

Press ③ or select FILE / 3D RESTORE with the mouse. Select the same GIF file from the FILE SELECTION screen that you created before (follow the instructions above to make it if you haven't already). At the 3D OPTIONS screen, there is a set of radio buttons labeled STEREO 3D. Click on the SUPERIMPOSE button. This is the superimpose option, which describes how the red and blue colors will be combined on the screen. The superimpose method combines colors red and blue to make magenta and pink, giving sharper results, but fewer color shades. The alternate option alternates red and blue dots on the screen, sacrificing resolution but allowing more color shades. The photo mode is for photographing the screen and making stereo slides. Chapter 4 explains all this in more detail.

Just below the 3D STEREO radio buttons you will find a larger set of radio buttons labeled FILL TYPE. Click the SURFACE FILL (COLORS INTERPOLATED) radio button. Click on OK. You will then come to the FUNNY-GLASSES PARAMETERS screen, which you did not see in the previous examples. The defaults are all right, so click on OK. If you changed the SURFACE SCALE parameter on the PLANAR 3D PARAMETERS screen in the previous examples, change it back to 30, and change PERSPECTIVE DISTANCE [1–999, 0 FOR NO PERSP] back to 120, and click on OK.

This time you will see the solid Mandelbrot image you generated a moment before. First a red image is generated, then a blue image. These images should look like the Mandelbrot cliffs image of the previous example, shown in Figure 2-16. Put on the red/blue glasses that came with this book and view the image, making sure the red lens is over the left eye. There you are in living 3-D—a Mandelbrot mountain outlined in a grid!

Clouds, Mountains, and Plasma

Until now we have restricted this tour to the Mandelbrot fractal type, except for a brief interlude with the Julia types. Many hours of fascinating fractal explorations are possible with this type, especially given the options of zooming, color cycling, and 3-D transformations. There are, however, other kinds of fractals that produce radically different images and effects. One such fractal that is particularly interesting is the plasma type. This fractal allows the creation of both cloud and mountain range images. Who would have guessed that mountains and clouds are so closely related? The plasma type makes a random pattern of smoothly changing colors that look like clouds.

Select Plasma

You can select the plasma fractal type by clicking on FRACTALS from the menu bar and then FRACTAL FORMULA from the submenu, or you can use the (T) hotkey. You can then pick the plasma type from the list. Figure 2-18 shows the fractal type pick list.

After you double-click on a fractal type name, Winfract will present you with the FRACTAL PARAMETERS dialog box. This is the same dialog box that you access via the FRACTAL PARAMS submenu under FRACTALS, or with the (Z) hotkey. In the case of the plasma type, the graininess factor parameter affects how gradually the colors on the screen merge with one another. For now, click on OK to accept the default value of 2.0. You might want to come back later and experiment. You can return to the parameter screen of the current fractal at any time with the (Z) hotkey.

As soon as you click on OK to accept your parameters choice, the plasma calculation will begin. What you are seeing on the screen is a fascinating algorithm that recursively subdivides the screen, randomly choosing colors with values between surrounding colors. To see this better, click on PIXEL-BY-PIXEL UPDATE under VIEW—this will slow down the generation of the fractal, but let you see all the pixels as they are written to the screen. After you have watched a while, you can click again on PIXEL-BY-PIXEL UPDATE to speed up the fractal. No two plasma images are quite the same because of the random element of the calculation. When the image is complete, start color cycling with the (·) command. *Now* you understand why this type is called plasma! The screen colors

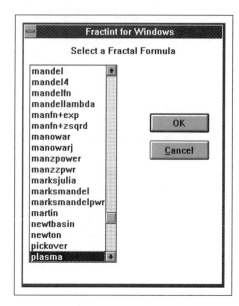

Figure 2-18
Fractal types pick list

ooze and writhe in graceful undulations of ethereal plasma waves. Be sure to try the options under COLORS / COLOR-CYCLING while color cycling. Turn on NEW COLOR GENERATION and try the different NEW COLOR FREQUENCY options.

Turning a Cloud into a Mountain

Take a good, long time playing with the plasma type, which is certainly one of the more colorful and dramatic fractals that you can create with Winfract. Be sure to press the (ENTER) key occasionally while it's color cycling; this instantly changes the colors. We should have convinced you that Winfract can make clouds, but what about mountains? To create mountains you have to first save a plasma image. You can stop color cycling with the (SPACEBAR) key. Press (S) to save the plasma screen, once again making a note of the filename that is reported on the screen. You are probably up to file FRACT022.GIF by now, right?

You can turn a cloud into a mountain by doing a 3-D transformation on the colors of the cloud. A cloud image can be considered a continuously color-coded contour map of a mountain, where areas of similar color are nearly the same height. By performing a 3-D transformation, you are transforming the contour map back into the mountain it represents.

Press the (3) key to invoke the 3-D function, and select the just-saved file from the file list. At the 3D OPTIONS screen, click on the SURFACE FILL

(COLORS INTERPOLATED) radio button and click on OK. This will bring you to the PLANAR 3D PARAMETERS screen. Click on OK, and watch a mountain emerge before your eyes!

Variations
Here are a few variations on the theme of fractal mountains.

Variation #1: Make the Mountain Emerge from Water

Repeat all the instructions for making a mountain from a saved plasma cloud in the previous paragraph, until you reach the PLANAR 3D PARAMETERS screen. Then set the WATER LEVEL (MINIMUM COLOR VALUE) item to 47. This will cause all color values less than 47 to be mapped to a flat lake surface. You can begin to see why George Lucas developed Pixar to use computers to simulate real terrain. After the mountain landscape has been created, click on COLORS / LOAD COLOR-MAP

There is a special map called TOPO.MAP that has color values tailored to plasma mountains, complete with water, rocks, greenery, and snow. Select TOPO.MAP from the file list. If it is not in the list, scroll down to the bottom of the list, where you will find the directory ".." which means "up one directory," as well as a list of drive letters. By clicking on these to move up a directory or change drives, you can navigate to the directory where you installed Winfract (probably C:\WINFRACT) where TOPO.MAP should be located. Select TOPO.MAP and double-click on it. You should then see a plasma mountain with more realistic landscape coloring—blue water, green hillsides, brown fields, and snow-capped mountains. Figure 2-19 shows an example.

Variation #2: Make a Red/Blue 3-D Glasses Plasma Mountain

Repeat the plasma mountain instructions above, beginning with the ③ command and selecting the same plasma file. At the 3D OPTIONS screen, click on the SUPERIMPOSE radio button in the STEREO 3D group, and the SURFACE GRID radio button in the FILL TYPE group. Click on OK. Continue to click on OK, accepting all the defaults for the remaining screens. The result is a wire-frame mountain, which makes an excellent red/blue 3-D glasses stereo image. The grid fill type has the virtue of being very fast, so it is an excellent means to play with 3-D parameters. When you have an image the way you want it, you can apply a slower fill type.

Variation #3: Make a Plasma Planet

Repeat the plasma mountain instructions above, beginning with the ③ command, selecting the same plasma file. At the 3D OPTIONS screen, click

Figure 2-19 A plasma mountain rising from a lake

in the SPHERICAL PROJECT box and click on the NONE radio button in the STEREO 3D group. Click on OK, and continue to click on OK, accepting all the defaults for the next screens. The plasma image will be projected onto the surface of a sphere, making a plasma planet. You can project any GIF image onto a sphere in this way, whether or not it originated in Winfract.

You can press ③ again and try some of the other 3-D options—a good strategy for learning. One piece of advice, though: just change one or two things at a time so you get an idea of what you are doing! For instance, try combining your plasma landscape with your planet by first creating the landscape, and then adding the planet, using the ⓪ key or FILE / 3D OVERLAY instead of the ③. The ⓪ key is just like ③ except the previous image is not erased.

This concludes the tutorial, but not your own Winfract explorations. You can launch off on your own, or turn to Chapter 3 and try some colorful fractal recipes for more fractal fun!

Fractal Recipes

Creating fractals is a little like cooking. You can have a lot of fun using your creativity to make a tasty dish out of whatever ingredients are at hand. Sometimes, however, you yearn for the exquisite taste of a gourmet dish, so you search through your favorite recipe book for a treat invented by some extraordinary culinary genius. Seeing the fractals a Winfract expert has made is a lot like tasting a prize-winning chef's favorite dish. Despite Winfract's multitude of options and possibilities, you may think you have seen everything after many hours of experimenting. Then you try a new fractal recipe and discover a whole new universe waiting to be explored. Some very talented people have used Winfract to make images in their own inimitable style. In this chapter, you'll find their best recipes, and you can try them out for yourself!

FRACTAL COOKING SECRETS

What makes a spectacular fractal? Each of the artists whose work you will find in this chapter has a different answer to this question. Here are a few tips gleaned from the experts.

1.   Don't jump to conclusions about the initial appearances of a fractal. Fractals that look superficially the same from a "zoomed out"

perspective may be extraordinarily different when viewed at high magnifications.

2.   Spend time coloring your fractals. You can do this with the color-cycling options (COLORS / COLOR-CYCLING) or by loading different color maps (COLORS / LOAD MAP). Fractals typically contain far more detail than the eye or the mind can absorb. Assigning the colors differently can completely alter what you see in a fractal image. Later in this chapter you'll see examples of this.

3.   Experiment with Winfract's basic and extended options (FRACTALS / BASIC OPTIONS and FRACTALS / EXTENDED OPTIONS). The inside and outside coloring options, or the use of features like continuous potential or binary decomposition, can completely alter the appearance of a fractal. Don't forget the fractal parameters (FRACTALS / FRACTAL PARAMS). Remember that you really don't have to fully understand these options in order to test them out! Experiment with them and see what happens!

4.   Try your hand at inventing your own formula types. You can use a text editor, such as the Windows Notepad application, to edit the file FRACTINT.FRM. The easiest way to invent a whole new fractal is to copy an existing formula type and change the formula around. Once again, do not be deterred if you have no idea what a complex hyperbolic tangent is. We'll let you in on a deep secret: a bright mathematician having fun with Winfract probably has no more idea than you do of the effect of making a fractal from a formula like $z = \tanh(z)/(z^2 - \cos(z/2))$.

USING PARAMETER FILES

The best way to share fractal recipes is by using Winfract parameter files, better known as PAR files because their filename extension is PAR. The PAR format is a compact way of saving the fractal parameters used to make a fractal. This format is shared by Winfract and the various incarnations of Fractint running on PCs and workstations. PAR files are a great way to share your fractals with others because they are small and compact and still hold all the information needed to reproduce a fractal. You will find them on computer bulletin boards and conferencing systems wherever fractals are discussed. On CompuServe, look in library 15 of the GRAPHDEV forum for many examples.

Writing Parameter Files

When, in the midst of your fractal explorations, you have created a fractal you want to save in a parameter file, press Ⓑ or click on FILES / SAVE

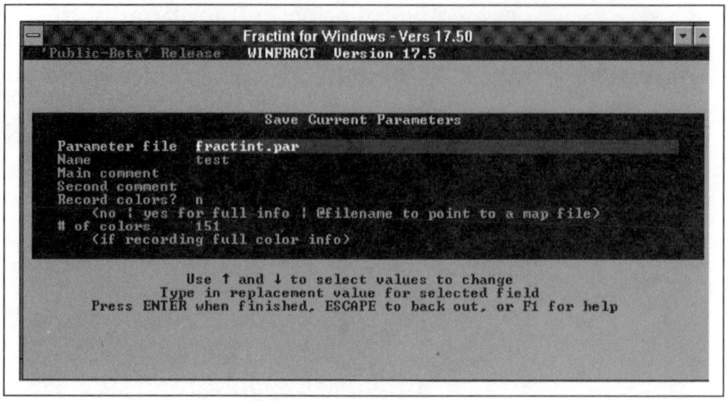

Figure 3-1 SAVE @BATCHFILE dialog box

@BATCHFILE. You will then see a dialog box that looks like Figure 3-1. Fill in the name of the parameter file and the name you want to give to the fractal. The name of the parameter file entry must be different than any of the names already used in the file; one parameter file can hold many entries, each with a unique name. You also have the option of having the colors written in compressed form in the parameter file, or of using the colors already saved in a separate color map file. Note that if you specify a color map file, Winfract will not automatically create the map file if it doesn't exist, but you can create it in a separate step using the COLORS / SAVE COLOR-MAP menu items. The parameters will be written in a file you can edit.

A parameter file entry looks like this:

```
Hypnoteyes2 { ; by Pieter Branderhorst
  reset type=julia corners=-0.162458/0.17487/0.734422/0.984935
  params=0.258919/1.76951e-007 decomp=256 colors=@blues.map
}
```

The name of the image is Hypnoteyes2. This is the name the Winfract user sees when opening the parameter file. The curly braces contain all the fractal options. To make changes, you can edit this file with a text editor such as Notepad.

Remember that Winfract saves this same fractal information with the GIF89a format images. You can convert your previously saved Winfract GIF files to PAR files by using FILE / OPEN to read in the GIF file and then FILE / SAVE @BATCHFILE to save as a PAR file entry.

Reading Parameter Files

All of the fractal recipes in this chapter are stored on this book's companion disk in PAR files. The easiest way to try the recipes is to read in the PAR file entry. To do this, click on FILES and then READ @BATCHFILE, and use the dialog box to select the desired PAR file. Once the PAR file is opened, you will be presented with a list of named PAR entries. Double-click on the example you want to run, and Winfract will go to work generating it.

THE RECIPES

For each of these fractal recipes, you'll find the following information:

1. **Name of the Image**: the image name as stored in the parameter file.

2. **PAR File:** where the image parameters are stored.

3. **Image Credits**: who created this fractal parameter entry.

4. **Parameter File Listing:** the listing of the parameter file entry.

5. **About the Image:** notes about particularly interesting parameters used and how the parameters affect the appearance of the image.

6. **Variations:** other options to try out with this fractal image.

The Best of FRACTINT.PAR

The first few recipes are taken from the FRACTINT.PAR file that has been distributed with Fractint and Winfract since version 16.

HYPNOTEYES

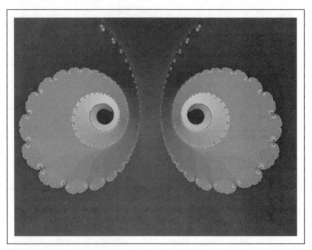

Figure 3-2 Hypnoteyes

PAR File: FRACTINT.PAR

Image Credits: Pieter Branderhorst

Parameter File Listing:

```
Hypnoteyes        { ;Try color cycling, by Pieter Branderhorst
  reset type=julia corners=-0.162458/0.17487/0.734422/0.984935
  params=0.258919/1.76951e-007 colors=@chroma.map
}
```

About the Image: This image, as shown in Figure 3-2 and color plate 5, is proof that fractals can express a sense of humor. This Julia set image contains two opposite spirals that look for all the world like two eyes. The real fun starts when you use the ⊙ to start color cycling and the eyes go bonkers! This image is a wonderful example of how cycling colors gives a sense of animation.

Variations: Try pressing (ENTER) during color cycling to get different color effects.

HYPNOTEYES2

Figure 3-3 Hypnoteyes2

PAR File: FRACTINT.PAR

Image Credits: Pieter Branderhorst

Parameter File Listing:

```
Hypnoteyes2          { ; with decomp, try fast cycling
                     ;            Pieter Branderhorst
   reset type=julia corners=-0.162458/0.17487/0.734422/0.984935
   params=0.258919/1.76951e-007 decomp=256 colors=@blues.map
   }
```

About the Image: The image in Figure 3-3 and color plate 6 is the same as Hypnoteyes with two differences: the decomposition option was used, and a different color map was used. Here you have proof positive that the Winfract options can totally transform an image. Recall that the escape-time algorithm colors points according to the number of iterations it takes for the orbit defined by the iterating expression to escape a circle. The decomposition option uses information about the direction the orbit was heading when it escaped to color the image. In this case, the decomp variable is set to 256, which means that the 360^0 circle is divided into 256 different directions for the purpose of coloring.

Variations: Try different values of the decomp= parameter. You will find it under FRACTALS / BASIC OPTIONS.

INSECTARM

Figure 3-4 Insectarm

PAR File: FRACTINT.PAR

Image Credits: Pieter Branderhorst

Parameter File Listing:

```
Insectarm            { ; barnsleyj2 with decomp
  ;  by Pieter Branderhorst
  reset type=barnsleyj2
  corners=0.220596/0.3306656/0.2319299/0.2133/0.2663158/0.1675801
  params=0.757642/1.07726 decomp=256
  colors=A0AJ0S<13>p0u8B36B34B32B32B52B7000<100>000zzK<2>_yHRxGIw\
  F8vD0uB<3>Usu<8>tcl<6>tlc000<96>000U0m<4>A0K
  }
```

About the Image: What have we here, a closeup of the arm of a praying mantis? The fractal in Figure 3-4 and color plate 7 has a discontinuous, patchwork appearance that is different from the standard Mandelbrot images, but typical of the Barnsley types. The use of the decomposition option also adds to the patchwork effect.

If you have not studied many parameter files before, you are probably wondering what that puzzling colors=gibberish line means. Winfract has a way to compress the 256 palette colors into a few symbols. The colors= line is not really meant to be understood by humans, but Winfract understands it quite well. You can decipher it by loading the parameter file into Winfract, and then using the COLORS / SAVE COLOR-MAP function to save as a human-readable color map file which has red, green, and blue color values. (You can learn more about color maps in Chapter 4).

Variations: Try without the decomposition option.

COOLCOMPLEXNEWTON

Figure 3-5 CoolComplexNewton

PAR File: FRACTINT.PAR

Image Credits: Michael Coddington

Parameter File Listing:

```
CoolComplexNewton  { ; complexnewton      Michael Coddington
  reset type=complexnewton corners=-2.0/2.0/-1.5/1.5
  params=4/-3/1/1 float=y invert=0.5/0.125/-0.125
  colors=CCCssC<20>sECsCCqCC<21>ACCCC<21>sCs<20>ECsCCsCEs<19>Cqs\
  CssCsq<8>Cs_CsYECE<20>sCs<20>ECsCCsCEs<19>CqsCssCsq<19>CsECsCE\
  sE<19>qsqsssssq<19>ssE
  }
```

About the Image: This fractal, as shown in Figure 3-5 and color plate 8, uses the inversion option to turn itself inside out. The invert=0.5/0.125/–0.125 parameters means that the circle of inversion has a radius of .5 and is centered on the point (0.125,–0.125). What inversion does is reflect all points outside the circle to points inside the circle and vice versa.

Variations: Use the FRACTALS / EXTENDED OPTIONS menu to turn off inversion. Then you will see the classic Complex Newton image with a discontinuity along the negative real axis.

DINNERPLATE

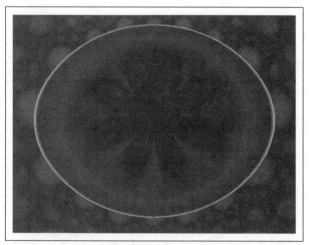

Figure 3-6 DinnerPlate

PAR File: FRACTINT.PAR

Image Credits: Dan Farmer

Parameter File Listing:

```
DinnerPlate          { ; Looks like china on tablecloth          Dan Farmer
  reset type=formula
  formulafile=fractint.frm formulaname=LeeMandel2
  corners=-0.0233229/0.0233249/0.2569835/0.291958 inside=0
  potential=255/500/500
  colors=000DP_Uoq<20>A4XVqq<18>nwjoIRFnsOkuUqq<22>ieiUqo<19>HjCT\
  qq<17>4riUqq<20>9ggUqq<14>SxqRyqTpq<6>LgmUqp<11>Pm'XfjPlZ<4>Mj\
  Sy3J<5>YEB<15>e0Fe0Fd0F<11>ZMAl'AzoAIjb<10>s0D<22>1ZC<3>9SS }
```

About the Image: The world of fractals may be a mysterious and bizarre world of exotic shapes and impossible patterns, but here we have a simple dinner plate on an attractive green table cloth, as shown in Figure 3-6 and color plate 9. This type illustrates the use of the user-defined formula. In this case, the formula is in the file FRACTINT.FRM, and is:

```
LeeMandel1(XYAXIS) {; Kevin Lee
  z=Pixel:
    c=sqr(pixel)/z, c=z-c, z=sqr(c),
     |z|<4
  }
```

Variations: Try different colors for the plate.

MANDALA

Figure 3-7 Mandala

PAR File: FRACTINT.PAR

Image Credits: Richard Hughes

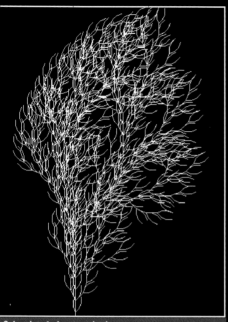

Color plate 1 - Lsystems bush

Color plate 2 - IFS Fern

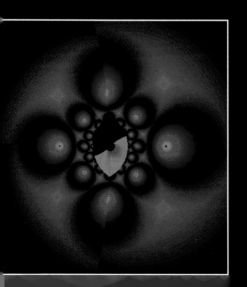

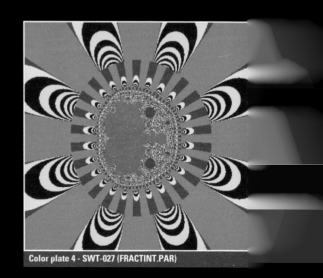

Color plate 4 - SWT-027 (FRACTINT.PAR)

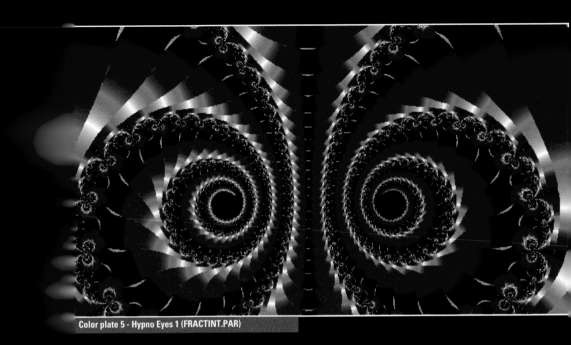
Color plate 5 - Hypno Eyes 1 (FRACTINT.PAR)

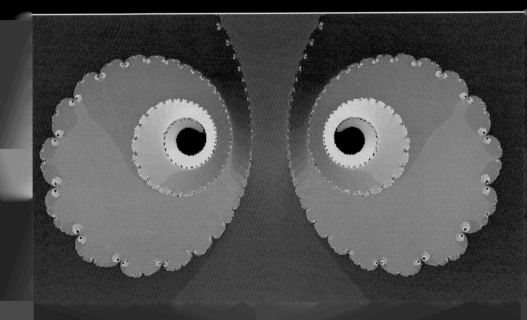

Color plate 7 - Insect Arm (FRACTINT.PAR)

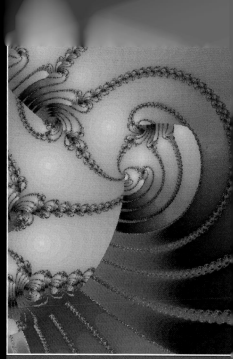

Color plate 8 - Cool Complex Newton (FRACTINT.PAR)

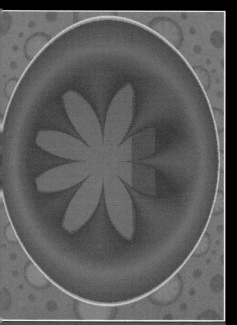

Color plate 9 - DinnerPlate (FRACTINT.PAR)

Color plate 10 - Mandalla (FRACTINT.PAR)

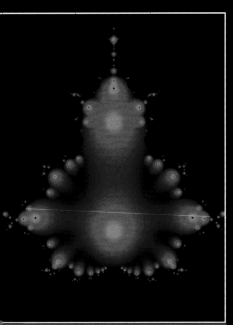

Color plate 11 - Nodule Mandelbrot (RECIPES.PAR)

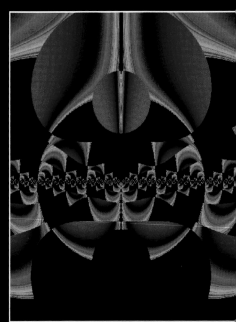

Color plate 12 - Newton's Headache (RECIPES.PAR)

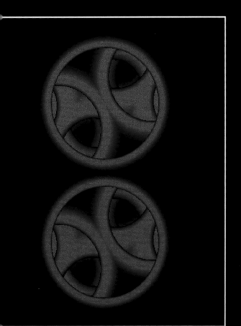

Color plate 13 - Red Holes (RECIPES.PAR)

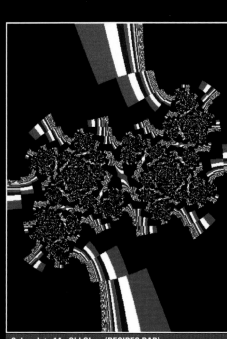

Color plate 14 - Old Glory (RECIPES.PAR)

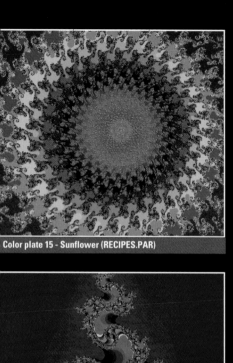

Color plate 15 - Sunflower (RECIPES.PAR)

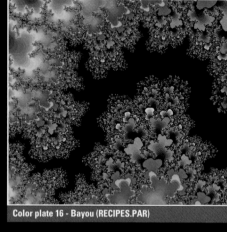

Color plate 16 - Bayou (RECIPES.PAR)

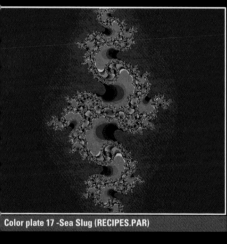

Color plate 17 -Sea Slug (RECIPES.PAR)

Color plate 18 - Medallion RHS-01 (RECIPES.PAR)

Color plate 19 - Injector (FRACTINT.PAR)

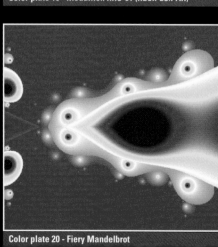

Color plate 20 - Fiery Mandelbrot

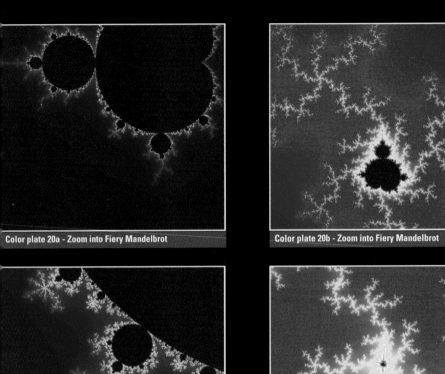

Color plate 20a - Zoom into Fiery Mandelbrot

Color plate 20b - Zoom into Fiery Mandelbrot

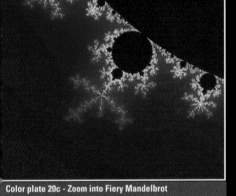

Color plate 20c - Zoom into Fiery Mandelbrot

Color plate 20d - Zoom into Fiery Mandelbrot

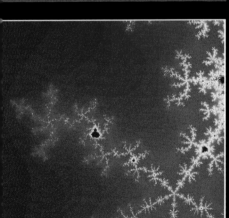

Color plate 20e - Zoom into Fiery Mandelbrot

Color plate 20f - Zoom into Fiery Mandelbrot

Color plate 21 - Lambdafn (FRACTINT.PAR)

Color plate 22 - Spiral (FRACTINT.PAR)

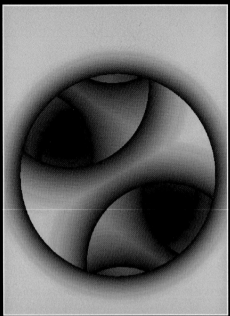

Color plate 23 - Not Your Usual Fractal 8 (FRACTINT.PAR)

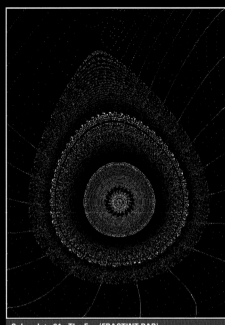

Color plate 24 - The Eye (FRACTINT.PAR)

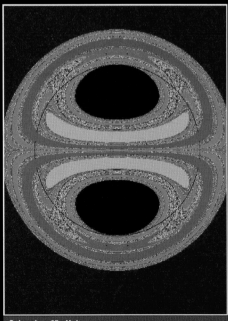

Color plate 25 - Unity

Color plate 26 - Distance Estimator Mandelbrot

Parameter File Listing:

```
mandala          { ; Sqr(1/FN)  ident              Richard Hughes
  reset type=sqr(1/fn) function=ident
  corners=-1.984573/1.98143/-1.486908/1.487839 maxiter=256 inside=0
  outside=real
  colors=000ztn<49>zV1zU0zU0zT0<28>z10z00z00y00<30>c00b11a11'22_22\
  <23>GEEFFFFFFFFFF<29>x11z00z10<29>zx0zz0zz1<29>zzxzzzzzz<10>zto
  }
```

About the Image: This image is a beautiful mandala with a pleasing circular symmetry. The example shown in Figure 3-7 and colorplate 10 illustrates two unusual features. The first is the use of a function variable fractal type. In this case, the iterated formula is $z' = sqr(1/fn)$ and the function variable is ident, or the identity function. Therefore, the actual formula is $z' = sqr(1/z)$ or $z' = 1/z^2$. The second unusual feature is the option outside=real. This option was added by the author of this Fractal. It changes the normal coloring scheme which assigns colors to iteration values to a similar scheme that adds the real value of the escaped orbit to the iteration.

Variations: To see the effect of outside=real, try turning it off by changing it to outside=iter. You will see that the fractal reduces to concentric circles; the beautiful symmetrical patterns of the mandala fractal are entirely due to the outside=real coloring scheme!

Fishing in Fractal Lakes

Winfract renders the Mandelbrot set in a stylish blue. Throughout this book we have referred to this blue area as the "lake." Fractal images require two elements: a chaotic dynamic system and a scheme for graphically rendering the chaos. The classic escape-time rendering of the Mandelbrot set appears as a solid blue lake only because the algorithm renders the nonescaping points using a single color. Within this lake area lurk fractal structures waiting to be caught. The bait to attract the mysteries under the lake are Winfract's optional parameters, which you can set using the BASIC OPTIONS and EXTENDED OPTIONS menus. These options allow you to select alternatives to the escape-time method of rendering that reveal structure inside the lake. Try the next few examples and go on a fractal fishing expedition!

PLAIN MANDELBROT

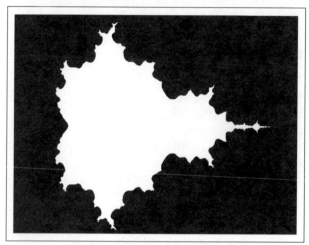

Figure 3-8 Plain Mandelbrot

PAR File: RECIPES.PAR

Image Credits: Authors

Parameter File Listing:
```
Plain_Mandelbrot  { ; Same as Nodule_Mandelbrot with inside=1
  reset type=mandel corners=0.929333/-2.206666/1.160014/-1.191986
  maxiter=9 inside=2 outside=0
    }
```

About the Image: We admit it: this is a pretty boring image. It is presented here and shown in Figure 3-8 only to make a dramatic contrast with the next recipe. Since the outside parameter is set to 0, the escape-time stripes are gone. All that is left is the bare outline of the Mandelbrot, and even that is less interesting than usual because the MAXIMUM ITERATIONS (maxiter=) parameter is set to the extremely low value of 9.

Variations: Even this plain example can be spiced up. In the FRACTALS / BASIC OPTIONS menu set Passes to 1-Pass and set Maximum Iterations to 30,000. Then on the FRACTALS / EXTENDED OPTIONS menu set DISTANCE ESTIMATOR to 1. You will be treated to a fascinating solid blue Mandelbrot with the normally invisible, super thin tendrils made visible by the distance estimator algorithm. See Figure 3-9 and colorplate 26.

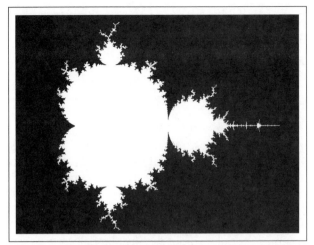

Figure 3-9 Mandelbrot with the distance estimator

NODULE_MANDELBROT

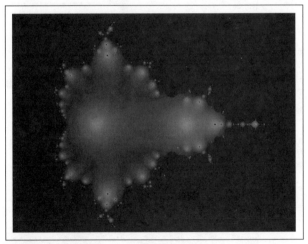

Figure 3-10 Nodule Mandelbrot

PAR File: RECIPES.PAR

Image Credits: BG Dodson

Parameter File Listing:

```
Nodule_Mandelbrot  { ; The "set" from my "Nodule" period
                   ; BG Dodson 1992 71636,1075
```

```
reset type=mandel corners=0.929333/-2.206666/1.160014/-1.191986
maxiter=9 inside=bof60 outside=0
colors=000oZK<6>xE2<8>'94Y90W84<10>336559000<27>000W00000000000
gHoYMiOScHGa<6>FXYOOOOOOFcXFeWXFx<3>FgW<13>la'vWg<6>eiTfhB<9>\
_onenw<6>Npb5lg<4>WsWpOZ<4>bkU'tU_rV<4>VhZXdU<6>PmiOnkKrp<14>fa\
Utce<12>FVO<19>gDBv8UqANlCHi61<12>e_ejWi<16>ZiheyyKuM<8>dp_fp'\
hmY<3>maN
}
```

About the Image: One line tells the tale of this image: inside=bof60. The Inside parameter, which you can set from the FRACTALS / BASIC OPTIONS menu, allows you to select different methods of rendering the area of the fractal where the orbits never escape. The BOF60 value for the Inside parameter is named after a method described on page 60 of our copy of *Beauty of Fractal*. The lake area will be broken into colored areas where the iteration number of the closest orbit approach to the origin is identical. With this method of rendering, rounded nodules sprout within Mandelbrot lake. The startling effect of the Inside BOF60 option can be seen by comparing Figures 3-8 and 3-10. The color version is shown in color plate 11.

Variations: Try rotating the colors using the ⊙ key, and watch the nodules dance!

NEWTON'S_HEADACHE

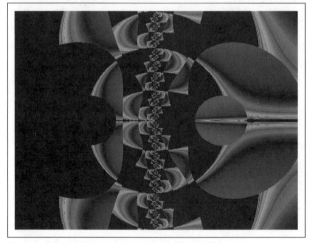

Figure 3-11 Newton's_Headache

PAR File: RECIPES.PAR

Image Credits: BG Dodson

Parameter File Listing:

```
Newton's_Headache  { ; A thoroughly freaked out Newton
                   ; BG Dodson 1992 71636,1075
  reset type=newton corners=-2.0/2.0/-1.5/1.5 params=2 float=y
  maxiter=400
  outside=mult
  colors=000rD3<19>336<17>RQkLXs<13>YMiqBu<2>0ScHGa<10>FeWXFx<3>\
  FgW<13>la'vWg<6>eiTfhB<9>_onenw<6>Npb5lg<4>WsWpOZ<4>bkU'tU_rV<4>\
  VhZXdU<6>Pmi0nkKrp<14>faUtce<12>FVO<19>gDBv8UqANlCHi61<12>e_ejWi\
  <16>ZiheyyKuM<8>dp_fp'hmY<11>xE2uD3
  }
```

About the Image: Figure 3-11 and color plate 12 illustrates another case of a plain fractal made fascinating by an option. The Newton fractal plots the chaos generated by the Newton's method algorithm for finding the roots of polynomials. The fractal arises from the uncertainty of the algorithm when there are more than two roots. When there are two roots, this is a fairly plain fractal, if indeed it is a fractal at all. The secret of this parameter file is setting the Outside parameter to MULT.

If you are used to thinking of inside and outside in terms of the Mandelbrot set, you might find their application to the Newton fractal a little strange. The *outside* points of the Mandelbrot set are the points that escape to infinity; the *inside* points are those that never escape. In the case of the Newton fractal, the attractor is not infinity but the roots of the polynomial, and virtually all the points are attracted to the roots. Therefore, all the points are "outside." Setting Outside to MULT colors the points according to the product of the iteration when the orbit was captured and the real part of the orbit value, divided by the imaginary part of the orbit value. This coloring method completely changes the appearance of the fractal.

Variations: Set Outside to ITER to see the plain second degree Newton fractal.

RED_HOLES

Figure 3-12 Red_Holes

PAR File: RECIPES.PAR

Image Credits: Bill Potter

Parameter File Listing:
```
Red_Holes  { ; (c) 1992 Bill Potter/Red holes on black background
           ; have fun use & abuse but no commercial use wo permission
  reset type=barnsleyj1 passes=g float=y
  corners=2.524975/-3.004308/2.540056/-1.606958
  params=0.599999905/1.099998949  maxiter=6000 inside=0
  potential=255/1000/1 colors=000<126>y00z00y00<125>000
```

About the Image: Winfract's philosophy is to give you the ability to apply options in as many combinations as possible and ask questions later. If you ask questions first you might never attempt absurd combinations! The continuous potential option is a case in point. This option has a physical meaning when used with the classic Mandelbrot set: the resulting image graphs the electrostatic potential surrounding a charged Mandelbrot set. Apart from the physical meaning, the value of the continuous potential option for fractal artists is that colors vary smoothly rather than in striped bands as they do with escape-time rendering. Winfract allows you to use continuous potential with any of the escape-time fractals. Generally it works best, and is the most accurate, with a large bailout value. (Bailout is the third potential parameter on the FRACTALS / EXTENDED OPTIONS menu.)

The Red_Holes fractal (see Figure 3-12 and color plate 13) uses continuous potential in combination with the barnsleyj1 fractal type, which is very different from the original Mandelbrot formula. All bets are off concerning the physical meaning of this combination of fractal type and rendering option. Maybe a physicist will write and tell us! Furthermore, the bailout is set to the extremely low value of 1; values more like 200 or 500 are more typical. You can see the result in Figure 3-12. You can see two identical wheels built from nested cycloid shapes. The delicate shading resulting from continuous potential gives a distinct 3-D effect.

Variations: Try changing the continuous potential bailout value on the FRACTALS / EXTENDED OPTIONS menu from 1 to 2, and then try 3 and 4. The rings fly apart and decompose, and completely vanish. You can achieve the same results by editing the Red_Hole parameter entry in RECIPES.PAR, modifying the line

```
potential=255/1000/1
```

to read

```
potential=255/1000/2
```

and then

```
potential=255/1000/3
```

The bailout is the third potential parameter.

Finally, to fully appreciate just what magic is being accomplished with this fractal, you should try turning potential off completely, and generate a picture of the regular barnsleyj1 fractal. To do this, change the

Figure 3-13 The regular barnsleyj1 fractal

Potential Max Color entry from 255 to 0. The result is shown in Figure 3-13. See if you can perceive any relationship between Figure 3-12 (barnsleyj1 with potential) and Figure 3-13 (barnsleyj1 without potential). A real mystery!

OLD_GLORY

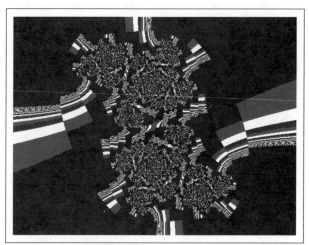

Figure 3-14 Old_Glory

PAR File: RECIPES.PAR

Image Credits: Ronald C. Lewen

Parameter File Listing:
```
Old_Glory           { ; A Very Patriotic Fractal
                    ; Ronald C. Lewen, 76376,2567
  reset type=cmplxmarksjul corners=-2.0/2.0/-1.5/1.5
  params=0.3/0.6/1.1
 outside=mult
  colors=000z00zzz00zz00zzz00zz00zzz00zz00zzz00zz00zzz00zz00zzz00zz00zzz\
  00zz00zzz00zz00zzz00zz00zzz00zz00zzz00zz00zzz00zz00zzz00zz00zzz\
  00zz00zzz00zz00zzz00zz00zzz00zz00zzz00zz00zzz00zz00zzz00zz00zzz\
  00zz00zzz00zz00zzz00zz00zzz00zz00zzz00zz00zzz00zz00zzz00zz00zzz\
  00zz00zzz00zz00zzz00zz00zzz00zz00zzz00zz00zzz00zz00zzz00zz00zzz\
  00zz00zzz00zz00zzz00zz00zzz00zz00zzz00zz00zzz00zz00zzz00zz00zzz\
  00zz00zzz00zz00zzz00zz00zzz00zz00zzz00zz00zzz00zz00zzz00zz00zzz\
  00zz00zzz00z
  }
```

About the Image: Here is another example of fractal magic accomplished by setting the Outside parameter to MULT. A cmplxmarksjulia fractal is broken into striped fragments, and then colored with a repeating red, white, and blue palette. Don't judge this one by the grayscale version in Figure 3-14 and color plate 14; you have to see it in full color!

Color Magic

Outstanding fractal images achieve distinction in different ways. The shape can be intriguing, perhaps suggestive of real-life objects. Fractal patterns can contain intriguing repetitions and symmetries that excite those with mathematical imagination. But the best fractal artists spend a lot of time manipulating the colors of their finished fractals. The next few examples have many admirable qualities, but have particularly striking color schemes.

SUNFLOWER

Figure 3-15 Sunflower

PAR File: RECIPES.PAR

Image Credits: Lee H. Skinner

Parameter File Listing:

```
Sunflower              { ; Mandelbrot
                         ; Lee H. Skinner
 reset type=mandel
 corners=-0.7454172061/-0.7454162868/0.112995187399/0.112995876899
  maxiter=16383 inside=0 logmap=yes symmetry=none
 colors=000DZS0gMSMW<6>q3QITJBY6Q0T<5>YJ6WHYbA'j2cOPU<3>GTLTOU<4>\
 nSHYqDTT'<4>puyFP_5RdPPG0Q0PRV<5>TkOsP_YRPgVIqZBP0W<4>U0Z2yDMRW\
 <6>0oUP0W<3>PSWPTVNRW<6>8rQJJVDEU78TRRT<3>'dFQUX<4>VyfQMZ<5>W7s\
 0PY<3>KXeTQX<5>vddPNZ<5>UDrPMZ<4>RBoW0bbNjqzFZWdicmtkv969'YYmh_\
```

```
zsbONjNLzFZH5i1ozYMOZ<5>4Mt<6>F2v<2>ptI<4>DB1<4>iNO<5>cDj<3>OtS\
<7>LLcV'jepqmrS<3>7FQ<4>2Zs1bz2_w<6>ACZ<4>_1w<4>2Zvaix<7>'Vs<3>8\
sh<2>Z_D<6>T5H3Vz<4>YtP<4>2QY
}
```

About the Image: With all the exotic fractal types possible with Winfract available to fractal artists, you might think that no one would bother making Mandelbrot images. The example in Figure 3-15 and color plate 15 demonstrates why the reputation of the Mandelbrot set is well deserved. The image shows a fascinating spiral of self-similar details swirling into oblivion. It looks like a sunflower because of the way the artist has colored the inside of the spiral.

Variations: This image begs for color cycling. Press (SPACEBAR) or ⊙ while viewing the image. Reverse the spiral by alternating between the ⊕ and ⊖ keys.

BAYOU

Figure 3-16 Bayou

PAR File: RECIPES.PAR

Image Credits: Lee H. Skinner

Parameter File Listing:

```
Bayou              { ; Water plants along a winding inlet
                   ; Lee H. Skinner
   reset type=mandel
```

```
corners=-0.235176302/-0.235075312/0.827176269/0.827251988
maxiter=255
inside=0 symmetry=none
colors=000LKMTYbF69<14>uGtK6D<3>o3eK6E<4>v4vF68<5>T8LD66<11>IGG\
D8A<8>5YkD88<14>Rhc<3>1on<11>vWN<12>v8'<13>2K74II6GT8Dd<9>rtR<7\
>dRg<3>8ke<10>h4ueVrbvo'ulLHT<4>TRlD99<12>AmsD86<12>Ed5JD8<5>vx\
MD96<6>CX5B'4D99<8>Jg'FAA<8>XjoC66<4>444H67<7>r3ID96<8>5'5DW4Cv\
12on
}
```

About the Image: Another gorgeous Mandelbrot image. (See Figure 3-16 and color plate 16.) This one traces an impossibly jagged Mandelbrot coastline. The colors include some wonderful greens and blues that suggest foliage, as well as a yellow fringe that highlights fractal tendrils. One way to achieve these color effects is by patient manipulation of colors while color cycling, using the COLORS / COLOR-CYCLING menu.

SEASLUG

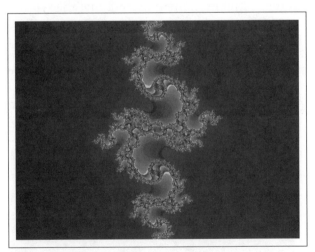

Figure 3-17 Seaslug

PAR File: RECIPES.PAR

Image Credits: Lee H. Skinner

Parameter File Listing:

```
SeaSlug               { ; Swimming near the coral reef
                      ; Lee H. Skinner
  reset type=marksjulia corners=-2.0/1.999996/-1.49998/1.5
  params=0.1/0.9 maxiter=1023 inside=0 symmetry=none
  colors=000F4E<11>7DdG66<8>1tHmsmIDB<3>MxbJ79<6>YobH25<18>DWLCYM\
  E6E<3>1Um<18>fgzcWh_JQ<22>XpZWr_YDg_EkH26<21>G0_FPaH58<10>CvoI5\
```

```
6<9>TrMMBA<4>kxaJ49<4>YKXG5B<4>7TeI35<16>lcGJ16<13>vARI26<20>r'\
fH25<20>QQ2H17G29G3B
}
```

About the Image: This image, as shown in Figure 3-17 and color plate 17, was made with the Marksjulia fractal type. The coloring scheme highlights a green seal slug wiggling in a dark blue ocean. This image demonstrates that the human mind cannot absorb all the information available in a fractal image. This is the point of experimenting with color schemes: how you assign the colors affects what details the viewer sees.

Variations: Seaslug is another image born to be color cycled. This time, however, instead of using the (SPACEBAR) key, try repeatedly pressing ⊙ (comma) and ⊙ (period). These keys cycle one color band at a time. You can fine-tune the coloring effects using these keys in a way that is impossible when the colors move rapidly.

Magic Symmetry

Fractals often exhibit symmetry. Sometimes the symmetry is exact, a consequence of the underlying symmetry of the generating formula. In other cases, the symmetry is approximate, and the curious mind struggles to grasp the underlying order of a very visible pattern. Symmetrical shapes have a beauty of their own, as the next few images attest.

MEDALLION (RHS-01)

Figure 3-18 Medallion (RHS-01)

PAR File: RECIPES.PAR

Image Credits: Richard H. Sherry

Parameter File Listing:

```
rhs-01            { ; (c) 1992 Richard H. Sherry
                  ; Please give recognition for commercial purposes
  reset type=fn(z)-fn(pix) function=sin/sqr
  corners=1.315946/-1.474307/-1.906889/1.813447/-1.474307/1.813447
  params=0/0/6 maxiter=32000 inside=0 potential=255/200/32000
  colors=000HF6<11>FZSJD2<9>ieGHB4<9>MCeGD8<6>8XyGC3<11>4V'HB3<14\
  >4HhIC6<7>XKjJE3<10>dt_HF1HJ1HO2HH7<3>GeXGF1<10>3y30CB<3>pGpKF8\
  <3>ZZ_HD3<7>ITQIVSGG5IXV<2>Jbc<8>SqFUsCTrD<14>2P'<10>0b9Qd7Se4V\
  g1Ve3<14>_1f<3>_7b<2>LHIKMMJPOJRRIUTGa_FdaFfcDnjCqlBto<2>DumDul\
  Evi<6>IxcVnU<3>tUA<14>fJ3hPCohbrokpkjmghhZelJ3<2>tM4HC2HE4
  }
```

About the Image: This image is a four-fold shape inscribed in a series of concentric circles. (See Figure 3-18 and color plate 18.) The serrated edging effect looks very much like the biomorph option, but is instead the result of using the sine function in the fractal formula. (The sine graph function repeats, and fractals made using sine often have repeating edges.) The pseudo 3-D appearance of the concentric circles on the oustside is due to the continuous potential coloring scheme.

YELLOW LEAVES (RHS-20)

Figure 3-19 Yellow Leaves (RHS-20)

PAR File: RECIPES.PAR

Image Credits: Richard H. Sherry

Parameter File Listing:

```
rhs-20          { ; (c) 1992 Richard H. Sherry
                  ; Please give recognition for commercial purposes
  reset type=lambdafn function=exp
  corners=-0.143341/0.119919/1.097198/1.292023 params=1/0.4
  maxiter=5000
  decomp=256
  colors=000DHZSH9SH8SH7RI5<14>NP8MQ9MP9<13>LCCLCCMDC<14>\XN8Y07X\
  07<14>CF0ebK<33>eYEeYEfZDg_Bh'Aja8<6>meDmfEngFohF<37>uoAuoAuoAu\
  p9vp9vp9<20>yw2yw2yw2yw2yw1yw1<6>zx0zx0zw0QF9<39>TP7TP7T07<13>\
  TI9
  }
```

About the Image: A green vine with yellow petals graces this image, but not just any petals—a pattern of infinitely nested fractal petals! The famous woodcut artist Escher would have loved this image. (See Figure 3-19 and color plate 19.) Try to follow the pattern of the yellow petals, and see if you can sort out the branching system! The petal effect is due to the use of the decomposition option—look for it on the BASIC OPTIONS menu, or use the decomp= parameter in the PAR file.

More Recipes!

You will find many more recipes in your Winfract directory than we had time to discuss here. Just look for files with the .PAR extension, open with the READ @BATCHFILE command, and enjoy!

Winfract Reference

Winfract's commands are your way of telling the program what to do. This chapter is a reference section for Winfract commands and options.

WINFRACT COMMANDS

There are several alternative methods of telling Winfract what to do. You can use Windows-style menus, hotkeys that directly operate from the keyboard, Fractint-style menus, the mouse for zooming, and command-line arguments. Which method you use in a particular situation is a matter of convenience and personal style.

Windows-Style Menus

When you first fire up Winfract, it comes up with a window displaying a small Mandelbrot image and a menu bar of Windows commands (FILE, FRACTALS, VIEW, COLORS, and HELP). You can select among these menu items using your mouse or the Alt key combined with the underlined character in each menu item in standard Windows fashion. For example, to access the FILE menu, click on FILE or press (ALT)-(F). Either of these actions will cause the FILE submenu to drop down. If there is more than one menu item with the same Alt key letter, repeatedly pressing that Alt key combination will cause the cursor to jump between the various items selected by that Alt key. An example of this is found in the BASIC OPTIONS menu under FRACTALS, where INSIDE:MAXIT, OUTSIDE:MULT, and MAXIMUM ITERATIONS all use the (ALT)-(M) Alt key.

Sometimes we'll ask you to select a submenu item, and we will give you both the main menu name and the submenu item separated by a /. For example, when we say "set FRACTALS / BASIC OPTIONS / MAXIMUM ITERATIONS to 200," we mean click on FRACTALS from the main menu, then click on the BASIC OPTIONS submenu item, then fill in the MAXIMUM ITERATIONS input field with the number 200.

Hotkeys

Winfract also responds to a number of hotkeys. They are also known in Windows circles as accelerator keys because they often perform functions available via the Windows menu bar, but with somewhat less fussing about. Hotkeys are keystrokes you can use to cause Winfract to perform some actions immediately. For example, the (SPACEBAR) key toggles color cycling on and off. There are also a number of hotkeys which bring up Fractint-style prompting screens (described in Table 4-1).

The Mouse

In addition to using the mouse to select menu items, Winfract uses the mouse to select areas for zooming and pinpointing where on your image to perform Mandelbrot/Julia toggles.

Fractint-Style Screens and Hotkeys

Winfract was originally developed as a Windows port of the DOS-based Fractint program, and there are a number of people around (including the authors) who use both programs. For those of us who do, Winfract includes the option to use many of Fractint's text-based prompting screens, implemented as pop-up text windows. This option is disabled by default, but can be enabled by selecting the VIEWS / HOTKEY ACTIONS / FRACTINT-STYLE PROMPTS menu item. When that option is enabled, Winfract pops up windows containing Fractint-style prompts whenever you use appropriate hotkeys. (When it is disabled, the same hotkeys bring up Winfract's equivalent Windows-style dialog boxes.)

Fair warning: the hotkeys used to bring up Fractint-style prompts follow Fractint's somewhat esoteric keystroke conventions (such as the (X) key, which brings up the BASIC OPTIONS screen—go ahead, attempt to figure out how *that* particular keystroke was originally selected to mean "basic options").

Winfract's Fractint-Style Hotkeys	
(R)	FILE / OPEN
(S)	FILE / SAVE AS
(P)	FILE / PRINT
(3)	FILE / 3D RESTORE
(O)	FILE / 3D OVERLAY
(@)	FILE / READ @BATCHFILE
(B)	FILE / WRITE @BATCHFILE
(T)	FRACTALS / FRACTAL FORMULA
(X)	FRACTALS / BASIC OPTIONS
(Y)	FRACTALS / EXTENDED OPTIONS
(Z)	FRACTALS / FRACTAL PARAMS
(I)	FRACTALS / 3D PARAMS
(INS)	FRACTALS / RESET ALL OPTIONS
(A)	FRACTALS / STARFIELD
(DEL)	VIEW / IMAGE SETTINGS
(TAB)	VIEW / STATUS
(L)	COLORS / LOAD COLOR-MAP
(W)	COLORS / WRITE COLOR-MAP
(C)	COLORS / COLOR-CYCLING

Table 4-1 Winfract hotkeys

Color-Cycling Hotkeys	
(→)	Start Color Cycling "outward"
(←)	Start Color Cycling "inward"
(▸)	Color Cycle outward one step and pause
(◂)	Color Cycle inward one step and pause
(SPACEBAR)	Pause Color Cycling
(ENTER)	Start Color Cycling with new random colors
(↑)	Speed up Color Cycling
(↓)	Slow down Color Cycling

Table 4-1 Winfract hotkeys, continued

Using the Windows menu interface always brings up the Windows-style menus and dialog boxes.

Command-Line Arguments

A *command-line argument* is an option that you give a program "on the command line" as you start it up. It is more commonly used in the MS-DOS world than in the Windows environment, but works in either one. For example, if you are starting Winfract using the Windows Program Manager FILES / RUN command, and you want it to start up calculating the Julia fractal type instead of the default Mandelbrot, you could click on FILES and then RUN, and type in `Winfract type=julia` in the RUN dialog box. Winfract accepts arguments letting you give it your own choice of fractal type, starting coordinates, and just about every other option selectable via its online menus.

Winfract has several alternate ways to use these command-line arguments besides being used on Winfract's command line. In fact, referring to them as "command-line" arguments is a bit of an anachronism—you usually start Winfract not by using the RUN command, but by clicking on the Winfract icon with the mouse, so these alternate methods of applying command-line arguments are the ones you typically use.

By whatever name they are called, command-line arguments are extremely useful. Command-line arguments are used inside startup files

Command	Meaning
COMMAND=<nnn>	Enter a number in place of <nnn>.
COMMAND=<filename>	You supply the filename.
COMMAND=yes|no|<whatever>	Type in exactly one of "yes", "no", or another command to replace <whatever>. The "|" means "or."
COMMAND=1st[/2nd[/3rd]]	You supply the slash-separated parameters to replace 1st, 2nd, and 3rd. The brackets [] mean that 2nd and 3rd are optional. You do type in the slashes.

Table 4-2 Command-Line Arguments

such as the SSTOOLS.INI file described below. Winfract can also load and save fractal images using parameter files, which are files containing the instructions for generating fractal images rather than their actual bitmap instructions stored in the form of command-line arguments.

The syntax for command-line arguments is as follows:

```
argument argument argument...
```

where the individual arguments are separated by one or more spaces (an individual argument may *not* include spaces). Either upper- or lowercase may be used, and arguments can be in any order. A typical sequence of arguments might be

```
type=julia inside=10
```

This example selects fractal type Julia and sets the inside color to color number 10 in the color palette. Both of these settings can also be made using submenus under Fractals.

Table 4-2 lists terminology we will use throughout the rest of this chapter as the commands are documented.

Commands in the SSTOOLS.INI File

When Winfract is first started, it always looks along the DOS path for any file called SSTOOLS.INI (which stands for Stone Soup Tools) and reads start-up variables and commands from that file. Then it looks at its own command line; arguments there will override those from the .INI file. The SSTOOLS.INI command file is used in the same way as Microsoft's TOOLS.INI or WINDOWS.INI configuration files. Sister Stone Soup Group programs, such as Lee Crocker's Piclab and our own DOS-based Fractint fractal program also use the SSTOOLS.INI file. In particular, you designate a section of SSTOOLS.INI as belonging to a particular program by beginning the section with a label in brackets. Winfract looks for the labels [fractint] and [winfract] and ignores any lines it finds in the file belonging to any other labels.

Command-line parameters always appear in the [fractint] section. All parameters in this section are processed by both Winfract and Fractint. (Winfract calmly ignores all Fractint-specific parameters that aren't relevant to the Windows environment, such as the video= parameter.) The commands do not have to be all on the same line. For clarity, you may prefer to put each command on its own line. Comments can be added to indirect files by preceding the comment with a semicolon. For example, if an SSTOOLS.INI file looks like this:

```
[fractint]
type=julia        ; start up with a Julia set
inside=0          ; using traditional black
printer=hp        ; my printer is a LaserJet
[startrek]
Aye, captain, but I dinna think the engines can take it!
[winfract]
FractintMenus=False
```

Winfract will read only the second, third, fourth, and last lines. (The fourth line, applying only to the DOS-based Fractint program, is quietly ignored.) The fifth and sixth lines are for a fictitious program called Startrek.

You can place any sort of Winfract command you like in SSTOOLS.INI, but the intent is to place commands there that you want to *always* take effect. The printer=hp entry, for instance, is a perfect example for an MS-DOS program.

When you select Windows-specific options, such as the Zoom bar and the hotkey action settings, Winfract automatically updates the [winfract] section, saving this information for future sessions. You do not normally need to modify the [winfract] section manually.

Commands in Parameter Files

A powerful extension of the command-line concept is the parameter file. Parameter files contain lists of named fractal images, called parameter entries, and all the command-line arguments needed to generate them. Parameter files have a .PAR filename extension. An example distributed with Winfract is FRACTINT.PAR, which you will find on your book disk. A parameter file entry is shown in Figure 4-1 along with labels for the component parts. The name of the parameter entry, in this case Spiral1, is followed by a list of commands contained within curly brackets ({}).

You can display parameter file entries using the FILE / READ @BATCHFILE command, described later in this chapter. You can create

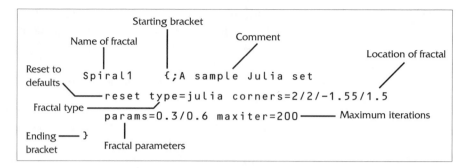

Figure 4-1 An annotated parameter file entry

parameter file entries by hand using a text editor such as the Windows Notepad program, but you will find it easier to generate them automatically using the FILE / SAVE @BATCHFILE command.

Commands in Indirect Files

There is one final method for running Winfract commands that is a holdover from the earlier Fractint program, but is mentioned here for completeness. When Winfract is invoked using the Program Manager RUN command, arguments can be put in an *indirect* file. If @filename appears in the command line right after typing Winfract, it causes Winfract to read the filename for any arguments that it contains. When it finishes, it resumes reading its own command line. For example, the command line:

```
winfract maxiter=250 @myfile passes=1
```

sets the maximum iterations to 250, opens the file MYFILE, reads and executes the commands in it, and then sets the number of passes to 1. The indirect file option is valid only on the original command line, as Winfract cannot deal with multiple indirection (putting the indirect file @filename commands within other indirect files).

For example, if MYFILE contains:

```
corners=-4/4/-2/2    ; set the image boundary
type=manowar         ; use this fractal type
biomorph=yes         ; and the Biomorph option
```

then the effect of starting Winfract with:

```
winfract @filename
```

is exactly the same as starting it with:

```
winfract corners=-4/4/-2/2 type=manowar biomorph=yes
```

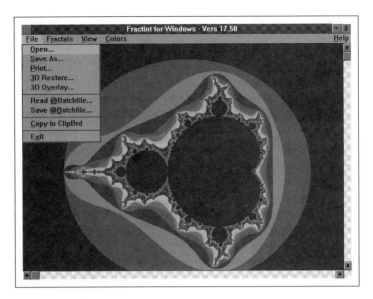

Figure 4-2 The File menu item list

WINFRACT COMMAND REFERENCE

The rest of this chapter documents all the Winfract commands and options. It is organized in the sequence of the Windows-style menus, with those functions available only via other actions (such as using the mouse to zoom in on an image) described at the end of the chapter. Commands are listed by the menu item that accesses the command function. Then any alternative means of accessing that function using the menus, such as using hotkeys or Fractint-style prompts, are given.

Any entries under FRACTINT-STYLE PROMPTS ACCESS only activate Fractint-style prompting screens if you have set your HOTKEY ACTIONS option to Fractint-style Prompts—otherwise, all hotkeys take you to the Windows-style dialog boxes. Also, Fractint-style prompting screens aren't really discussed except to mention where they exist, under the assumption that folks who use those prompts do so because they're used to them, are familiar with them, and aren't thumbing through this chapter to figure out what they do.

THE FILE MENU ITEM

The FILE menu items deal with those Winfract commands that involve loading, saving, and copying images to and from Winfract and other devices, such as the printer and clipboard. In true Windows tradition, the EXIT command is in this selection as well. Figure 4-2 shows the drop-down list of menu items that are displayed when you select this menu item. The following section is organized according to the menu items on the File menu.

File / Open

Command Function
The OPEN menu item is used to select a previously saved image for viewing. The menu is a standard Windows-style, open-files menu and can be used to wander through your various disk drives and directories searching for images to display.

Menu Access
The OPEN menu item of the FILE menu.

Fractint-Style Prompts Access
The Ⓡ hotkey brings up the Fractint-style prompt sequence.

Command-Line Access
        [filename=]<filename>

For backwards compatibility, the filename= prefix is optional when used on the actual command line. Elsewhere, the filename= prefix is required. The .GIF extension is assumed if no extension is specified.

Comments
GIF files created by Winfract contain not just fractal images but also information about how the fractal was generated. Thus, loading Winfract-created files not only allows you to view the image, but also resets Winfract to regenerate that image. Winfract is also capable of being used as a GIF decoder to view files not created by Fractint, such as pictures. Since Winfract has no way of knowing how these GIFs were generated, it sets the current fractal type to plasma.

Although Winfract can save images as BMPs, it cannot read them back. Any image you want to access later using Winfract should be saved as a GIF image.

High-Resolution Modes
Winfract can display and access images that are larger than its display window, and even larger than your physical screen. If a displayed image is larger than Winfract's display window, you can use the scrollbars at the side and bottom of the window to move to various points of the image. This feature is extremely useful, since it allows you to create and view images at resolutions greater than those supported by your video hardware.

File / Save As

Command Function

The SAVE AS menu item is used to save the current image for later use by Winfract or other programs. The menu is a standard Windows-style, save-as menu and can be used to navigate through your various disk drives and directories searching for an appropriate place to create your files.

Menu Access

The SAVE AS menu item of the FILE menu.

Fractint-Style Prompts Access

None. The Ⓢ Hotkey always brings up the Windows-style menu.

Command-Line Parameters Access

None.

Comments

Winfract can save its images as either GIF89a, GIF87a, or BMP files. GIF89a is the default format type. If you are saving an image that you may want to use with Winfract again later, use the GIF89a format. That's because the GIF89a format includes a feature that allows Winfract to include fractal-specific information in a special extension block. The saved information includes the fractal type, current coordinates, and even information about a partially calculated image that will let it resume calculating it when reloaded. The older GIF87a format does not have this feature, and Winfract currently can't read BMP files.

The default filename is FRACT001.GIF (FRACT001.BMP if you're saving BMP files). If you save more than one time during a session, the last character of the name will be a number that is incremented, resulting in FRACT002.GIF and so forth. You can change the default filename in the dialog box.

Normally, Winfract avoids overwriting existing files when it selects a default filename for you. If you would like to reuse existing filenames to conserve disk space, you can override these default names by entering the exact name that you want to use and clicking on OK when Winfract asks you if you want to replace the file.

Winfract's GIFs Store Partial States

Understand that Winfract remembers the state of a partial calculation when saving in the GIF89a file format. Although Winfract is the world's second-fastest fractal program (Fractint is faster), calculations with high maximum iterations in the floating-point mode, extreme resolutions, or running on a slow PC can take a long time. For example, the feather image on the cover of the *Fractal Creations* book took a week to generate on a 25-MHz 80386 machine. (The image was done using a 2048 x 2048 video mode with a very high maximum iteration value.) Many times throughout that week the image was saved when the computer had to be used for other purposes; and when it was restored, the calculation picked right up where it left off!

Winfract stores GIFs using the GIF89a format. If you need to make a GIF file that you can view with software that does not support the new GIF89a standard, or that requires the BMP format popular with Windows programs, you can select one of those formats when you save your images. However, they will not contain any information about the Winfract parameters that created them. You can also convert GIF89a files to alternate formats at any time by reading them in and then saving them again.

File / Print

Command Function
The PRINT menu item is used to send the current image to the printer.

Menu Access
The PRINT menu item of the FILE menu.

Fractint-Style Prompts Access
None. The Ⓟ hotkey always brings up the Windows-style menu.

Command-Line Parameters Access
None.

Comments
This command brings up a dialog box with several options as to the size and orientation of the printed image (see Figure 4-3). The image can either be printed in Portrait or Landscape format, and either in full-page mode (the default) or a user-selectable image size.

If your printer supports color, Winfract asks the Windows printer driver to print the image using the colors closest to those on your screen. Otherwise, Winfract uses a simple candy-stripe technique, alternating between black and white for consecutive palette values. Winfract makes no attempt to dither images into grayscale (other programs do, and you may prefer to save your really good images to a file for printing later by one of those other programs).

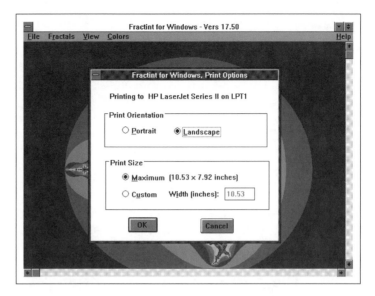

Figure 4-3 The PRINTER OPTIONS dialog box

File / 3D Restore

Command Function
The 3D RESTORE menu item is used to load and display a GIF image using 3-D transformations.

Menu Access
The 3D RESTORE menu item of the FILE menu.

Fractint-Style Prompts Access
The ③ hotkey brings up the Fractint-style prompt sequence.

Command-Line Parameters Access
    3D=yes

Comments
Most of the fractals created by Winfract are inherently two-dimensional, meaning they are flat in the x-y plane. The 3D RESTORE feature allows you to transform any fractal into a three-dimensional image with depth and an x-y-z-axis. The 3-D function treats a fractal's colors (specifically, their associated palette indexes) as the third dimension and performs various 3-D and rendering transformations on the image, so it appears on the screen projected realistically. Another feature of Winfract is that the 3-D

transformations are not limited to Winfract-generated files, but they can also be performed on GIF files created by other software. Indeed, some scientists use Winfract's sister program Fractint's 3-D capabilities to enhance electron microscope pictures!

Using 3-D involves several successive and somewhat complex-looking screens (Figures 4-4 through 4-13), but it is really quite easy to use. The 3D RESTORE menu item leads you to the first of these screens for entering all the parameters that affect 3D. Do not be dismayed by the number of possibilities: usually the default values are something reasonable, and you just press (ENTER) to move to the next screen. Follow the defaults at first, and then try changing the parameters a few at a time.

The 3D RESTORE menu begins with a file selection menu that works the same as the file selection for the OPEN menu (in fact, it looks like the same menu because it is the same menu). Select a GIF file, and then select a 3-D mode (see below).

File / 3D Restore (3-D Options)

Command Function
After 3-D transformation has been selected, choose a specific 3-D mode.

Menu Access
Automatically selected as part of the 3D RESTORE and 3D OVERLAY functions.

Fractint-Style Prompts Access
Automatic, if the Fractint-style 3D RESTORE sequence is used. There are several Fractint-style prompting screens that perform the same function as this one Windows-style menu.

Command-Line Parameters Access
```
3D=yes
preview=yes|no
showbox=yes|no
sphere=yes|no
coarse=<nnn>
stereo=0|1|2|3
filltype=0|1|2|3|4|5|6|7
ray=0|1|2|3|4|5|6
brief=yes|no
```

Comments
After the filename prompt, Winfract presents a 3-D mode selection screen as shown in Figure 4-4. Each selection will have defaults entered. If you want to change any of the defaults, use the (TAB) key to move through the menu. When you're satisfied, press (ENTER) to accept your choices and move

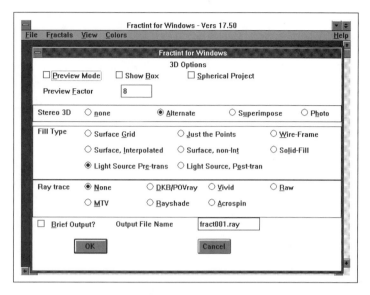

Figure 4-4 The 3-D mode selection dialog box

to the next 3-D screen. (ESC) allows you to back out at any time. Here are the options and what they do:

Preview Mode

Preview mode provides a rapid look at your transformed 3-D image by skipping a lot of rows and filling in the image. It is good for quickly discovering the best parameters. Once the 3-D parameters look good, you can turn off the preview mode and generate the full image.

Show Box

If you have selected Preview Mode, you have another option to consider. This is the option to show a rectangular image box around the image boundaries in scaled and rotated coordinates x, y, and z. The bottom of this box is the original x-y plane of your fractal, and the height is the dimension where the colors in your fractal will be interpreted as elevations. The box appears only in rectangular transformations and shows how the final image will be oriented; it doesn't draw the actual transformation. If you select one of the Light Source options, it will also show you the light source vector so you can tell where the light is coming from in relation to your image.

Spherical Projection

The spherical projection parameter allows you to select a sphere projection of your fractal. If you check this box, your image will be mapped onto a spherical surface. If not, it is mapped onto a plane as described above. Therefore you can take your favorite fractal, wrap it around a sphere, and turn it into a planet, an asteroid, a moon, or whatever. Winfract allows you to use any GIF image whatsoever and make a planet out of it— even a digitized photograph of your loved one! Planets can be smooth or rough, large or small, and they can be illuminated with the light from an imaginary sun.

Preview Factor

This parameter sets how many divisions the image will be divided into in the y direction, and it is needed if you select preview mode as described above or grid fill in the Select Fill Type screen described below. The default is 20 divisions; a larger number makes a finer (and slower) grid.

Stereo

Winfract allows you to create 3-D images for use with red/blue glasses like those found in 3-D comic books. NONE turns off the stereo effect. ALTERNATE and SUPERIMPOSE require the special red/blue glasses. They are meant to be viewed right on the screen or on a color print of the screen. The image can be made to hover entirely or partially in front of the screen.

The ALTERNATE STEREO 3D option gives 64 shades of red and blue, but with half the spatial resolution you have selected. It works by writing the red and blue images on adjacent pixels, which is why it removes half the picture's resolution. In general, we recommend you use this with resolutions above 640 x 350 only. Use this mode for continuous potential landscapes where you need all those shades.

The SUPERIMPOSE STEREO option gives you full spatial resolution but with only 16 shades of gray. If the red and blue pixels overlap, the colors are mixed, and the pixel is colored magenta. This option is good for wire-frame images (we call them surface grids), lorenz3d, and ifs3d. It works fine in 16-color modes.

The PHOTO STEREO option is for creating full-color stereo pair images for viewing with more specialized equipment. The left image is presented on the screen first. You may photograph it or save it as a GIF for later processing into a slide. Then the second image is presented, and you may do the same with it as you did with the first image. You can then take the two images and convert them to a stereo image pair.

Fill Type

In the course of any 3-D projection, portions of the original image must be stretched to fit the new surface. Points of an image that formerly were right next to each other may now have a space between them. The FILL

TYPE options generally determine what to do with the space between the mapped dots.

Surface Grid

If you select the SURFACE GRID option, Winfract will make an unfilled wire-frame grid of the fractal surface that has as many divisions in the original y direction as were set in coarse in the first screen. This wire-frame view of your image is generated very quickly and can reveal a quick approximation of what the final 3-D fractal will look like.

Just the Points

The second option, JUST THE POINTS, means Winfract just maps points in the 2-D image to corresponding points in the 3-D image. Generally, this will leave empty space between many of the points, and this space will appear black.

Wire-Frame (Connect the Dots)

This fill method simply connects the points in the hope that the connecting lines will fill in all the missing pixels. This option is rarely used, because it has been supplanted by the superior surface fill methods that were developed later.

Surface, Interpolated
Surface, Non-Interpolated

The surface fill options fill in the areas between the 3-D dots with small triangles formed from the transformed points. If the corners of the triangles are different colors, the INTERPOLATED fill colors the interior of the triangle with colors that smoothly blend between the corner colors. The NON-INTERPOLATED fill simply colors the whole triangle the color of one of the corners. Interpolating the colors makes the little triangles blend better but only works if the color palette is continuous, meaning that colors with near color numbers are a similar color. If the results look strange, try the colors not interpolated fill.

Solid-Fill

The SOLID FILL method works by using a kind of bar graph approach. A line is drawn from each point to its projection in the x-y plane.

Light Source, Pre-Transformation
Light Source, Post-Transformation

The two light source fill options allow you to position an imaginary sun over your fractal landscape. Winfract colors each pixel of the landscape

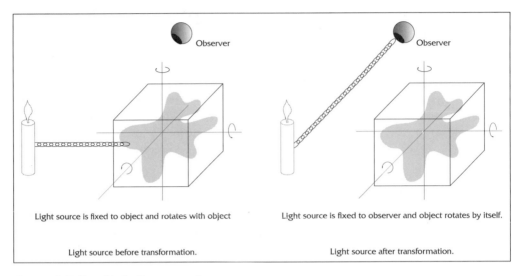

Light source is fixed to object and rotates with object   Light source is fixed to observer and object rotates by itself.

Light source before transformation.   Light source after transformation.

Figure 4-5 Two Light Source options

according to the angle the surface makes with an imaginary light source. This creates the appearance of shadows and can be used to create realistic mountains. One of the following screens will ask you to enter the three coordinates of the vector pointing toward the light.

The option called LIGHT SOURCE BEFORE TRANSFORMATION calculates the illumination before doing the coordinate transformations, and it is slightly faster. If you generate a sequence of images where one rotation is progressively changed, the effect is as if the image and the light source are fixed in relation to each other and you orbit around the image.

LIGHT SOURCE AFTER TRANSFORMATION applies the transformations first, then calculates the illumination. If you generate a sequence of images with progressive rotation as above, the effect is as if you and the light source are fixed and the object is rotating. Figure 4-5 shows the relationship between the fractal object, the viewer, and the light source for these two options.

If you select either light source fill, you will be prompted for a color map, which is a file assigning colors to the color numbers. You can try ALTERN.MAP, which is a grayscale palette that represents the light source shading as shades of gray. However, any map that has continuous shades of color works well with the light source options, although they may not look as realistic as with the gray palette in ALTERN.MAP. Try color cycling to get some interesting effects.

Ray Tracing Options

Winfract can create files of its 3-D transformations which are compatible with many ray tracing programs. Currently, four are supported directly: DKB/POVRAY, VIVID, MTV, and RAYSHADE. In addition, a RAW output is supported which can be relatively easily transformed into a format many other products can use. ACROSPIN is included as a ray tracing output option, even though it's not really a ray tracer, because the same Winfract options apply. All ray tracing files consist of triangles which follow the surface created by Winfract during the 3-D transform. Triangles which lie below the waterline are not created in order to avoid causing unnecessary work for the poor ray tracers which are already overworked. A simple plane can be substituted by the user at the waterline if needed.

The size (and, therefore, the number) of triangles created is determined by the Preview Factor setting. While generating the ray tracing file, you will view the image from above and watch it partitioned into triangles.

The color of each triangle is the average of the color of its vertices in the original image, unless BRIEF OUTPUT is selected.

If BRIEF OUTPUT is selected, a default color is assigned at the beginning of the file and is used for all triangles.

The ray tracing OUTPUT FILE NAME is used to specify the name of the file to be written. The default name is FRACT001.RAY. Note that the ray tracing files generated by Winfract are not ready to be traced by themselves. For one thing, no light source is included. They are actually meant to be included within other ray tracing files.

Because the intent is to produce an object which may be included in a larger ray tracing scene, it is expected that all rotations, shifts, and final scaling will be done by the ray tracer. Thus, in creating the images, no facilities for rotations or shifting is provided. Scaling is provided to achieve the correct aspect ratio.

The files created using the RAY TRACE option can be huge. Setting Preview Factor to 40 will result in over 2,000 triangles. Each triangle can take from 50 to 200 bytes to describe, so your ray tracing files can rapidly approach or exceed 1MB. Make sure you have enough disk space before you start.

Ray Tracing Files: Technical Info

Each ray tracing file starts with a comment identifying the version of Winfract that generated it and ends with a comment giving the number of triangles in the file.

Winfract's coordinate system has the origin of the x-y plane at the upper left-hand corner of the screen, with positive x to the right and positive y down. The ray tracing files have the origin of the x-y plane moved to the center of the screen with positive x to the right and positive y up. Increasing values of the color index are out of the screen and in the +z direction. The color index 0 will be found in the x-y plane at z = −1.

When x, y, and z scale are set to 100, the surface created by the triangles will fall within a box of +/− 1.0 in all three directions. Changing scale will change the size and/or aspect ratio of the enclosed object.

We will describe only the structure of the RAW format here. If you want to understand any of the ray tracing file formats besides RAW, please see your favorite ray tracer documentation.

The RAW format simply consists of a series of clockwise triangles. If BRIEF OUTPUT is checked, each line is a vertex with coordinates x, y, and z. Each triangle is separated by a couple of CRs from the next. If BRIEF OUTPUT is not checked, the first line in each triangle description is the red, green, blue value of the triangle.

Selecting BRIEF OUTPUT produces shorter files with the color of each triangle removed. All triangles will be the same color. These files are otherwise identical to normal files, but they will run faster than the non-Brief Output files. Also, with BRIEF OUTPUT selected, you may be able to get files with more triangles to run than otherwise.

For DKB, when BRIEF OUTPUT is selected and the WATER LEVEL value (specified on the next screen) is nonzero, you may get empty COMPOSITE/END_COMPOSITE pairs (i.e., containing no triangle info). These are harmless and may be edited out of the file if desired.

File / 3D Restore (Planar 3D Parameters)

Command Function
Chose various planar 3-D parameters such as axis rotation, water level, etc.

Menu Access
Automatically selected as part of the 3D RESTORE and 3D OVERLAY functions.

Fractint-Style Prompts Access
Automatic, if the Fractint-style 3D RESTORE sequence is used.

Command-Line Parameters Access
```
rotation=<xrot>[/<yrot>[/<zrot>]]
scalexyz=<scalex>[/<scaley>[/<scalez>]]
roughness=<scalez>
waterline=<level>
perspective=<distance>
xyshift=<xshift>[/<yshift>]
xyadjust=<xadjust>[/<yadjust>]
transparent=<startcolor>/<stopcolor>
randomize=<nnn>
```

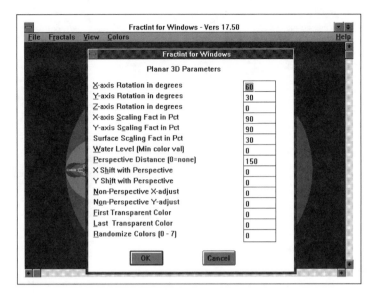

Figure 4-6 The PLANAR 3D dialog box

Comments

The number of 3-D parameters in this menu (Figure 4-6) is a bit daunting; however, most have reasonable default values, so you can usually press (ENTER) to accept them all. Thus you do not need to understand all of them to get 3D working. You'll usually change only a few of these parameters, unless you want to explore.

x-axis Rotation in Degrees
y-axis Rotation in Degrees
z-axis Rotation in Degrees

The first entries are rotation values around the x-, y-, and z-axes. Think of your starting image as a flat map: the x value tilts the bottom of your monitor towards you by x degrees, the y value pulls the left side of the monitor towards you, and the z value spins it counterclockwise. The final result of combining rotations depends on the order in which they are done. Fractint always rotates first along the x-axis, then along the y-axis, and finally along the z-axis. All rotations actually occur through the center of the original image. Figure 4-7 shows the effect of these three rotations.

A more detailed explanation of this rotation process, including a quick demonstration walk-through that you can perform using a Lorenz3D fractal, is in the description of the FRACTALS / 3D PARAMETERS menu item later in this section.

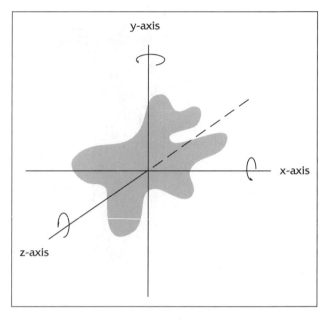

Figure 4-7 Rotating fractal objects

x-axis Scaling Factor in Pct
y-axis Scaling Factor in Pct
Surface Roughness Scaling Factor in Pct

Following the three rotation parameters are three scaling factors that control the resulting size of each axis of the image. Initially, leave the x- and y-axes alone and try changing the surface roughness factor (really z-axis scaling). High values of roughness assure your fractal will be translated into steep Alpine mountains and improbably deep valleys; low values make gentle, rolling terrain. Negative roughness is legal. For example, if you're doing a Mandelbrot image and want the solid Mandelbrot lake to be below the ground, instead of eerily floating above, try a roughness of about −30 percent.

Water Level (Minimum Color Value)

When a file is loaded into Winfract using the 3-D option, the colors are interpreted as elevations according to the number of the color. The WATER LEVEL option creates a minimum elevation in the resulting image. The result is exactly like flooding a valley. The higher the water level value, the more of the scene will be underwater. This works well with plasma landscapes.

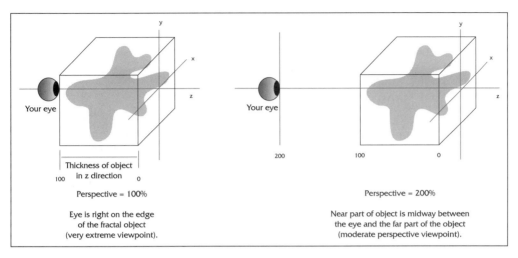

Figure 4-8 The Perspective parameter

Perspective Distance [1–999, 0 for No Persp]

Perspective distance can be thought of as the distance from your eye to the image. A zero value (the default) means no perspective calculations, which makes the image appear flat, as though photographed through a telephoto lens. If you set perspective to a nonzero value, features nearer to the observer will be larger than features farther away. To understand the effect of the perspective number, picture a box with the original x-y plane of your flat fractal on the bottom and your 3-D fractal inside. A perspective value of 100 percent places your eye right at the edge of the box and yields fairly severe distortion, like a close view through a wide-angle lens. A value of 200 percent puts your eye as far from the front of the box as the back is behind. A value of 300 percent puts your eye twice as far from the front of the box as the back is, and so on. Try about 150 percent for reasonable results. Much larger values put you far away for even less distortion, while values smaller than 100 percent put you inside the box. Try larger values first, and work your way in. Figure 4-8 shows how the perspective parameter relates to the distance from the viewer to the object.

X Shift with Perspective (positive = right)
Y Shift with Perspective (positive = up)
Non-Perspective X Adjust (positive = right)
Non-Perspective Y Adjust (positive = up)

There are two types of x and y shifts that let you move the final image around if you'd like to recenter it. The first set, x and y shift with perspective, moves the image and changes the viewing perspective as well. The second set, x and y adjust without perspective, simply moves the image without changing the perspective viewpoint. They are used just for positioning the final image on the screen.

First Transparent Color
Last Transparent Color

You may define a range of transparent colors. This option is most useful when using the Overlay command (see Menu Access) to place one image on top of another, so parts of the bottom image show through. Enter the color-range minimum and maximum value for which you do not want to overwrite whatever may already be on the screen. The color ranges refer to the color numbers in the original image. The default is no transparency (overwrite everything).

Randomize Colors (0–7, 0 Disables)

The randomize option will smooth the transition between colors and reduce the banding that occurs with some maps. Select the value of randomize to between 0 (for no effect) and 7 (to randomize your colors almost beyond use). A setting of 3 is a good starting point.

File / 3D Restore (Spherical 3D Parameters)

Command Function
Chose various spherical 3-D parameters such as axis rotation, water level, etc.

Menu Access
Automatically selected as part of the 3D RESTORE and 3D OVERLAY functions.

Fractint-Style Prompts Access
Automatic, if the Fractint-style 3D RESTORE sequence is used.

Command-Line Parameters Access
```
longitude=<startdegree>/[<stopdegree>]
latitude=<startdegree>/[<stopdegree>]
radius=<scaleradius>
roughness=<scalez>
waterline=<level>
perspective=<distance>
xyshift=<xshift>[/<yshift>]
xyadjust=<xadjust>[/<yadjust>]
transparent=<startcolor>/<stopcolor>
randomize=<nnn>
```

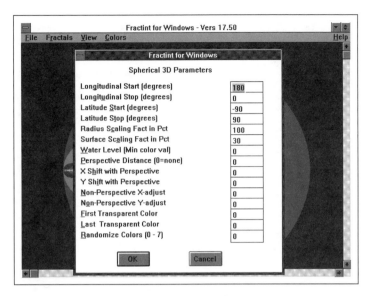

Figure 4-9 The SPHERICAL 3D dialog box

Comments

The SPHERICAL 3D PARAMETERS function (Figure 4-9) controls the wrapping of a fractal image around the surface of a sphere. In fact, you can project any GIF file image, whether from Fractint or not, onto the surface of a sphere.

Longitude Start (Degrees)
Longitude Stop (Degrees)
Latitude Start (Degrees)
Latitude Stop (Degrees)

Picture a globe lying on its side, north pole to the right. You will be mapping the x- and y-values of the starting image to latitude and longitude on the globe, so that what was a horizontal row of pixels becomes a line of longitude, and what was a vertical column of pixels becomes a line of latitude. The default values exactly cover the hemisphere facing you, from longitude 180 degrees (top) to 0 degrees (bottom) and latitude –90 (left) to latitude 90 (right.) By changing these values, you can map the image to a piece of the hemisphere or wrap it clear around the globe. Figure 4-10 shows how this works.

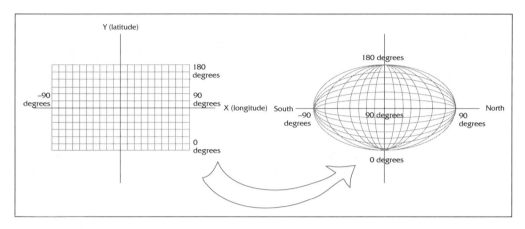

Figure 4-10 Mapping a fractal to a sphere

Radius Scaling Factor in Pct

The radius factor controls the overall size of the globe and is the sphere analog to the x and y scale factors. Use this parameter to enlarge or shrink your globe as you want.

Surface Roughness Scaling Factor in Pct

The roughness factor in the sphere context controls the bumpiness of the surface of the sphere. A value of zero makes the sphere perfectly smooth.

The remaining screen items have the same meaning for a sphere transformation as they do for a plane transformation—see the PLANAR 3D PARAMETERS screen for the explanation.

When the wraparound construction process begins at the edge of the sphere (the default) or behind it, it is plotting points that will be hidden by subsequent points as the process sweeps around the sphere toward you. Winfract's hidden-point algorithms know this, and the first few dozen lines may be invisible unless a high mountain happens to poke over the horizon. If you start a spherical projection and the screen stays black, wait a while (a longer while for higher resolution or fill type 6) to see if points start to appear.

File / 3D Restore (Light Source Parameters)

Command Function

After a 3-D transformation has been selected, and if an appropriate light source has been selected, set various light-source parameters.

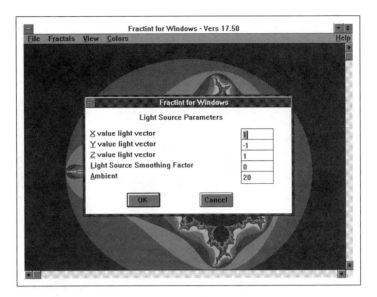

Figure 4-11 The 3D LIGHT SOURCE dialog box

Menu Access
Automatically selected as part of the 3D RESTORE and 3D OVERLAY functions.

Fractint-Style Prompts Access
Automatic, if the Fractint-style 3D RESTORE sequence is used.

Command-Line Parameters Access
```
lightsource=<x>[/<y>[/<z>]]
smoothing=<nnn>
ambient=<nnn>
```

Comments
The purpose of this screen (Figure 4-11) is to control the details of an internal, simulated light that is shining on your fractal. You will need patience when using the light source option because figuring out light directions can be confusing.

X Value Light Vector
Y Value Light Vector
Z Value Light Vector

First, if you have selected a light source fill, you must choose the direction of the light from the light source. This will be scaled in the x, y, and z directions the same as the image. For example, the values 1,1,3 position

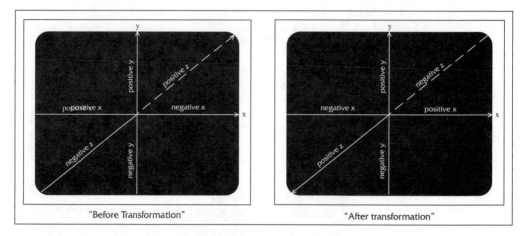

Figure 4-12 Two light coordinate systems

the light to come from the lower right front of the screen in relation to the untransformed image. It is important to remember that these coordinates are scaled the same as your image. Thus 1,1,1 positions the light to come from a direction of equal distances to the right, below, and in front of each pixel on the original image. However, if the x,y,z scale is set to 90,90,30, the result will be from equal distances to the right and below each pixel but from only 1/3 the distance in front of the screen; that is, it will be low in the sky, as if it were afternoon or morning.

Figure 4-12 shows the coordinate system used for defining the light vectors in the two light source modes. This coordinate system is not the same for the before transformation and after transformation light source options we explained earlier. For the light source before transformation option, the positive x-axis is on the left, the positive y-axis is up, and the positive z-axis is behind the screen. A good light vector to try would be x=1, y=1, and z=−3. With this light vector and rotations of 0,0,0, the light would appear to come from the upper right. For the light source after transformation option, the positive x-axis is on the right, the positive y-axis is up, and the positive z-axis is in front of the screen. To get the same effect as the above vector, the signs of the x- and z-coordinates of the light vector have to be reversed, yielding x=−1, y=1, and z=3. Confusion can be avoided by using one of the two light source options until you are familiar with the effects.

Light Source Smoothing Factor

Unless you use continuous potential (described below) when generating the starting 3-D image, the illumination when using light source fills may appear sparkly, like a sandy beach in bright sun. This is because with only

256 colors in the original image, the z-coordinate has only 256 possible values, and the transformed image surface is broken into tiny facets. With continuous potential, there are 64,000 possible z-coordinate values, so a very smooth surface is possible. The smoothing factor averages colors in each line of the original image, smearing them together. A smoothing factor of 2 or 3 will allow you to see the large-scale shapes better. If you did use continuous potential and are loading in a *.POT file, you should turn off smoothing. If your fractal is not a plasma cloud and has features with sharply defined boundaries (e.g., a Mandelbrot lake), the smoothing may cause the colors to run.

Ambient Light (0–100, 0 = Black Shadows)

If a surface has no direct lighting at all, the ambient option sets the minimum light value for the surface. All light values are scaled from this value to white. This effectively adjusts the depth of the shadows and sets the overall contrast of the image.

File / 3D Restore (3D Funny-Glasses Parameters)

Command Function

After 3-D transformation has been selected, and if an appropriate Stereo 3-D option has been selected, you need to set various Stereo 3-D parameters. This dialog box is also brought up as part of the FRACTAL OPTIONS / 3D PARAMETERS option if appropriate.

Menu Access

Automatically selected as part of the 3D RESTORE and 3D OVERLAY functions.

Fractint-Style Prompts Access

Automatic, if the Fractint-style 3D RESTORE sequence is used.

Command-Line Parameters Access

```
interocular=<distance>
converge=<distance>
crop=<red-left>/<red-right>/<blue-left>/<blue-right>
bright=<red>/<blue>
map=<mapfilename>
```

Comments

Figure 4-13 shows the Funny-Glasses dialog box.

Interocular Distance

The interocular distance is the distance between the left and right viewpoints measured as a percent of the screen width. It should be set small

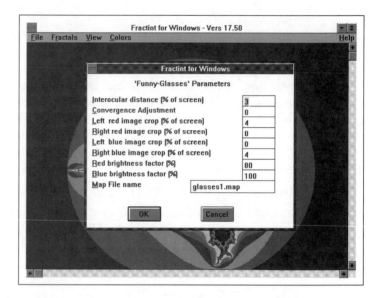

Figure 4-13 Funny-Glasses dialog box

enough so that your eyes can easily converge the two images, but large enough that there is an adequate stereo effect. The default of 3 usually works quite well if the perspective value is not extremely close.

Convergence Adjustment

The convergence parameter adjusts the relative position of the two images in the horizontal dimension. The effect is to move the apparent image into or out from the screen. A larger value makes the image appear in front of the screen, while a smaller (possibly negative) value makes the 3-D object appear to be inside the monitor.

Left Red Image Crop
Right Red Image Crop
Left Blue Image Crop
Right Blue Image Crop

The red and blue images need to be clipped on the left and right differently to make a proper 3-D effect. The edge of the image should appear to be in the same place for both eyes. Setting this properly can be very tricky because it interacts strongly with the convergence parameter. The default is about right for images that appear near the screen surface. Cropping is only an issue when the screen edge clips the image. If a lorenz3d image is completely contained within the screen, for example, so the black background goes right up to the screen edge, then cropping is not needed.

Red Brightness Factor
Blue Brightness Factor

The brightness parameters allow adjustment for differences in the red and blue screen color saturation and glasses filter properties. You can adjust these values so that both the red and blue images look equally bright. The correct settings are dependent on the color properties of your monitor, the quality of your funny-glasses filters, and the color sensitivity of your eyes. Try to find values that minimize the ghost image caused by bleed-through of the left (red) image through the blue lens to the right eye, and the right (blue) image through the red lens to the left eye. If you can see a faint, green, ghost image when you place the blue lens over the red image, it means there is too much yellow in the red image. Try turning down the monitor intensity until the ghost disappears.

Map File Name

The alternate and superimpose methods of displaying red and blue images on your screen each require special palette mappings. They are stored in the files GLASSES1.MAP and GLASSES2.MAP that come with Winfract. The files GLASSES1.MAP and GLASSES2.MAP are designed to allow the greatest number of different shades of red and blue. If you are using superimpose, try substituting the file called GRID.MAP and see if it works any better, especially for wire-frame images or other images that do not need shades of red and blue.

File / 3D Overlay

Command Function

The 3D OVERLAY menu item is used to load and display a GIF image overlaid on the current image using 3-D transformations.

Menu Acces

The 3D OVERLAY menu item of the FILE menu.

Fractint-Style Prompts Access

The (O) hotkey brings up the Fractint-style prompt sequence.

Command-Line Parameters Access

None.

Comments

This function is identical to the normal 3-D transformation accessed with the 3D RESTORE menu, with one important difference: the existing image

Figure 4-14 Moons over landscape

is not cleared prior to the drawing of the 3-D image. The new image is pasted on top of the old image. For example, if the first image is a plasma landscape, and you use the 3D OVERLAY command to make a sphere, the sphere image will be added to the plasma landscape picture. Figure 4-14 shows the kind of images that are possible with this command.

File / Read @Batchfile

Command Function
The READ @BATCHFILE menu item is used to load and generate a fractal image from a file of preselected instructions stored as parameter entries.

Menu Access
The READ @BATCHFILE menu item of the FILE menu.

Fractint-Style Prompts Access
The @ hotkey brings up the Fractint-style prompt sequence.

Command-Line Parameters Access
None.

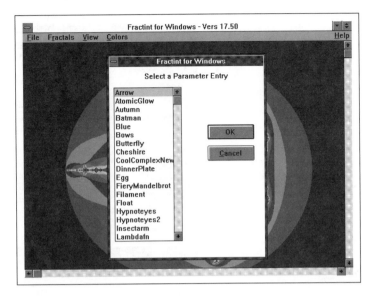

Figure 4-15 Selecting a parameter file entry

Comments

Parameter files (also called batch files) can be used to save/restore all the options and settings required to re-create particular images. The parameters required to describe an image require very little disk space, especially compared with that of saving the image itself.

The FILE / READ @BATCHFILE command loads a set of parameters describing an image. When you start up this command, Winfract first brings up a standard FILE / OPEN dialog box letting you select which parameter file you want to use. (Winfract comes with a sample parameter file, FRACTINT.PAR.) Once you select a parameter file, Winfract displays the names of the entries in that file (Figure 4-15). When you select an entry, Winfract reads the command-line parameters in that entry and generates a fractal image based on them.

File / Save @Batchfile

Command Function

The SAVE @BATCHFILE menu item saves the command-line parameters that can be used to regenerate the currently displayed fractal image into a file of preselected instructions stored as parameter entries.

Menu Access

The SAVE @BATCHFILE menu item of the FILE menu.

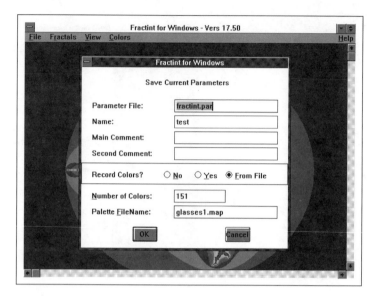

Figure 4-16 Saving a parameter file entry

Fractint-Style Prompts Access
The ⒷB hotkey brings up the Fractint-style prompt sequence.

Command-Line Parameters Access
None.

Comments
Parameter files (also called batch files) can be used to save and restore all options and settings required to re-create particular images. The parameters required to describe an image require very little disk space, especially compared with that of saving the image itself.

The FILE / SAVE @BATCHFILE command saves a set of parameters describing the current fractal image. When you start up this command, Winfract brings up a dialog box (Figure 4-16) letting you select a parameter file (see the following description), the name of your entry, and several options.

Parameter File
The name of the file to store the parameters in. You may want to consider using some name like MYIMAGES.PAR instead of the default FRACTINT.PAR, so that your images are kept separate from the ones released with new versions of Winfract.

Name

The name you want to assign to the entry to be displayed when the FILE / READ @BATCHFILE command is used.

Main Comment
Second Comment

These comments are stored with the parameter entry. They are not displayed during the FILE / READ @BATCHFILE display in the current versions of Winfract. However, this may change (and they *are* displayed in the current Fractint program), so you may want to keep your comments suitable for public viewing.

Record Colors

This selection governs whether color information should be included in the entry. Usually the default value displayed by Winfract is what you want, as Winfract is pretty clever about remembering whether you've used a palette file or done any color cycling lately. The RECORD COLOR options are:

> NO—Don't record colors. This is the default if the image is using Winfract's default colors.
> FROM FILE—Load the colors from the named color map file. This is the default if you are currently using colors from a color map file.
> YES—Record the colors in the parameter entry in detail. This is the default when you've changed the display colors by color cycling.

Number of Colors

This only matters if RECORD COLORS is set to YES. It specifies the number of colors to record. Recording fewer colors takes less space. Usually, the default value displayed by Winfract is what you want.

Palette FileName

This only matters if RECORD COLORS is set to FROM FILE. This entry is the name of the last palette map file you've used.

File / Copy to Clipboard

Command Function

The COPY TO CLIPBOARD menu item is used to copy the currently displayed fractal image to the Windows clipboard for future use by other Windows programs.

Menu Access
The COPY TO CLIPBOARD menu item of the FILE menu.

Fractint-Style Prompts Access
None.

Command-Line Parameters Access
None.

Comments
Many Windows programs, including most of the ones that specialize in manipulating graphics images, can collect images from the Windows clipboard. This feature comes in particularly handy if your favorite Windows graphics packages don't handle Winfract's default GIF format.

File / Exit

Command Function
The EXIT menu item is used to end the Winfract program.

Menu Access
The EXIT menu item of the FILE menu.

Fractint-Style Prompts Access
None.

Command-Line Parameters Access
None.

Comments
The standard (ALT)-(F4) sequence of exiting Windows applications also causes Winfract to end.

THE FRACTALS MENU

The FRACTALS menu items deal with those Winfract commands that involve selecting and modifying the fractal parameters of the image that is displayed in the window. The following section is organized according to the menu items on the FRACTALS menu.

Fractals / Fractal Formula

Command Function
The FRACTAL FORMULA menu item is used to select a new fractal type for viewing.

Menu Access
The FRACTAL FORMULA menu item of the FRACTALS menu item.

Fractint-Style Prompts Access
The (T) hotkey brings up the Fractint-style prompt sequence.

Command-Line Parameters Access
```
type=<type>
params=<nnn>[/<nnn>[/<nnn>[/<nnn>]]]
bailout=<nnn>
corners=xmin/xmax/ymin/ymax
center-mag=[Xctr/Yctr/Mag]
```

Comments
Winfract generates fractal images from an incredible number of different fractal types. See Chapter 5, Fractal Types, for a detailed description of these fractal types.

When you select the FRACTALS / FRACTAL FORMULA menu item, Winfract displays a standard list box containing all of its available fractal types sorted in alphabetical order. Select the fractal type you want to display, either by double-clicking on its name using your mouse or by moving the selection highlight to it using your cursor keys and then pressing (ENTER). If the fractal type you want isn't listed in the visible portion of the listbox, you can use the scrollbar or cursor keys to scroll through the list until it becomes visible.

After you select a fractal type, Winfract prompts you for any parameters related to the selected fractal type, along with the coordinates of the image corners of the initial display. All parameter and corner values are given with defaults that generate interesting (or at least nonboring) images, although we're confident that you can do better than the images generated using the defaults. The types formula and lsystem read in a complete list of subtypes from files you can edit, allowing you to create new types. See Figure 4-17 for the parameter dialog box for the Mandelbrot fractal type.

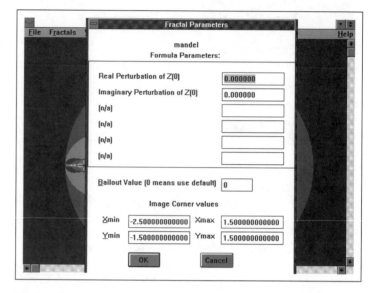

Figure 4-17 The FRACTAL PARAMETER dialog box for the
Mandelbrot fractal

Fractals / Basic Options

Command Function
The BASIC OPTIONS menu item is used to view and modify any of a number of options used in generating the current fractal image.

Menu Access
The BASIC OPTIONS menu item of the FRACTALS menu item.

Fractint-Style Prompts Access
The ⓧ hotkey brings up the Fractint-style prompt sequence.

Command-Line Parameters Access
```
passes=1|2|guess|btm
float=yes
maxiter=nnn
inside=<nnn>|maxiter|bof60|bof61|zmag|eps|star
outside=<nnn>|iter|real|imag|mult|summ
logmap=yes|old|<nnn>
biomorph=<nnn>
decomp=0|2|4|8|16|32|64|128|256
fillcolor=<nnn>
```

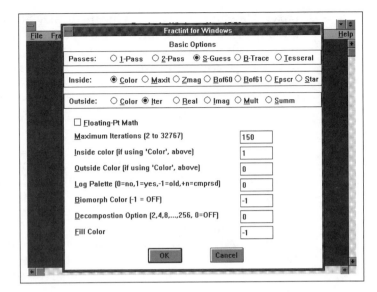

Figure 4-18 The BASIC OPTIONS dialog box

Comments

The distinction in Winfract between basic and extended options is somewhat arbitrary. The authors resent the common assumption that the basic options are just the ones they thought up first, mostly because it's true. The BASIC OPTIONS menu (Figure 4-18) lets you select and modify any of the following options:

Passes

The passes options, only one of which can be selected at a time, determine which of several algorithms are used to generate your fractal image. There are five algorithms available: single-pass, dual-pass, solid-guessing mode, boundary tracing, and tesseral. The SINGLE-PASS mode draws the image pixel by pixel and is the simplest (and slowest) of the five. The DUAL-PASS mode generates a coarse screen first as a preview using 2 x 2-pixel boxes, and when the image is filled generates the rest of the dots with a second pass. The effect is to quickly get a coarse view of the fractal. Remember, you don't have to wait for a fractal image to complete before selecting a new image or a new place to zoom in on the current one. SOLID-GUESSING is the fastest mode, because it attempts to avoid calculations by guessing the color of pixels surrounded by pixels of one color. It performs from two to four visible passes—more on higher-resolution images. Its first visible pass works much like the first pass of the dual-pass algorithm, except that it performs fewer calculations and uses larger pixel boxes. Subsequent passes fill in the display at the next-finer resolution, but skip blocks that are surrounded by a single color (making the assumption that those blocks are in the middle of a solid band of color). The multiple passes are for two reasons. The first is to give you a quick preview of the image in case you don't want to wait for it to complete. The second reason is that the guessing algorithm works in stages, starting with a rough approximation. Solid-guessing can guess wrong when it assumes that a block completely surrounded by a single color is that same color, but it guesses wrong quickly.

The TESSERAL algorithm is a variant of the super-solid guessing algorithm that works by continually dividing the screen into quarters, calculating all of the pixel values of the rectangular border of each quadrant, and filling in an entire rectangle if its boundary is all the same color.

BOUNDARY TRACING is a completely different approach from the others. It only works with fractal types that do not contain islands of colors, such as the Mandelbrot set (but not the Newton type). Boundary tracing works by finding a color boundary, tracing it around the image, and then filling in the enclosed area. The idea of this algorithm is to speed up calculations, but in Winfract solid-guessing is almost always faster. We have included boundary tracing anyway because it is fun to watch! Boundary tracing does not work when the inside color is set to 0 (black) because it uses 0 to determine if a color has been written to the screen already.

Understand that the single- and dual-pass modes result in exactly the same image and take the same amount of time. They work best for fractal purists who do not want to risk the occasional inaccuracies of the default guessing mode. Most of the time, the solid-guessing mode is the one to use, and it's usually the default. If you are the type who is fascinated by watching intriguing algorithms at work, by all means try the boundary tracing and tesseral options.

Inside Color

The INSIDE option lets you set the color of the lake area of a fractal. (Recall from Chapter 1's discussion that the lake area consists of the points whose orbits had still not escaped when the maximum iteration cutoff was reached.) For example, setting INSIDE to COLOR and the INSIDE COLOR to 0 makes the Mandelbrot-fractal interior lake black, since color 0 is black in the standard Windows palette. (If you change the palette by cycling colors, 0 might be a different color.) Setting INSIDE to MAXITER makes the inside color the same as the maximum iteration value you are using, which is useful for 3-D purposes.

Three more INSIDE options reveal hidden structures inside the lake. They are BOF60 and BOF61, named after the page numbers in our copy of

Beauty of Fractals where we first saw these plotted, and ZMAG. If you set INSIDE to BOF60, the lake area will be broken into colored areas where the iteration number of the closest orbit approach to the origin is identical. If you set INSIDE to BOF61, you will see the lake broken into colored areas where the closest value of the orbit to the origin is the same. Setting INSIDE to ZMAG colors the inside pixels based on the magnitude of their order point when maxiter was reached.

Getting confused yet? Well then, consider the EPSCROSS option, which colors the inside pixels based on whether their orbits swung close to the x- or y-axis, and the STARCROSS option, which colors them based on clusters of points in the orbits.

Don't worry if you don't understand all these options, just try them to see what they look like!

Outside Color

As you might guess, this function is the opposite of the INSIDE option. The INSIDE option sets the color of the lake, which is to say the points of the Mandelbrot set. The OUTSIDE option concerns itself with all the areas outside the lake.

Throughout this book we have discussed the Mandelbrot fractal or image instead of the Mandelbrot set. The reason is that the Mandelbrot set consists of just the interior lake; all the striped colors of the usual fractal image of the Mandelbrot are not part of the set at all! The first outside option was born when the authors received a letter from a high school math teacher who wanted to see just the Mandelbrot set (the part colored with the inside option) and not the distracting stripes outside the set.

The classic method of coloring outside the fractal is to color according to how many iterations were required before *z* reached the bailout value, usually 4. This is the method used when OUTSIDE is set to ITER.

Setting OUTSIDE to COLOR and setting OUTSIDE COLOR to NNN sets the color of the exterior to some number of your choosing. For example, if OUTSIDE COLOR is 1, all points not inside the fractal set are displayed as color 1 (blue). Note that defining an outside color forces any image to be a two-color one: either a point is inside the set, or it's outside it.

However, when *z* reaches bailout, the real and imaginary components can be at very different values. Setting OUTSIDE to REAL or IMAG colors the outside pixels using the iteration value plus the real or imaginary values. If OUTSIDE is SUMM, Winfract uses the sum of all these values to determine the pixel color. These options can give a startling 3-D quality to otherwise flat images and can change some boring images to wonderful ones. The OUTSIDE MULT option colors outside pixels by multiplying the iteration by the real part divided by the imaginary part. There was no mathematical reason for this coloring scheme; it just seemed like a good idea.

Floatin-Point Math

Most fractal types have both a fast integer math and a floating-point version. The much faster, but sometimes less accurate, integer version is the default. If you have an Intel 80386-based PC or other fast machine with a math coprocessor, or if you are using the continuous potential option (which looks best with high bailout values not possible with our integer math implementation), you may prefer to use floating-point instead of integer math. In fact, with the latest round of speed-em-up coding in Winfract's floating-point algorithms, Intel 80486-based PCs generate the Mandelbrot image using Winfract's floating-point math almost as fast as they do using Winfract's integer math. 486 chipsets with floating-point math have an internal, floating-point unit that is much faster than the external FPU their predecessors use.

To enable floating-point math, set the FLOATING-POINT flag in this menu. Winfract automatically changes to floating-point math when you zoom deeply into an image and the limited range of the faster integer math is encountered.

Maximum Iterations

Recall that the escape-time algorithm creates fractal images by repeatedly iterating a formula and testing whether the orbit wanders outside the bailout threshold. Because many orbits never do escape the bailout radius, Winfract must have a limit to how many iterations it will try before giving up, or the computation will go on forever. That limit is the MAXIMUM ITERATIONS value, and it has a default of 150. The limit causes some inaccuracy in the final fractal. For example, there are points near the lake shore of the Mandelbrot set whose orbits have not escaped after 150 iterations, but they would have escaped after a few more iterations if the calculation had been extended. These points might be plotted as part of the lake, when they really belong on the shore. The higher the maximum iterations cutoff, the more accurate the final image, but also the slower the calculation. As a practical matter, the default Mandelbrot image looks fine with 150 iterations. As you zoom in further, however, you will need to increase the iteration limit when the inaccuracies become visible.

To see the effect of setting the maximum iteration limit, select the BASIC OPTIONS menu while viewing a fractal, and set the MAXIMUM ITERATIONS (2 to 32,767) value to 3. (The value 2 creates a solid blue image unless the INSIDE value is set to something other than 2.) You will see a single oval band surrounding the lake, which consists of all the points whose orbits did not escape after 3 iterations. Now try again and set maximum iterations to 4. You will see one more band, and the lake will be a little smaller. After trying a few higher values, you will see why the value

150 is fine for the default Mandelbrot. A higher value makes no visual difference at that magnification.

Log Palettes

Normally, escape-time iterations are mapped one-to-one to palette colors (the normal case, when LOG PALETTES is set to 0), which causes areas with a high iteration count to lose detail because the colors change so rapidly that the stripes are too close together for you to see any pattern. Turning this option on by setting LOG PALETTES to 1 causes colors to be mapped to the logarithm of the iteration, revealing structure in the featureless areas of more chaotic coloring. Entering a number larger than 1 enables logarithmic palette mapping but also forces a "compression" of this mapping by forcing all iteration counts lower than the specified number to use the first palette color. This option is particularly useful when you're in a highly zoomed portion of a fractal image where every pixel has a high iteration count. Setting LOG PALETTES to –1 forces Winfract to use an older logarithmic palette algorithm used in earlier versions of Fractint, an option useful only for backward compatibility.

When using a logarithmic palette in a 256-color mode, we suggest changing your colors from the usual defaults.

Decomposition

Most fractal types are calculated by iterating a simple function of a complex number to produce another complex number, until either the number exceeds some predefined bailout value or the iteration limit is reached. The pixel corresponding to the starting point is then colored based on the result of that calculation.

The DECOMPOSITION option turns on another coloring method. Here the points are colored according to which section of the complex plane the final value is in. The decomposition parameter determines how many sections the plane is divided into for this purpose. The result is a kind of warped checkerboard coloring, even in areas that would ordinarily be part of a single contour. Figure 4-19 shows what the default Mandelbrot looks like with decomp=2.

Biomorph Color

Related to binary decomposition are the biomorphs invented by Clifford Pickover and discussed by A. K. Dewdney in his Computer Recreations column in the July 1989 *Scientific American*, page 110. They are so-named because this coloring scheme makes many fractals look like one-celled animals. Figure 4-20 shows an example of what appears to be a giant biomorph with baby biomorphs inside.

Figure 4-19 The Mandelbrot fractal using decomposition

To create BIOMORPHS, the normal escape-time coloring is modified so that if either the real *or* the imaginary component is less than the bailout, then the pixel is set to the biomorph color. The effect is a bit better with higher bailout values: the bailout is automatically set to 100 when this option is in effect. You can try other values with the bailout option. When toggling to Julia sets, the default corners are three times bigger than normal to allow one to see the biomorph appendages. This option does not work with all types; in particular it fails with any of the mandelsine family. However, if you are stuck with monochrome graphics, you should try it, as it works very well in two-color modes. Try it with the marksmandel and marksjulia types.

Fill Color

The FILL COLOR option only affects the Boundary-Tracing and Tesseral algorithms. It causes them to use a fixed color instead of the boundary color whenever they fill in an area. This gives you a pretty clear idea of just how much of the fractal image these algorithms avoided calculating.

Fractals / Extended Options

Command Function

The EXTENDED OPTIONS menu item is used to view and modify any of a number of options used in generating the current fractal image.

Figure 4-20 A Pickover biomorph

Menu Access
The EXTENDED OPTIONS menu item of the FRACTALS menu item.

Fractint-Style Prompts Access
The Ⓨ hotkey brings up the Fractint-style prompt sequence.

Command-Line Parameters Access
```
finattract=no|yes
potential=<maxcolor>[/<slope>[/<bailout>[/16bit]]]
invert=<radius>/<xcenter>/<ycenter>
distest=<nnn>
cyclerange=<nnn>/<nnn>
```

Comments
The distinction in Winfract between basic and extended options is some-what arbitrary. The options that were selected as being extended (Figure 4-21) are detailed here:

Finite Attractor
This is an option that colors some Julia lakes, showing the escape time to finite attractors. It works with the lambda and magnet types as well as others.

A finite attractor is a point within a Julia set that captures the orbits of points that come near. By capture we mean that if this option is turned

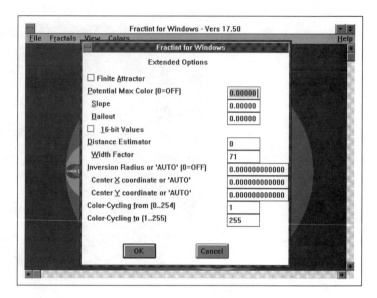

Figure 4-21 The EXTENDED OPTIONS dialog box

on, Winfract attempts to locate such a finite attractor and then to color the inside of the lake according to the time of escape of that attractor. This is an exact analogy to the way the normal escape-time algorithm colors points according to escape time to infinity. Another way to put this is that this option graphs the level sets of the basin of attraction of a finite attractor.

For a quick demonstration, select a fractal type of lambda using the FRACTALS / FRACTAL FORMULA menu item, changing the real and imaginary parts of the parameter from their default values to .5 and .5. You will obtain an image with a large blue lake. Now go back to the FRACTALS / EXTENDED OPTIONS menu and check the FINITE ATTRACTOR option. The image will be redrawn from scratch, this time with a much more multicolored lake. A finite attractor lives in the center of one of the resulting ripple patterns in the lake. Figure 4-22 shows the result. The code and original documentation for this option were provided by Kevin Allen of Australia.

Potential Max Color
Slope
Bailout

Winfract's escape-time fractal images are usually calculated by the level set method, producing bands of color. Each of these bands consists of all points whose orbit exceeded the bailout threshold at the same iteration. The continuous potential option makes colors change continuously, rather

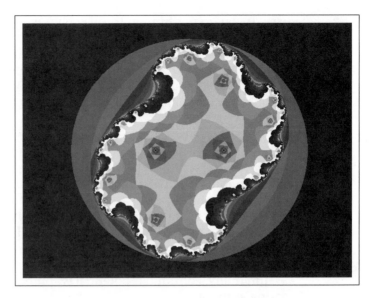

Figure 4-22 Finite attractors in lambda lake

than breaking the image into bands or stripes. A 256-color video mode is mandatory to appreciate this effect, as it is impossible to show continuous variation with only 2 or 16 colors. Non-3-D continuous potential images sometimes have a 3-D appearance because of the smoothly changing colors. Color cycling a continuous potential image gives a totally different effect than you experience with a normal striped fractal. The colors ooze rather than flash.

POTENTIAL MAX COLOR is the color corresponding to zero potential, which plots as the top of the mountain. Generally, this should be set to one less than the number of colors. (235 is a good Windows 256-color value, as it avoids the 20 palette values reserved by the Windows video driver for system use.)

SLOPE is a number that determines how fast the colors change (try 2,000 or so). If this value is too high, there will be large solid areas with the color 0; if it is too low, only a limited segment of possible colors will appear in the image. In 3-D transformations, this value determines the steepness of the mountain slopes.

BAILOUT is a number that replaces the normal escape-time bailout (set at 4). Larger values give more accurate and smoother potential—try 200.

16-BIT VALUES is a flag that makes Winfract save the file as a double-wide, 16-bits-per-pixel GIF file. Use this flag if you want to try a 3-D transformation of the image. The 16 bits per pixel results in a smoother 3-D image. If you do not turn on this flag but save the file in the normal way, then the potential value will be truncated to an integer, resulting in a rougher 3-D image. When this flag is turned on, saved filenames will have the extension .POT, short for potential. You can load these files back into Winfract the same way normal GIF files are loaded back in. However, the .POT files will look strange when viewed with GIF decoders other than Winfract.

Creating 3-D Landscapes

Continuous potential is particularly useful when creating 3-D landscape images from fractals. When viewed in 3D, the stripes of a typical noncontinuous potential image turn into something like Chinese terraces; most of the surface appears to be made up of colorful horizontal steps. This effect may be interesting, but it is not suitable for use with the 3-D light source fill options. Continuous potential smooths the steplike terraces into a continuous surface, so that the illumination results in graduated shades of color.

Internally, continuous potential is approximated in Winfract by calculating as follows:

$$potential = \log(modulus)/2^{iterations}))$$

where modulus is the magnitude of the iterations orbit value—the first orbit value that exceeded the bailout. The term potential comes from the fact that this value is related to the electrical potential field surrounding the lake that would result if it were electrically charged.

Here is a pointer for using continuous potential. Winfract's criterion for halting a fractal calculation, the bailout value, is generally set to 4, but continuous potential is inaccurate at such a low value. The integer math that makes the mandel and Julia types so fast imposes a hard-wired maximum bailout value of 127. You can still make interesting images with these bailout values, such as ridges in the fractal hillsides. However, this bailout limitation can be avoided by turning on the floating-point algorithm option from the BASIC OPTIONS menu.

Distance Estimator
Width Factor

This option is Phil Wilson's implementation of an alternate method for rendering the Mandelbrot and Julia sets, based on work by mathematician John Milnor and described in *The Science of Fractal Images*. While this alternative method takes full advantage of your color palette, one of its best uses is in preparing monochrome (single-color) images for a printer. Using a high-resolution monochrome image and an HP LaserJet, you can generate fractals of quality equivalent to the black-and-white illustrations of the Mandelbrot set in *The Beauty of Fractals*.

The distance estimator method has the effect of widening the very thin strands which are part of the inside of the set. Instead of hiding invisibly between pixels, these strands are made one pixel wide. This method is designed to be used with the classic Mandelbrot and Julia types, and it may work with other escape-time fractals.

To turn on the distance estimator method, set the DISTANCE ESTI-MATOR value to a nonzero value.

The DISTANCE ESTIMATOR option interacts with a number of fractal generation options that are located in the FRACTALS / BASIC OPTIONS menu. If you set DISTANCE ESTIMATOR to 1, you should also set the inside color to something other than 1, or you will get a solid blue fractal (set-ting inside color to 0 gives you a black interior). You should use the one-pass or two-pass algorithms—solid-guessing and boundary tracing can miss some of the thin strands made visible by the distance estimator method. For the highest-quality images, maxiter should also be set to a high value, say 1,000 or so.

In color modes, the distance estimator method also produces more evenly spaced contours. Set the distance estimator value higher for nar-rower color bands and lower for wider ones. 1,000 is a good value to start with. Using this option automatically toggles to floating-point mode. When you disable this option by seting its value back to zero, remember to turn off floating-point mode if you want it off.

Unfortunately, images using the distance estimator method can take many hours to calculate even on a fast machine with a coprocessor. There-fore, you should not use this option for exploration, but use it only after you have found interesting fractals.

Inversion
Inversion Radius
Center X Coordinate
Center Y Coordinate

The INVERT IMAGE function has three parameters. The INVERSION RA-DIUS must be set; the default 0 value means inversion is turned off. The CENTER X- and CENTER Y-coordinates default to 0 if not set.

Many years ago there was a brief craze for anamorphic art: images painted and viewed with the use of a cylindrical mirror, so that they looked weirdly distorted on the canvas but correct in the distorted reflection. In other words, you could see the paintings correctly if you looked at the image in the cylindrical mirror.

Winfract's inversion option performs a related transformation on most of the fractal types. You define the center point and radius of a circle on your fractal; Winfract maps each point inside the circle to a corresponding point outside, and vice versa. This is known to mathematicians as "everting

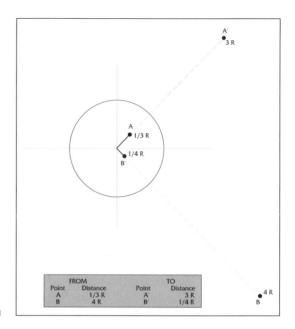

Figure 4-23
The inversion transformation

FROM		TO	
Point	Distance	Point	Distance
A	1/3 R	A'	3 R
B	4 R	B'	1/4 R

the plane." John Milnor made his name in the 1950s with a method for everting a seven-dimensional sphere, so Winfract still has a "ways to go" in this particular area.

As an example, if a point A inside the circle is 1/3 of the way from the center to the radius, it is mapped to a point A' along the same radial line, but at a distance of (3 × radius) from the origin. An outside point B' at 4 times the radius is mapped to a point B inside at 1/4 the radius. Figure 4-23 shows the transformation that inversion accomplishes.

Entering the word Auto for the INVERSION RADIUS sets the radius at 1/6 the smaller dimension of the image currently on the screen. The auto values for center X and center Y use the coordinates currently mapped to the center of the screen.

The Newton fractal is a good one to try with the inversion option because it has well-defined radial spokes that make it easy to visualize the before and after effects of inverting. Select the Newton fractal type using the FRACTALS / FRACTAL FORMULA menu. Then return to the FRACTALS / EXTENDED OPTIONS menu and enter inversion parameters, using a radius of 1 with the center coordinates set to 0. The center has exploded to the periphery. Inverting through a circle not centered on the origin produces bizarre effects that we're not even going to try to describe. Do this by entering nonzero values for center X and center Y.

Color-Cycling From
Color-Cycling To

Normally, color cycling cycles through the entire palette, except for the background color (0), which stays constant. Setting these values restricts the color-cycling range for some interesting effects.

Fractals / Fractal Params

Command Function

The FRACTAL PARAMS menu item contains parameters specific to the current fractal type. It is used to view and modify any of a number of options used in generating a fractal image.

Menu Access

The FRACTAL PARAMS menu item of the FRACTALS menu item.

Fractint-Style Prompts Access

The (Z) hotkey brings up the Fractint-style prompt sequence.

Command-Line Parameters Access

```
params=<nnn>[/<nnn>[/<nnn>[/<nnn>]]]
bailout=<nnn>
corners=xmin/xmax/ymin/ymax
center-mag=[Xctr/Yctr/Mag]
```

Comments

The FRACTAL PARAMETERS menu brings up the same dialog box that the FRACTAL FORMULA menu item (Figure 4-17) does when you select a fractal type. Adding this dialog box as a direct menu item lets you change fractal parameters without resetting your image boundaries and vice versa. It also avoids wandering through the fractal types dialog box when you're not interested in changing fractal types.

Fractals / 3D Params

Command Function

The 3D PARAMS menu item is used to view and modify any of a number of options related to the 3-D display used in generating the current fractal image.

Menu Access

The 3D PARAMS menu item of the FRACTALS menu item.

Fractint-Style Prompts Access

The (I) hotkey brings up the Fractint-style prompt sequence.

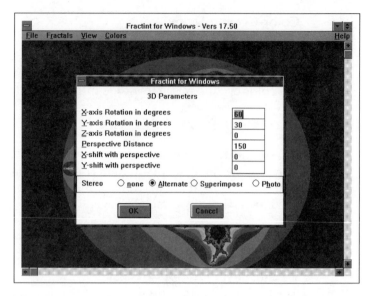

Figure 4-24 The fractal 3D PARAMS dialog box

Command-Line Parameters Access

```
rotation=<xrot>[/<yrot>[/<zrot>]]
perspective=<nnn>
xyshift=<xshift>/<yshift>
stereo=0|1|2|3
```

Comments

All the 3-D capabilities in Winfract use the same variables. These 3-D parameters are also settable via the 3D RESTORE menu item on the FILES menu. The fractal types that use 3D are ifs3D, lorenz3d, rossler3d, kamtorus3d, and henon. Figure 4-24 shows the 3D PARAMS dialog box.

Imagine that the x-axis runs horizontally across the middle of your computer screen, with zero in the middle. The y-axis runs vertically through the computer screen with zero in the middle. The z-axis is perpendicular to the plane of the screen with the positive end toward you.

Here is what each of the 3-D parameters do:

X-axis Rotation
Y-axis Rotation
Z-axis Rotation

The first three parameters allow setting the rotations that cause the fractal objects to be viewed from different angles. Refer to Figure 4-25 as you

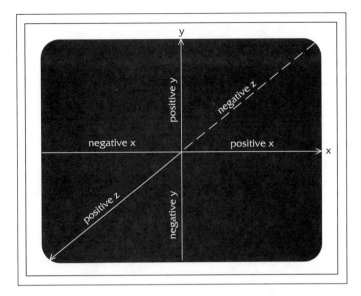

Figure 4-25 The 3-D coordinate system

follow this example. From the FRACTALS / FRACTAL FORMULA menu, select a fractal type and choose type lorenz3d. Now select the FRACTALS / 3D PARAMS menu item and change the x-, y-, and z-axis rotation values to 0, 0, 0. Press (ENTER) to accept these values. You now see the Lorenz orbit as it is with no 3-D rotations. The Lorenz orbit is the path of a wildly orbiting particle under the influence of two invisible attractors. It spirals around one, then the other, back and forth, forming two flat spirals in two different planes at an angle to each other.

Now select the FRACTALS / 3D PARAMS menu item, but change the X-AXIS ROTATION to 30. The image has rotated around the x-axis 30 degrees, with the top of the image coming toward you. One of the two spirals now looks very thin because you are viewing it end-on. Now change the Y-AXIS ROTATION to 30, so both x and y rotations are now 30. The skinny spiral now looks fuller because the image has rotated around the y-axis and the right-hand side of the screen has moved away from you.

Finally, set all three rotation values to 30. The last rotation is the easiest to understand, because the z-axis is coming right out of the screen, and the rotation just moves the image clockwise around the screen. To get a little better feel, you might try repeating this whole experiment with red/ blue glasses—just set the stereo option to superimpose. Figure 4-26 specifically shows the first three of these Lorenz images with superimposed axes,

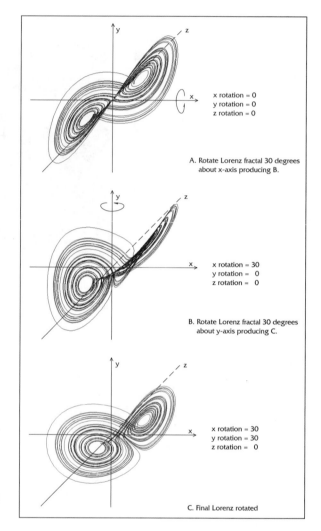

x rotation = 0
y rotation = 0
z rotation = 0

A. Rotate Lorenz fractal 30 degrees about x-axis producing B.

x rotation = 30
y rotation = 0
z rotation = 0

B. Rotate Lorenz fractal 30 degrees about y-axis producing C.

x rotation = 30
y rotation = 30
z rotation = 0

C. Final Lorenz rotated

Figure 4-26
A Lorenz fractal rotated about the three axes

with arrows indicating the direction of rotation. The fourth image with all three rotations is not shown.

Perspective Distance [1–999, 0 for No Persp]

The perspective parameter causes the 3-D projection to use a viewpoint from different distances. The effect is to make closer parts of the fractal larger, and farther parts smaller, as seen by an imaginary observer. The value entered for PERSPECTIVE DISTANCE allows you to control how close this observer is to the fractal object. Imagine the 3-D object inside a box and touching all the sides. A perspective value of 100 is an extreme perspective where your viewpoint is right on the near edge of the box, with parts of the object very close. This can be considered a close-up of the image. A value of 200 means that the near edge of the box is halfway between your eye and the far edge of the box.

X Shift and Y Shift with Perspective

The x and y shift move the position of the observer. If perspective is also turned on, the image is not just moved on the screen, but the point of view is also changed. Shifting to the left and then to the right changes the image in exactly the same way as when you close your right eye and look through your left, and then look at the same scene through your right eye.

Stereo (R/B 3D)

Stereo viewing is a technique whereby two distinct views of a 3-D object are created, one as if seen by the right eye, the other a little offset and as if seen by the left eye. What is needed to reproduce stereo vision is a way to get the left and right images to the correct eye. One method of doing that is to use the red/blue funny glasses. The red filter blocks the blue image and lets the red image through, and the blue filter does the opposite. Winfract can put the left and right images on the screen at the same time, using red and blue colors. The two images overlap, so some method of combining the two colors is needed. Winfract provides two methods, each with its advantages. The ALTERNATE and SUPERIMPOSE options are the two different ways that the red and blue are combined. In the ALTERNATE approach, the screen is divided so that every other pixel in each row is designated to be either a red or blue pixel. The red and blue aren't really combined except in your mind. When your eye sees red and blue pixels close together, your mind sees the color magenta. The alternate approach does offer less resolution because each image is formed from only half the screen pixels, but it allows more shades of red and blue—128 shades with a 256-color Windows video driver.

The SUPERIMPOSE option combines overlapping red and blue pixels in a single magenta pixel, allowing higher effective resolution but fewer shades of red and blue. Even in a 256-color mode, there are only 16 visible shades of red and blue; all the colors are taken up with combinations of these shades. Use superimpose for lorenz3d. Put on your 3-D glasses and regenerate the lorenz3d example.

The PHOTO stereo option makes two separate images and pauses so that pictures can be taken of the screen. The two pictures can be mounted and viewed with a stereo slide viewer. This kind of stereo doesn't use red and blue; it provides full-color stereo. You need a camera to photograph the images, or you can save the left and right views and have slides made by a slide service.

Fractals / Reset All Options

Command Function
The RESET ALL OPTIONS menu item is used to reset all fractal-specific options back to the values they were when your Winfract session first started.

Menu Access
The RESET ALL OPTIONS menu item of the FRACTALS menu item.

Fractint-Style Prompts Access
None.

Command-Line Parameters Access
```
reset
```

Comments
The RESET ALL OPTIONS command is a handy shortcut after you have been modifying all sorts of parameters, can no longer remember which ones you've modified and what they all were set to originally, and want to start all over. It is also used (in command-line argument form) as a safety measure as the first entry in every parameter file.

Fractals / Starfield

Command Function
The STARFIELD menu item is used to convert your currently displayed image into a starfield.

Menu Access
The STARFIELD menu item of the FRACTALS menu item.

Fractint-Style Prompts Access
The (A) hotkey brings up the Fractint-style prompt sequence.

Command-Line Parameters Access
None.

Comments
Once you have generated your favorite fractal image, you can convert it into a fractal starfield using the STARFIELD transformation. The screen is

filled with random-appearing distributions of individual pixels of different degrees of brightness. Stars are generated on a pixel-by-pixel basis—the odds that a particular pixel will coalesce into a star are based (partially) on the color index of that pixel.

If the screen is entirely black and the star density per pixel is set to 30, then a starfield transformation will create an evenly distributed starfield with an average of one star for every 30 pixels. Therefore, if you're using a 320 x 200 image, you have 64,000 pixels and will end up with about 2,100 stars. By introducing the variable of clumpiness, we can create more stars in areas that have higher color values. At 100 percent CLUMPINESS, a color value of 255 will change the average of finding a star at that location to 50:50. A lower clumpiness value will lower the amount of probability weighting. To create a spiral galaxy, draw your favorite spiral fractal (IFS, Julia, or Mandelbrot) and perform a starfield transformation. For general starfields, we recommend transforming a plasma fractal. For starfields based on fractals with lakes, such as the Mandelbrot fractal, be sure to set the inside color to 255 using the FRACTALS / BASIC OPTIONS menu item for the best effect.

Real starfields have many more dim stars than bright ones because very few stars are close enough to appear bright. To achieve this effect, the program will create a bell curve based on the value of the *ratio of dim stars to bright stars*. After calculating the bell curve, the curve is folded in half and the peak is used to represent the number of dim stars.

The starfield transformation should be used only with 256-color images (and Windows video drivers that can display them). Winfract will automatically try to load ALTERN.MAP and abort if the map file cannot be found.

THE VIEW MENU

The VIEW menu items deal with those Winfract commands that involve selecting and modifying the image that is displayed in the window (as opposed to the parameters of the fractal formula that is being displayed there). The following section is organized according to the menu items on the VIEW menu.

View / Image Settings

Command Function
The IMAGE SETTINGS menu item is used to select the size of the generated image and the number of colors it contains.

Menu Access
The IMAGE SETTINGS menu item of the VIEW menu item.

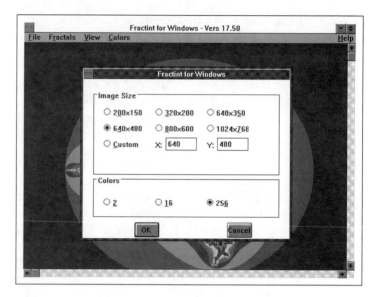

Figure 4-27 The IMAGE SETTINGS dialog box

Fractint-Style Prompts Access

The (DEL) hotkey brings up the Fractint-style prompt sequence.

Command-Line Parameters Access

None.

Comments

When this menu item is selected, Winfract brings up a dialog box (Figure 4-27) letting you select the size of your image and the number of colors it contains. The dialog box consists of two sections:

Image Size

This section of the dialog box contains radio buttons for a number of preselected image sizes (preselected only because they're popular resolutions in the MS-DOS world) and a button labeled CUSTOM. If you want to select a resolution other than one of the preselected image sizes, first modify the X and Y entries and then select the CUSTOM radio button. Otherwise, just pick from any of the preselected image sizes. Winfract has an internal resolution limit of 2,048 pixels: if you ask for an X or Y value larger than this limit, Winfract will silently reduce it to 2,048.

Colors

Here you have three choices: 2-color, 16-color, and 256-color. When Winfract first starts up, it selects one of these entries based on the capabilities of your Windows video driver. You don't have to limit yourself to this selection. Winfract will cheerfully let you generate a 256-color image using a standard, 16-color video driver. However, the subsequent mapping that your Windows video driver goes through to convert Winfract's 256-color image to a 16-color display (mapping each image color to the closest available display color) may not look all that great.

Image Sizes and Memory

Once you've selected an image size and number of colors, Winfract releases whatever memory it was using for the previous image and then asks Windows for enough memory to store the new one. The amount of memory requested can be substantial: 256-color images require one byte of memory for every pixel, and a 256-color 2048 x 2048 image requires 4MB of memory. If Windows is unable to give Winfract the memory it requires, Winfract pops up a message box informing you of the problem and then switches to a small image size that it knows it can access. If that happens, you will have to select a smaller image size that your hardware can handle. Table 4-3 shows the memory requirements of selected image sizes.

A word about Windows 3.0 standard mode, 386-enhanced mode, and memory. In standard mode, Windows 3.0 cannot give memory to its applications in chunks larger than 1MB—if you're running Windows 3.0 in standard mode, you won't be able to select 256-color image sizes of 1,024 x 1,024 or larger or 16-color image sizes of (roughly) 1,400 x 1,400 or larger. Windows 3.0 in 386-enhanced mode and Windows 3.1 in either standard or 386-enhanced mode don't have this problem—in fact, in 386-enhanced mode you can use a full 2,048 x 2,048 image size even if you don't have the real memory to hold it, as long as Windows is able to grab enough space out of its swap file somewhere.

View / Zoom In Box

Command Function

The ZOOM IN box toggle is used to set Winfract's zooming logic to use a "Zoom In" box to select a region of the image for zooming purposes. This menu item is checked when the ZOOM IN box logic is selected.

Menu Access

The ZOOM IN box menu item of the VIEW menu item.

Image size	Number of Colors	Memory Required
320x200	256	64K
640x480	256	307K
800x600	256	480K
1,024x768	256	786K
2,048x2,048	256	4MB
640x480	16	154K
800x600	16	240K
1,024x768	16	393K
2,048x2,048	16	2MB
640x480	2	38K
800x600	2	60K
1,024x768	2	98K
2,048x2,048	2	500K

Table 4-3 Image memory requirements

Fractint-Style Prompts Access
None.

Command-Line Parameters Access
None.

Comments
Winfract has three distinct methods of performing a zoom: the Zoom In box, the Zoom Out box, and the floating Zoom bar. Only one method is active at a time, and selecting any one of these three deselects the other two. Which of these methods you use is up to you.

To zoom in on a fractal image using the Zoom In method, move your mouse pointer to the center of the area you want to zoom in on, and press and hold down the left mouse button while moving the mouse pointer away from that centerpoint. As you do so, Winfract displays a rectangular zoom box that changes size as you move the mouse. When the zoom box is the size you want, release the left mouse button.

Don't worry if your zoom box isn't in exactly the right position on the image. If you want to move the zoom box to a different area, just move the mouse pointer to somewhere inside the zoom box, press and hold down the left mouse pointer, and move the mouse pointer with the left mouse button held down—the zoom box will follow the movement of the mouse.

When you have the zoom box where you want it, move the mouse pointer to a position inside the zoom box and double-click on the left mouse button. The program will immediately begin a new image using the zoom-box coordinates you selected.

If you decide that you don't want to perform a zoom, or that your zoom box is the wrong size after all, just move your mouse pointer somewhere outside the zoom box and double-click on the left mouse button. The zoom box will disappear.

Whenever you select one of the Zoom Box options, Winfract automatically saves the state of that item in the [winfract] section of your SSTOOLS.INI file. Subsequent Winfract sessions read this entry and use this setting as the default startup value.

View / Zoom Out Box

Command Function
The ZOOM OUT box toggle is used to set Winfract's zooming logic to use a "Zoom Out" box to select a region of the image for zooming purposes. This menu item is checked when the Zoom Out box logic is selected.

Menu Access
The ZOOM OUT box menu item of the VIEW menu item.

Fractint-Style Prompts Access
None.

Command-Line Parameters Access
None.

Comments
Winfract has three distinct methods of performing a zoom: the Zoom In box, the Zoom Out box, and the floating Zoom Bar. Only one method is

active at a time, and selecting any one of these three deselects the other two. Which of these methods you use is up to you.

The Zoom Out box option uses exactly the same logic as the Zoom In box option to size, move, and activate a zoom box. The only difference is that this zoom box is for zooming out purposes, and indicates where (and how small) your current image will be in the new image.

Whenever you select one of the Zoom box options, Winfract automatically saves the state of that item in the [winfract] section of your SSTOOLS.INI file. Subsequent Winfract sessions read this entry and use this setting as the default startup value.

View / Zoom Bar

Command Function
The ZOOM BAR menu item is used to activate or deactivate the optional floating Zoom bar window and its associated Zoom-box technique.

Menu Access
The ZOOM BAR menu item of the VIEW menu item.

Fractint-Style Prompts Access
None.

Command-Line Parameters Access
None.

Comments
Winfract has three distinct methods of performing a zoom: the Zoom In box, the Zoom Out box, and the floating Zoom bar. Only one method is active at a time, and selecting any one of these three deselects the other two. Which of these methods you use is up to you.

When you activate the ZOOM-BAR option, a floating zoom-box scrollbar (Figure 4-28) is displayed along with your fractal image. The zoom box defaults to the mid-position, in which your zoom box exactly covers the area of your fractal image and is invisible. Moving the scrollbutton up shrinks your zoom box (and makes it visible on the fractal image). You can then move the zoom box around by moving your cursor inside the zoom box and then holding down your left mouse button and moving the cursor and zoom box as a single unit. Double-clicking the left mouse button will cause your image to be redrawn using your current zoom-box coordinates.

You can also zoom out by moving the zoom-box scrollbar below the midpoint. When you do this, the zoom box that is displayed is actually

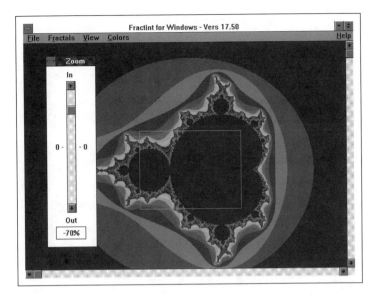

Figure 4-28 The Zoom bar in action

showing you where (and how small) your currently displayed image would be if you double-clicked the left mouse button at that point. Moving the zoom box and double-clicking to perform the zoom is done the same way as when you are zooming in.

Whenever you select one of the zoom box options, Winfract automatically saves the state of that item in the [winfract] section of your SSTOOLS.INI file. Subsequent Winfract sessions read this entry and use this setting as their default startup value.

View / Coordinate Box

Command Function
The COORDINATE box menu item is used to activate or deactivate the optional, floating Coordinate box window.

Menu Access
The COORDINATE box menu item of the VIEW menu item.

Fractint-Style Prompts Access
None.

Command-Line Parameters Access
None.

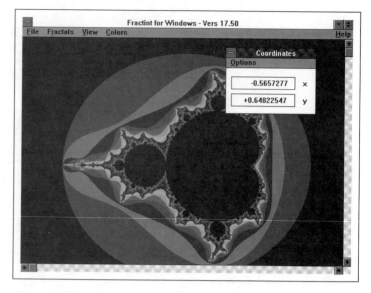

Figure 4-29 The COORDINATE box in action

Comments

When you have the COORDINATE box checked, a floating coordinate window (Figure 4-29) constantly displays the current position of your mouse pointer.

An OPTIONS menu in that COORDINATE box lets you select whether you want your coordinates to display in rectangular (default), polar, or pixel coordinates.

RECTANGULAR coordinates correspond to the Cartesian plane. The coordinates displayed are in absolute units relative to the origin. Winfract uses these coordinates to form a complex number. This complex number initializes one or more variables in the iterative calculation. The x-coordinate is used as the *real* portion of the complex number and the y-coordinate as the *imaginary* portion.

PIXEL coordinates display the position of a point in terms of the number of pixels, or color dots, relative to the pixel in the upper left-hand corner of the image. For example, if the image size is 200 x 150, then the pixel in the lower right-hand corner of the image is coordinate (199, 149.)

POLAR coordinates display the position of a point in terms of its distance and angle relative to the origin. The angle can be in units of degrees (default), radians, or grads. Most people are familiar with degrees which divide the circle into 360 *degrees*. Grads divide the circle into 400 *grads*. Radians divide the circle into units of 2 Pi *radians*.

Whenever you select or deselect the floating Coordinate box, Winfract automatically saves the state of that item in the [winfract] section of your SSTOOLS.INI file. Subsequent Winfract sessions read this entry and use this setting as their default startup value.

View / Window Sizing

Command Function
The WINDOW SIZING menu item is used to activate and deactivate the window sizing option, which disables the scrollbars and forces the image window to be the same size as the fractal image.

Menu Access
The WINDOW SIZING menu item of the VIEW menu item.

Fractint-Style Prompts Access
None.

Command-Line Parameters Access
None.

Comments
By default, the size of your fractal image and the size of the window in which it is displayed are independent. If the image size is larger than the window size, the scrollbars on the edges of the window can be used to scroll around the portion of the image that is displayed in the window. If the image is smaller than the window, the area of the window beyond the edge of the image is displayed as a black background.

If you select the WINDOW SIZING option, Winfract automatically sizes its window to match the size of the image. The scrollbars disappear from the window, as they no longer have any function. If the image size is larger than your entire screen, Winfract automatically switches to full-screen mode and only the upper left-hand section of the image is visible.

Whenever you select or deselect the WINDOW SIZING option, Winfract automatically saves the state of that option in the [winfract] section of your SSTOOLS.INI file. Subsequent Winfract sessions read this entry and use this setting as the default startup value.

View / Pixel-by-Pixel Update

Command Function
The PIXEL-BY-PIXEL UPDATE menu item is used to activate and deactivate the PIXEL-BY-PIXEL UPDATE option, which causes Winfract to update its image display every time a pixel is changed rather than in periodic sweeps.

Menu Access
The PIXEL-BY-PIXEL menu item of the VIEW menu item.

Fractint-Style Prompts Access
None.

Command-Line Parameters Access
None.

Comments
Windows extracts a heavy toll of overhead on applications that update their images a pixel at a time. For this reason, Winfract normally updates its images in periodic sweeps, tracking and periodically updating those rectangular sections of the image that have changed over the last few seconds. This approach has the advantage of offering a great improvement in execution speed, but a disadvantage in that you never actually see how Winfract is generating your images. This disadvantage is particularly distressing when it comes to the boundary-tracing and tesseral algorithms, as watching them generate an image is most of the fun.

By selecting this option, you can disable Winfract's speedy approach to updating its fractal images and force it to update the appropriate section of the image each and every time a pixel is modified. Compared to the normal approach, this can be excruciatingly slow—but sometimes speed isn't everything.

Whenever you select or deselect the PIXEL-BY-PIXEL UPDATE option, Winfract automatically saves the state of that option in the [winfract] section of your SSTOOLS.INI file. Subsequent Winfract sessions read this entry and use this setting as the default startup value.

View / Hotkey Actions

Command Function
The HOTKEY ACTIONS menu item is used to select between Windows-style menus and Fractint-style prompts when you use Fractint-style hotkeys.

Menu Access
The HOTKEY ACTIONS menu item of the VIEW menu item.

Fractint-Style Prompts Access
None.

Command-Line Parameters Access
None.

Comments

Winfract originated as a port of the MS-DOS Fractint program to the Windows environment, and many Winfract users (including the authors) use both programs regularly. In such cases, consistency is sometimes valued over ease of use, and some folks prefer to use Fractint-style hotkeys and Fractint-style prompting screens.

By default, Winfract responds to all hotkey activity by selecting the associated Windows menu (the (X) hotkey, for example, brings up the FRACTALS / BASIC OPTIONS menu). By setting the HOTKEY ACTIONS menu item you can tell Winfract to bring up Fractint-style prompting screens (where they exist) instead.

Using the Windows menu bar always causes Winfract to bring up a Windows-style menu. Also, some functions, such as printing and selecting a video mode, are so different in the Windows and DOS environments that the hotkeys for those actions *always* bring up the Windows-style menus.

Whenever you change the HOTKEY ACTIONS option, Winfract automatically saves the state of that option in the [winfract] section of your SSTOOLS.INI file. Subsequent Winfract sessions read this entry and use this setting as the default startup value.

View / Status

Command Function

The STATUS menu item displays a dialog box showing the status of the fractal image currently being displayed.

Menu Access

The STATUS menu item of the VIEW menu item.

Fractint-Style Prompts Access

The (TAB) hotkey brings up the Fractint-style prompt sequence.

Command-Line Parameters Access

None.

Comments

This command displays an information screen about the current image. The screen shows the fractal type, whether or not the fractal is completed, the corner values, and fractal-specific parameter values that were used to generate the current image (see Figure 4-30). This command is particularly useful for checking the completion status of an all-nighter image,

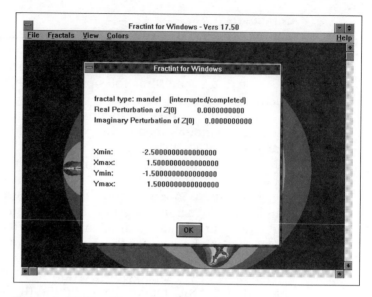

Figure 4-30 The STATUS display

but it's also a quick and handy way of answering the all-too-frequent "where the devil am I now?" question.

This screen does not give you a full list of all the parameters you've modified in order to create the image you're currently looking at. A quick-and-dirty way to answer that particular question is to use the FILE / SAVE @BATCHFILE command to generate a parameter entry for the current image, and then read the parameter file you've just created into the Windows Notepad to sneak a peek at the entry you've just created.

THE COLORS MENU

The COLORS menu items deal with those Winfract commands that involve palette manipulation loading, saving, and cycling through palette values.

Colors / Load Color-Map

Command Function
The LOAD COLOR-MAP menu item is used to modify the palette Winfract uses for its images.

Menu Access
The LOAD COLOR-MAP menu item of the COLORS menu item.

Fractint-Style Prompts Access
The Ⓛ hotkey brings up the Fractint-style prompt sequence.

Command-Line Parameters Access
None.

Comments
Colormap files are text files describing the palette maps used by Winfract and its MS-DOS cousin Fractint to display their images. These palette map files are 256 lines long, each line containing three intensity values for the Red, Green, and Blue components of a single palette entry. Component values range from 0 (not there at all) to 255 (the highest intensity). Bright red would be stored as '255 0 0'. Comments may be entered after the three numeric values.

When Winfract first starts up, it reads in the DEFAULTW.MAP colormap file and uses these values as its default palette map. Some fractal types (the plasma clouds, for instance) and some 3-D viewing options use alternate palette maps.

You can change the palette map Winfract uses in a number of ways. See the Color Cycling section below for some that are a lot of fun. One way is to use this command to have Winfract read and use a different colormap file.

When you select the LOAD COLOR-MAP menu, Winfract presents you with a standard Windows-style FILE / OPEN menu using a default filetype of MAP. Winfract is distributed with a number of MAP files that offer some interesting color combinations.

One caveat about Windows programs and palette maps: 16-color Windows drivers use fixed palettes, and Windows forces all displayed images into those 16 fixed colors using a best-fit algorithm that doesn't always fit so well. Even a 256-color Windows video driver reserves 20 palette values for its own use, and images that use all 256 palette values end up with their upper 20 palettes mapped into other palette values. Only a true-color Windows video driver (the kind capable of displaying 32,000 or more simultaneous colors) is going to actually use all 256 colors exactly as the MAP file specifies them.

Colors / Write Color-Map

Command Function
The WRITE COLOR-MAP menu item is used to save the palette used by Winfract's current image into a colormap file.

Menu Access
The WRITE COLOR-MAP menu item of the COLORS menu item.

Fractint-Style Prompts Access
The ⓦ hotkey brings up the Fractint-style prompt sequence.

Command-Line Parameters Access
None.

Comments
Colormap files are text files describing the palette maps used by Winfract and its MS-DOS cousin Fractint to display their images. These palette map files are 256 lines long, each line containing three intensity values for the Red, Green, and Blue components of a single palette entry. Component values range from 0 (not there at all) to 255 (the highest intensity). Bright red would be stored as '255 0 0'. Comments may be entered after the three numeric values.

This command lets you save the colors in use by your current image independently of the fractal formula used to generate that image.

When you select the WRITE COLOR-MAP menu item, Winfract brings up a standard FILE / SAVEAS menu displaying a list of the MAP files in your current directory. You can either select a MAP file to overwrite, or type in a new filename.

Colors / Color-Cycling

Command Function
The COLOR-CYCLING menu item is used to cycle and/or randomize the palette colors in your currently displayed image.

Menu Access
The COLOR-CYCLING menu item of the COLORS menu item.

Fractint-Style Prompts Access
The ⊕, ⊖, arrow, and (SPACEBAR) hotkeys.

Command-Line Parameters Access
None.

Comments
Color cycling is a term referring to the rapid modification of an image's colors by modifying the palette used to display the image. As such,

Winfract's color-cycling capabilities are available only if you are using a palette-based, Windows video driver, and only the 256-color. Windows video drivers are currently palette based. If your Windows video driver is not palette based, the COLOR-CYCLING menu item is grayed out, and any attempt to use the color-cycling hotkeys brings up a small "I'm sorry, but you can't do that message box."

Because color cycling is so popular, there are so many hotkeys available for it that the COLOR-CYCLING menu is almost superfluous. In fact, let's list the hotkeys first:

Hotkey Summary

(SPACEBAR)	Toggles cycling on and off
(←) and (→)	Set the cycling direction
(+) and (-)	Set the cycling direction
(>) and (<)	Single-step through a cycle
(↑) and (↓)	Speed up/slow down the cycling
(ENTER)	Randomizes the palette

The Color-Cycling dialog box contains the following items:

Start/Stop Control

The START radio button starts the color-cycling process as soon as you press the OK button to end the dialog, and the STOP button cancels it. A quicker way to start and stop color cycling is to use the (SPACEBAR), which acts as a Start/Stop color-cycling toggle. The directional color-cycling hotkeys also force color cycling on as a side-effect.

Rotate Direction

The two directions, IN and OUT, were selected arbitrarily based on their visual effect on the default Mandelbrot set. The (←) and (→) hotkeys also select the rotation direction (and have the side-effect of starting the color-cycling process), as do the (+) and (-) hotkeys. The (>) and (<) hotkeys select a cycling direction, single-step through one palette change, and stop the color cycling. (These keys are particularly useful when you've just missed the perfect color palette.)

New Color Generation

This selection governs whether color cycling continually rotates the current palette over and over, or randomly selects new palette values as the existing palette values are rotated off the current palette. New palette values are blended in with existing values by selecting a new target value and smoothly changing color values in successive palette entries until the target value is reached.

By default, color cycling starts up rotating the current palette. When color cycling is in progress, pressing the (ENTER) hotkey causes Winfract to randomly generate an entire new set of palette values and randomly generate new colors as existing values are rotated off the palette. (Pressing (ENTER) repeats it with a new set of random values.) Changing/setting the direction of the rotation or single-stepping through palette changes automatically disables any random generation and returns to pure rotation. (The assumption is that you changed direction because you just passed the perfect color combination and want to get back to it.)

New Color Frequency
This selection governs how frequently colors are changed during random color generation.

THE HELP MENU

The HELP menu items deal with the various help systems and commands available with Winfract. Winfract includes both its own Windows-style help system and the help system from its DOS-based sister program, Fractint.

Help / Index

Command Function
The INDEX menu item is used to bring up Winfract's main Help screen.

Menu Access
The INDEX menu item of the HELP menu item.

Fractint-Style Prompts Access
The (F1) hotkey always brings up the Windows-style Help screens.

Command-Line Parameters Access
None.

Comments
Winfract's online help system isn't nearly as complete as this book, but it is a handy way to look into the basic capabilities of Winfract.

Help / Using Help

Command Function
The USING HELP menu item is used to bring up Windows' generic How-to-use-Help screens.

Menu Access
The USING HELP menu item of the HELP menu item.

Fractint-Style Prompts Access
None.

Command-Line Parameters Access
None.

Comments
The USING HELP screens are supplied as a standard feature of Microsoft Windows. In fact, when you use this option, you've really launched an application supplied by Microsoft.

Help / Fractint Help

Command Function
The FRACTINT HELP menu item is used to bring up the Fractint-style help system.

Menu Access
The FRACTINT HELP menu item of the HELP menu item.

Fractint-Style Prompts Access
The (CTRL)-(F1) hotkey brings up the Fractint-style prompt sequence.

Command-Line Parameters Access
None.

Comments
When this item is selected, Winfract first looks for FRACTINT.HLP, which is a specially formatted file containing the online help screens from Winfract's sister program Fractint. If Winfract can't locate that file, it looks for a copy of FRACTINT.EXE and uses the Fractint help files that are embedded in that

program. If Winfract can't locate that file either, it displays a Fractint-style "Help is not available" message box.

The Fractint-style help system has the advantage of being both massive (there are over 350 screens of information in the current versions) and hypertext-like. It has the disadvantage that it is a help system for Fractint as opposed to Winfract, and it is loaded with information that is not applicable to Winfract and the Windows environment. (The detailed information about the DOS program's video modes and printer access are prime examples.)

Also, when used by Winfract, Fractint's help system is not context-sensitive. Regardless of what you are doing in Winfract, the Fractint help system always starts at the main help index.

Help / About Winfract

Command Function
The ABOUT WINFRACT menu item is used to bring up the About message box.

Menu Access
The ABOUT WINFRACT menu item of the HELP menu item.

Fractint-Style Prompts Access
None.

Command-Line Parameters Access
None.

Comments
Winfract's About message box displays Winfract's version number, copyright notice, and icon.

OTHER COMMANDS AND FUNCTIONS

Some of Winfract's functions aren't accessed via items on Winfract's menu system.

Mandelbrot/Julia Toggle

Command Function
The right mouse button is used as a Mandelbrot/Julia toggle for alternating between matched pairs of fractal formulas.

Menu Access
None.

Fractint-Style Prompts Access
None.

Command-Line Parameters Access
None.

Comments
As explained in Chapter 1, each point of a Mandelbrot set corresponds to a Julia set. Winfract allows you to see this connection very clearly, as follows. Create an image of a Mandelbrot set. This can be the classic Mandelbrot (mandel) fractal, or any of the types that have 'man' in their names. Point your mouse cursor to a region near the lake shore of the image, where blue meets the multicolor shore, but instead of zooming in on it, press the right mouse button. Winfract will display the Julia set corresponding to the point of the Mandelbrot set that was at the mouse location. Remember that each Julia type, is in fact, an infinite collection of quite different fractals, depending on the values of the parameters. The characteristics of each Julia set can be inferred from the appearance of the Mandelbrot set near the point that generates the Julia set. For example, if the selected point of the Mandelbrot set is deep in the lake, the corresponding Julia will have a large lake. Conversely, if you pick a point on land, the Julia will not have a large lake. The most interesting Julia sets may be found from points near the lake edge of the corresponding Mandelbrot set, where the chaos is the greatest.

Command-Line Functions

Command Function
Some command-line functions perform actions that just aren't available via the interactive menus. Others are technically available (in that Winfract doesn't complain if it runs into them), but are ignored by Winfract as not being applicable to the Windows environment. Both types of parameters are listed below.

Menu Access
None.

Fractint-Style Prompts Access
None.

Command-Line Parameters Access

Command-line parameters that Winfract uses

```
function=<fn1>[/<fn2>[/<fn3>[/<fn4>]]]
formulafile=
formulaname=
lfile=
lname=
initorbit=pixel
initorbit=<nnn>/<nnn>
periodicity=no|show|nnn
symmetry=<symmetry>
```

Command-line parameters that Winfract ignores

```
adapter=
askvideo=
batch=
exitmode=
gif87a=
hertz=
printer=
textcolors=
```

Comments

The command-line parameters listed below are used primarily by Winfract's parameter-file logic when it automatically saves and restores fractal images for you. They are also occasionally useful to the programmer who is attempting to add new fractal types to Winfract.

function=<fn1>[/<fn2>[/<fn3>[/<fn4>]]]

Allows setting variable functions found in some fractal-type formulas. Possible values of the functions are sin, cos, sinh, cosh, exp, log, and dsqr. The FILE / SAVE @BATCHFILE command uses this parameter when the saved fractal type includes these functions as parameters.

formulafile=<filename>
formulaname=<formulaname>

Allows specifying the filename and entry used in a parameter file entry using a formula fractal type. The FILE / SAVE @BATCHFILE command uses this parameter when the saved fractal type is formula.

lfile=<filename>
lname=<lsystemname>

Allows specifying the filename and entry used in a parameter file entry using an lsystem fractal type. The FILE / SAVE @BATCHFILE command uses this parameter when the saved fractal type is lsystem.

initorbit=pixel
initorbit=<nnn>/<nnn>

Allows control over the value used to begin each Mandelbrot-type orbit. The command initorbit=pixel is the default for most types; this command initializes the orbit to the complex number corresponding to the screen pixel. The command initorbit=nnn/nnn uses the entered value as the initializer.

periodicity=no | show | nnn

Allows control of periodicity checking. Periodicity checking is logic that checks consecutive iterations to detect if a particular pixel calculation is in a periodic loop, will never reach the escape value, and will reach the maximum iteration limit as a result. For most fractal images, periodicity checking greatly speeds up the calculations of those pixels that are in the internal lake regions. "No" turns it off, and "show" lets you see which pixels were painted the inside color due to being caught by periodicity. Specifying a number causes a more conservative periodicity test (each increase of 1 divides the test tolerance by 2). Entering a negative number lets you turn on "show" with that number. Type lambdafn function=exp needs periodicity turned off to be accurate. There may be other situations where this condition exists as well.

symmetry=<symmetry>

This option forces symmetry to one of None, Xaxis, Yaxis, XYaxis, Origin, or Pi symmetry. Some fractals are symmetrical and have parts that are reflections of their other parts. For example, the top and bottom of the Mandelbrot fractal are reflections of each other. The Mandelbrot fractal has x-axis symmetry, because the top points are the reflections of the bottom points about the x-axis. y-axis symmetry means the left and right sides of a fractal are reflections of each other. XY-axis symmetry is a combination of both of these. Origin symmetry reflects upper points to lower points on the opposite side. Finally, pi symmetry describes the symmetry of periodic fractals that repeat themselves every   units.

This command forces symmetry whether or not the fractal really exhibits it. A portion of the fractal is calculated, and the symmetrical parts are reflections of the calculated part. The Stone Soupers have attempted to automatically use symmetry when it exists, but they have not caught every case. For example, any of the fractal types with fn in their name (such as fn + fn) exhibit different symmetry depending on which functions are used to replace fn in the formula. If you are experimenting with a fractal and can see that it has symmetry that Winfract doesn't know about, you can set the symmetry with this command and make the fractal run faster because fewer points have to be calculated. You can also apply symmetry just to change any fractal and see how it looks.

5

Fractal Types

Winfract is capable of creating a tremendous variety of fractals. If you press ⓣ or click on FRACTAL FORMULA under the FRACTALS menu, you'll see a list of the built-in fractal types that Winfract can generate. Table 5-1 shows this list and tells you where to find it in this chapter. You should understand that there really isn't a whole lot of rhyme or reason to this list of fractal types or to their names. Whatever fractal algorithms tickled the Stone Soupers' fancy made their way into Winfract. In fact, fractal formulas have been contributed by enthusiasts in dozens of countries all around the world, and new ones are added constantly. Some of the algorithms in Winfract have been obtained from the classic fractal books such as Peitgen and Richter's *The Beauty of Fractals*, Peitgen and Saupe's *The Science of Fractal Images,* or Barnsley's *Fractals Everywhere.* All these fractals and their sources are described in this chapter. Despite the fact that Winfract already contains over 78 built-in fractals, as sure as fractals are infinitely complex, the abundance of contributions for Winfract will continue to grow!

Some of Winfract's "types" are specific fractals based on a particular formula. Other Winfract types allow you to custom design fractals by specifying your own equations for Winfract to calculate. The first section of this chapter, "Built-In Fractal Types," describes each of the types avail-

Winfract Type	Fractal Category	Chapter Section
barnsleyj1	Escape-time fractal	BARNSLEYJ1
barnsleyj2	Escape-time fractal	BARNSLEYJ2
barnsleyj3	Escape-time fractal	BARNSLEYJ3
barnsleym1	Escape-time fractal	BARNSLEYM1
barnsleym2	Escape-time fractal	BARNSLEYM2
barnsleym3	Escape-time fractal	BARNSLEYM3
bif+sinpi	Bifurcation	BIFURCATION SINEPI
bif=sinpi	Bifurcation	BIFURCATION SUMMATION SINEPI
biflambda	Bifurcation	BIFURCATION LAMBDA
bifstewart	Bifurcation	BIFURCATION STEWART
bifurcation	Bifurcation	BIFURCATION
circle	Moire pattern	CIRCLE
cmplxmarksjul	Escape-time fractal	COMPLEX MARK'S JULIA
cmplxmarksmand	Escape-time fractal	COMPLEX MARK'S MANDELBROT
complexbasin	Escape-time fractal	COMPLEX NEWTON'S BASIN
complexnewton	Escape-time fractal	COMPLEX NEWTON
diffusion	Random fractal	DIFFUSION LIMITED AGGREGATION
fn(z)+fn(pix)	Escape-time fractal	FUNCTION VARIABLE FRACTALS

Table 5-1 Winfract's fractal types

Winfract Type	Fractal Category	Chapter Section
fn(z×z)	Escape-time fractal	FUNCTION VARIABLE FRACTALS
fn×fn	Escape-time fractal	FUNCTION VARIABLE FRACTALS
fn×z+z	Escape-time fractal	FUNCTION VARIABLE FRACTALS
fn+fn	Escape-time fractal	FUNCTION VARIABLE FRACTALS
formula	Escape-time fractal	USER DEFINED FRACTALS
gingerbreadman	Orbital fractal	GINGER BREAD MAN
henon	Orbital fractal	HENON FRACTALS
hopalong	Orbital fractal	HOPALONG
ifs	Iterated function sys	ITERATED FUNCTION SYSTEMS
julfn+exp	Escape-time fractal	PICKOVER M/J FRACTALS
julfn+zsqrd	Escape-time fractal	PICKOVER M/J FRACTALS
julia	Escape-time fractal	JULIA SETS
julia4	Escape-time fractal	PICKOVER M/J FRACTALS
julibrot	Escape-time fractal	JULIBROT
julzpower	Escape-time fractal	PICKOVER M/J FRACTALS
julzzpwr	Escape-time fractal	PICKOVER M/J FRACTALS
kamtorus	Escape-time fractal	KAM TORUS
kamtorus3d	Escape-time fractal	KAM TORUS

Table 5-1 Winfract's fractal types (continued)

Winfract Type	Fractal Category	Chapter Section
lambda	Escape-time fractal	LAMBDA
lambdafn	Escape-time fractal	LAMBDA FUNCTION FRACTALS
lorenz	Escape-time fractal	LORENZ FRACTALS
lorenz3d	Escape-time fractal	LORENZ FRACTALS
lorenz3d1	Escape-time fractal	LORENZ FRACTALS
lorenz3d3	Escape-time fractal	LORENZ FRACTALS
lorenz3d4	Escape-time fractal	LORENZ FRACTALS
lsystem	L-system fractal	L-SYSTEM FRACTALS
lyapunov	Bifurcation	LYAPUNOV
magnet1j	Escape-time fractal	MAGNETISM FRACTAL TYPES
magnet1m	Escape-time fractal	MAGNETISM FRACTAL TYPES
magnet2j	Escape-time fractal	MAGNETISM FRACTAL TYPES
magnet2m	Escape-time fractal	MAGNETISM FRACTAL TYPES
mandel	Escape-time fractal	MANDELBROT SET
mandel4	Escape-time fractal	PICKOVER M/J FRACTALS
mandelfn	Escape-time fractal	MANDELBROT LAMBDA FUNCTION
mandellambda	Escape-time fractal	MANDELBROT LAMBDA
manfn+exp	Escape-time fractal	PICKOVER M/J FRACTALS

Table 5-1 Winfract's fractal types (continued)

Winfract Type	Fractal Category	Chapter Section
manfn+zsqrd	Escape-time fractal	PICKOVER M/J FRACTALS
manowar	Escape-time fractal	MANOWAR
manowarj	Escape-time fractal	MANOWAR
manzpower	Escape-time fractal	PICKOVER M/J FRACTALS
manzzpwr	Escape-time fractal	PICKOVER M/J FRACTALS
marksjulia	Escape-time fractal	MARK'S JULIA
marksmandel	Escape-time fractal	MARK'S MANDELBROT
marksmandelpwr	Escape-time fractal	MARK'S MANDELPOWER
martin	Escape-time fractal	MARTIN
newtbasin	Escape-time fractal	NEWTON'S BASIN
newton	Escape-time fractal	NEWTON
pickover	Orbital fractal	PICKOVER ATTRACTOR
plasma	Random fractal	PLASMA CLOUDS
popcorn	Orbital fractal	POPCORN FRACTALS
popcornjul	Escape-time fractal	POPCORN JULIA SET
rossler3d	Escape-time fractal	ROSSLER THREE D
sierpinski	Escape-time fractal	SIERPINSKI
spider	Escape-time fractal	SPIDER

Table 5-1 Winfract's fractal types (continued)

Winfract Type	Fractal Category	Chapter Section
sqr(1/fn)	Escape-time fractal	FUNCTION VARIABLE FRACTALS
sqr(fn)	Escape-time fractal	FUNCTION VARIABLE FRACTALS
tetrate	Escape-time fractal	TETRATION FRACTAL
tim's_error	Escape-time fractal	TIM'S ERROR
unity	Escape-time fractal	UNITY

Table 5-1 Winfract's fractal types (continued)

able when you select FRACTAL FORMULA under the FRACTALS menu. The second section, "User-Defined Fractals," describes how you can use Winfract to create your own fractal types.

BUILT-IN FRACTAL TYPES

In this chapter, each fractal type has a page or more describing the fractal. The following is a brief description of what you will find in these pages.

Fractal Screen Dump
Each fractal section begins with a grayscale screen dump showing what the fractal looks like.

Fractal Category
The fractal category tells to which of the fractal families this particular type belongs. Some of the possibilities are escape-time fractals, chaotic-orbit fractals, bifurcation fractals, iterated-function systems (IFS) fractals, L-systems fractals, and random fractals. These fractal families were discussed in Chapter 1.

Formal Name
The formal name is how the fractal is known to non-Winfract users.

Fractal Type
The name of the fractal as it appears in Winfract's list of types shown under the FRACTALS / FRACTAL FORMULA submenu or with the Ⓣ hotkey. Use this name when you want to identify or select the fractal and display it.

Formula

A mathematical description of the algorithm used to generate the fractal. For most fractals, the pixels on your computer screen are mapped to a rectangle in the complex plane, and the procedure for calculating the fractal must be repeated for each complex number located at every pixel in that rectangle. The variables z and c in these formulas appear repeatedly and refer to complex numbers. Generally, the pixel's x- and y-coordinates correspond to the real and imaginary portions for the values of z or c. For Mandelbrot sets, the screen pixel is used for the value of c, and the initial value of z is set to zero. For Julia sets, the value of c is kept constant, and the screen coordinates are used for the initial value of z. The variable *zpixel* is used in the formulas to designate the complex number corresponding to a particular screen pixel that is being colored. Many of the formulas have a calculation that is done once for each pixel on the screen. This calculation is designated the *initialization*. Following the initialization is another calculation specifying the computation that is repeated, or iterated. This second calculation is designated the *iteration*.

Occasionally, we will refer to the real or imaginary portions of a complex number using x and y, respectively, with a subscript denoting to which variable it belongs. For example, x_z refers to the real portion of the variable z, and y_z refers to the imaginary portion of the variable z, so that $z = x_z + iy_z$. A complex number enclosed in absolute value bars, such as $|z|$, means the modulus of the complex number. The *modulus* of a complex number is the distance of the number's corresponding point on the Cartesian plane from the origin.

Some fractals, however, do not use complex numbers at all, but rather treat the screen coordinates as two separate real numbers. For these variables we will use x and y without subscripts.

Parameter File Example

The parameter file example tells you how the image (usually shown at the top of the page) was generated. This uses the parameter file format that was introduced in Chapter 2. If you would like to duplicate the example, you can run it using the READ @BATCHFILE menu item under FILE, select the parameter file EXAMPLES.PAR in the SELECT A PARAMETER FILE dialog box, and click on OPEN. Then select the fractal name from the SELECT A PARAMETER ENTRY dialog box.

You can also enter the same information interactively. For example, if the parameter file example specifies type=mandel, you can use the FRACTAL FORMULA submenu under FRACTALS to select fractal type mandel. Similarly, if the parameter file entry contains the line inside=3, you can set this using the BASIC OPTIONS submenu under FRACTALS. These parameter file examples work with the DOS Fractint (version 16.0 or later) as well as the Winfract program that comes with this book. Parameter files are a popular and efficient means of sharing fractals with others.

Code

For the curious and the adventurous, the Winfract source code has been included with this book. The CODE section tells you exactly where to look to find the details of how each fractal is calculated. Winfract contains a number of different generalized fractal engines that organize the work of generating fractals. Each fractal engine calls several small routines to actually generate an image. For each fractal, the CODE section tells you which engine is used, and which routines are invoked once per pixel and once per iteration to generate that fractal. You should also look up the fractal's name in the large structure defined in FRACTALP.C. Most of the code for individual fractals uses the C language, but some fractals have been written in assembler. See Chapter 6 for more information about the Winfract source code and how to compile Winfract.

Description

The description covers facts about the fractal type. In this section, you'll find out more about the math behind the fractal, where the fractal came from, hidden or subtle facts, details on how it acts or looks, and the like.

Parameters

Most fractal types have numerical parameters that alter their appearance. When selecting a type from Winfract's type list, you are prompted for these. While normally you can just press (ENTER) or click on OK and accept the default values, here we tell you the meaning of the parameters, their default values, and the effect of changing them. For example, many of the Mandelbrot fractal types accept a perturbation parameter, which is used to warp the fractal. The effect of setting this to a nonzero value is similar to viewing the fractal through a carnival mirror. Internally, this is done by adding the perturbation variable to the initial value of z, but the on-screen effect causes the fractal to be pulled, stretched, and squeezed out of its original shape.

While you can just press (ENTER) and accept the defaults, changing parameters can often create some amazing effects and, in some cases, generate entirely new fractals to explore.

Explorer

This section tells you where to zoom in on the fractal for the most intriguing and interesting shapes. Suggested experiments are given either in command-line form that can be used in parameter files, or else as instructions for setting values using Winfract dialog boxes.

Special Effects
Collections of Winfract settings that give other means of viewing, such as 3D.

Warnings
Problems to avoid or machine-specific restrictions. For example, the Julibrot fractal can be generated only on a 256-color machine or using a 256-color disk video mode.

Alternate Color Maps
Suggested color maps to try. Color maps allow you to reset the color palette to bring out or enhance different characteristics of the fractal. A few selected maps can be found on the companion disk as files with the extension .MAP.

History and Credits
Who discovered this fractal, who contributed it to Winfract, or how it was obtained.

BARNSLEYJ1

Fractal Category: Escape-time fractal

Formal Name: None

Fractal Type: barnsleyj1

Formula: Initialize: *z = zpixel*
          Iterate: $(z - 1)c,$ if $x_z >= 0$
                     $(z + 1)|c|/c,$ if $x_z < 0$

Code

Routine type	Routine name	File
Fractal engine	StandardFractactal()	CALCFRACT.C
Integer math initialization	long_julia_per_pixel()	FRACTALS.C
Integer math orbit	Barnsley1Fractal()	FRACTALS.C
Floating-point initialization	otherjuliafp_per_pixel()	FRACTALS.C
Floating-point orbit	Barnsley1FPFractal()	FRACTALS.C

Parameter File Example
```
barnsleyj1  {
  reset maxiter=20000 inside=255 logmap=-1
  type=barnsleyj1
}
```

Description
Because the formula has two cases, depending on whether the real part of the orbit value (x_z) is positive or not, the image is broken up into a patchwork quilt of colored patterns.

This fractal type is a family of Julia sets corresponding to the Mandelbrot fractal type barnsleym1.

Parameters: Real part of parameter   0.6
                 Imaginary part of parameter   1.1
                 Bailout value (0 means default) 0.0

As with all Julia variants, the first two parameters determine the value of *c* in the formula, and they result in a different image. Even a small change will sometimes produce a radically different fractal. The best guide for how the parameters affect the image is to generate the Mandelbrot map of the formula (fractal type barnsleym1) and then use the right mouse button to toggle to the Julia set. Winfract will use the coordinates for the point in the center of the screen as the real and imaginary parameters.

Explorer
Interesting barnsleyj1 images can be discovered by zooming in near the lake edge in barnsleym1, which is the Mandelbrot set for this Julia family,

and toggling back to barnsleyj1 using the right mouse button. Try this in reverse, starting with barnsleyj1 using default parameters. You will notice that the image is a multicolored island surrounded by a blue ocean. Now click the right mouse button. This will show you a barnsleym1 image with the zoom box centered on the point that represents the parameter values of the barnsleyj1 you just generated. If you look closely, you will see that the zoom box is centered on a colored part of the barnsleym1 lagoon. Now center the zoom box on the edge of the lake, and click the right mouse button again. You will see the Julia set with the island reduced to disconnected colored fragments. By making a series of images with the parameter values varying smoothly from those of the default barnsleyj1 to one exploded into fragments, you can chronicle all the steps and produce the effect of a fractal explosion.

Special Effects
Here are some samples of an explosion sequence, created by heading due east on the barnsleym1 "map."

At the very start of the explosion

Real part of parameter   0.52
Imaginary part of parameter   1.1

During the explosion

Real part of parameter   0.50

After the explosion

Real part of parameter   0.48

History and Credits
Dr. Michael Barnsley of the Georgia Institute of Technology originated this fractal type, and it was adapted for Winfract from the description in the book *Fractals Everywhere* by Dr. Barnsley.

BARNSLEYJ2

Fractal Category: Escape-time fractal

Formal Name: None

Fractal Type: barnsleyj2

Formula: Initialize: $z = zpixel$
Iterate: $(z - 1)c$ if $x_z y_c + x_c y_z >= 0$
$(z + 1)c$ if $x_z y_c + x_c y_z < 0$

Code

Routine type	Routine name	File
Fractal engine	StandardFractactal()	CALCFRACT.C
Integer math initialization	long_julia_per_pixel()	FRACTALS.C
Integer math orbit	Barnsley2Fractal()	FRACTALS.C
Floating-point initialization	otherjuliafp_per_pixel()	FRACTALS.C
Floating-point orbit	Barnsley2FPFractal()	FRACTALS.C

Parameter File Example

```
barnsleyj2  {
  reset  maxiter=20000  inside=255  logmap=-1
  type=barnsleyj2
}
```

Description

This is a family of Julia sets corresponding to the Mandelbrot fractal type barnsleym2. Unlike the classic Mandelbrot, the Barnsley fractals tend to have a lot of chaotic patterns inland from the lake. These patterns are a mixture of large and small patches that arise from the two different formulas used for the generation.

A tremendous variety of images can be created with this type, many of which have a printed shirt design quality that is less fractal-like than some other types.

Parameters:

Real part of parameter	0.6
Imaginary part of parameter	1.1
Bailout value (0 means default)	0.0

The first two parameters determine the value of c in the formula. Small changes can sometimes give you a radically different image. For example, the following settings produce an image with very large lake areas:

Real part of parameter	−0.36
Imaginary part of parameter	1.14

But with a slight change in each parameter, as follows, almost all the lake region disappears:

Real part of parameter	−0.39
Imaginary part of parameter	1.21

Explorer

Interesting barnsleyj2 images can be discovered by zooming in near the lake edge in the barnsleym2 variant and toggling to barnsleyj2 using the right mouse button.

This time let's try varying values along the y-axis of the barnsleym2 Mandelbrot map. Start with the following settings:

Real part of parameter	0.0
Imaginary part of parameter	1.5

You will see a symmetrical barbell-shaped figure. Recalculate with the imaginary part of the parameter changed to 1.35, then 1.3, 1.29, and 1.28.

For another exploration, start with the generation of a barnsleym2 fractal. Note that the image has a horizontal discontinuity along the negative x-axis. Barnsleyj2 images corresponding to points in the top half of the image look very different than those corresponding to the bottom half. Zoom into the middle of the bottom island and click the right mouse button to generate a barnsleyj2. With a little luck you can create some very fashionable, designer Easter eggs this way!

Special Effects
Try the almost-exploded image from the "explorer" sequence:

Real part of parameter   0.0
Imaginary part of parameter   1.295

Now try the designer Easter egg:

Real part of parameter   –0.2
Imaginary part of parameter –0.8

History and Credits
Dr. Michael Barnsley of the Georgia Institute of Technology originated this fractal type, and it was adapted for Winfract from the description in the book *Fractals Everywhere* by Dr. Barnsley.

BARNSLEYJ3

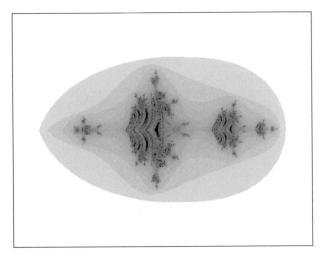

Fractal Category: Escape-time fractal

Formal Name: None

Fractal Type: barnsleyj3

Formula: Initialize: $z = zpixel$
　　　　　　Iterate:　$x_z^2 - y_z^2 - 1 + i2x_z y_z,$　　　　　if $x_z > 0$
　　　　　　　　　$x_z^2 - y_z^2 + x_c x_z + i(2x_z y_z + y_c x_z),$　if $x_z <= 0$

Code

Routine type	Routine name	File
Fractal engine	StandardFractactal()	CALCFRACT.C
Integer math initialization	long_julia_per_pixel()	FRACTALS.C
Integer math orbit	Barnsley3Fractal()	FRACTALS.C
Floating-point initialization	otherjuliafp_per_pixel()	FRACTALS.C
Floating-point orbit	Barnsley3FPFractal()	FRACTALS.C

Parameter File Example

```
barnsleyj3  {
  reset  maxiter=20000 inside=255 logmap=-1
  type=barnsleyj3
}
```

Description

This is the Julia variant corresponding to the barnsleym3 Mandelbrot map. It looks very different from the other Barnsley Julia sets. The default parameter values yield an image that has several distinct islands of chaotic colors. With the right change of parameters these become lakes.

Parameters:	Real part of parameter	0.1
	Imaginary part of parameter	0.36
	Bailout value (0 means default)	0.0

As with other Julia variants, the first two parameters determine the value of c in the formula, and give you a different image.

Explorer

Interesting barnsleyj3 images can be discovered by zooming in near the lake edge in the barnsleym3 variant and toggling to j3 using the right mouse button. To convert the chaotic islands to lakes, try the following:

Real part of parameter	0.1
Imaginary part of parameter	0.2

By creating a sequence of images with the imaginary part of the parameter moving from the default .36 to .2, you can watch the chaotic clumps explode, scatter into little islands, and then vanish into lakes. After you have created lakes with the above parameters, look closely at the right side of the image generated with the lake parameters above. There is a nested sequence of smaller and smaller little lakes. Try zooming into the sequence for a wonderful example of fractal self-similarity, using the following:

Real part of parameter	0.1
Imaginary part of parameter	0.2

Xmin   1.57668   Xmax   1.62464
Ymin   −0.016723   Ymax   0.0192422

Because of the self-similarity of the nested lakes, it is almost impossible to tell from this image how far you have zoomed in.

History and Credits
This type was originated by Dr. Barnsley. Tim Wegner modified the formula, which originally had only a real parameter, by making the parameter complex and adding the $y_c x_z$ term to take advantage of the imaginary part of the parameter.

BARNSLEYM1

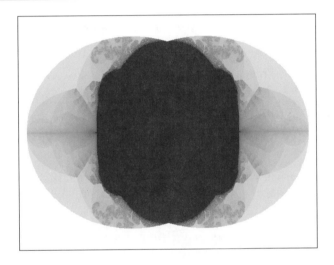

Fractal Category: Escape-time fractal

Formal Name: Called "M1" by Dr. Barnsley

Fractal Type: barnsleym1

Formula: Initialize: $c = z = zpixel$
  Iterate: $(z - 1)c$ if $x_z >= 0$
      $(z + 1)|c|/c$ if $x_z < 0$

Code

Routine type	Routine name	File
Fractal engine	StandardFractactal()	CALCFRACT.C
Integer math initialization	long_mandel_per_pixel,()	FRACTALS.C

Integer math orbit	Barnsley1Fractal()	FRACTALS.C
Floating-point initialization	othermandelfp_per_pixel()	FRACTALS.C
Floating-point orbit	Barnsley1FPFractal()	FRACTALS.C

Parameter File Example

```
barnsleym1  {
  reset  maxiter=20000 inside=255 logmap=-1
  type=barnsleym1
}
```

Description

This is the Mandelbrot map for the Julia family barnsleyj1. The original barnsleym1 is the inversion of Winfract's implementation, which means that we have turned the image inside out. Our version looks like a kind of barrier reef with a "maximum iterations" bay surrounded by a "minimum iterations" ocean. Barnsley's original was the reverse of this.

Parameters:		
Real perturbation of Z(0)	0
Imaginary perturbation	0
Bailout value (0 means default)	0

As with other Mandelbrot maps, the first two parameters warp the fractal by perturbing the initialization value of z_0.

Explorer

See the barnsleyj1 description for explorations that involve toggling to the Julia variant with the right mouse button.

Special Effects

Since the programmers of Winfract turned Dr. Barnsley's fractal inside out, you might try to experiment with the inversion option and restore his original. This is found under the FRACTALS / EXTENDED OPTIONS menu, or by using the (Y) hotkey. Leave the center of inversion at (0,0), and play with the radius of inversion. Try values from about .75 to 1.5. Note that the outside of the "reef" now has gravelly detail; whereas in the uninverted version, the inside has that appearance.

For an inverted barnsleym1, try the following. Under FRACTALS / EXTENDED OPTIONS, set:

Inversion Radius or 'Auto' (0=OFF)   .75

Then Under FRACTALS / FRACTAL PARAMS, set:

Xmin −0.835   Xmax 0.860
Ymin −0.636   Ymax 0.636

In command-line form:

```
type=barnsleym1 invert=0.75/0/0
corners=-.835/.860/-.636/0.636
```

For two zooms in a search of wallpaper patterns, try these corners values with the same example. The first is:

Xmin −0.686   Xmax −0.486

Ymin   0.978   Ymax   1.128

The second is:

Xmin −1.166   Xmax −0.966

Ymin   0.499   Ymax   0.649

The command-line versions of these corners values are:

```
corners=-.686/-.486/.978/1.128
corners=-1.166/-.966/.499/.649
```

History and Credits

Dr. Michael Barnsley of the Georgia Institute of Technology originated this fractal type, and it was adapted for Winfract from the description in the book *Fractals Everywhere* by Dr. Barnsley.

BARNSLEYM2

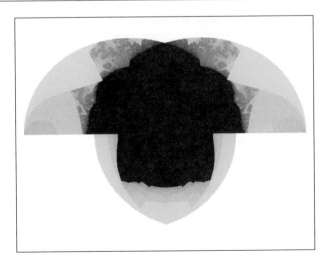

Fractal Category: Escape-time fractal

Formal Name: Called "M2" by Dr. Barnsley

Fractal Type: barnsleym2

Formula: Initialize: $c = z = zpixel$
Iterate: $(z - 1)c$ if $x_z y_c + x_c y_z >= 0$
$(z + 1)c$ if $x_z y_c + x_c y_z < 0$

Code

Routine type	Routine name	File
Fractal engine	StandardFractactal()	CALCFRACT.C
Integer math initialization	long_mandel_per_pixel,()	FRACTALS.C
Integer math orbit	Barnsley2Fractal()	FRACTALS.C
Floating-point initialization	othermandelfp_per_pixel()	FRACTALS.C
Floating-point orbit	Barnsley2FPFractal()	FRACTALS.C

Parameter File Example

```
barnsleym2 {
  reset  maxiter=20000  inside=255  logmap=-1
  type=barnsleym2
}
```

Description

This is a Mandelbrot map of the Julia family barnsleyj2. Related fractal types are barnsleym1 and barnsleym3.

Parameters:

Real perturbation of Z(0)	0
Imaginary perturbation	0
Bailout value (0 means default)	0

As with other Mandelbrot variants, the first two parameters warp the fractal by perturbing the initialization value of z_0.

Explorer

See the barnsleyj2 description for explorations that involve toggling to the Julia variant with the right mouse button.

History and Credits

Dr. Michael Barnsley of the Georgia Institute of Technology originated this fractal type, and it was adapted for Winfract from the description in the book *Fractals Everywhere* by Dr. Barnsley.

BARNSLEYM3

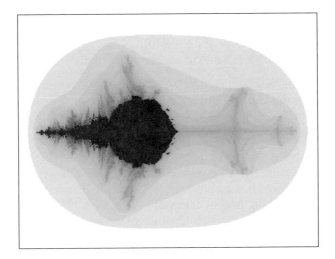

Fractal Category: Escape-time fractal

Formal Name: None

Fractal Type: barnsleym3

Formula: Initialize: $c = z = zpixel$

Iterate: $x_z^2 - y_z^2 - 1 + i2x_z y_z$ if $x_z > 0$

$x_z^2 - y_z^2 + x_c x_z + i(2x_z y_z + y_c x_z)$ if $x_z <= 0$

Code

Routine type	Routine name	File
Fractal engine	StandardFractactal()	CALCFRACT.C
Integer math initialization	long_mandel_per_pixel,()	FRACTALS.C
Integer math orbit	Barnsley3Fractal()	FRACTALS.C
Floating-point initialization	othermandelfp_per_pixel()	FRACTALS.C
Floating-point orbit	Barnsley3FPFractal()	FRACTALS.C

Parameter File Examples

```
barnsleym3  {
  reset  maxiter=20000 inside=255 logmap=-1
  type=barnsleym3
}
```

Description

This type looks very different from the other Barnsley fractal types. On the left is a lake area that looks somewhat like the Mandelbrot set. On the right are several star-like shapes. If you zoom in on the far right limit of those shapes, you will discover a never-ending sequence of those stars.

Parameters: Real perturbation of Z(0)   0

Imaginary perturbation   0

Bailout value (0 means default) 0

As with other Mandelbrot variants, the first two parameters warp the fractal by perturbing the initialization value of z_0.

Explorer
Try pointing the mouse to the center of the lake and clicking the right mouse button. This will generate the barnsleyj3 fractal corresponding to the position in the lake where you pointed. The result is a symmetrical fractal that also has a lake region. Contrast this with the result of pointing the mouse at one of the star shapes, which is a bowling pin shape with stars. See the barnsleyj2 description for other explorations that involve toggling to the Julia variant with the right mouse button.

Try zooming in on one of the stars. First generate the default barnsleym3 example, then use the mouse to zoom in on the star shape to the right of the lake. A parameter file example in EXAMPLES.PAR that does this is:

```
star {
  reset type=barnsleym3 corners=0.906367/1.022504/-0.042199/0.0457101
  maxiter=1000
  }
```

History and Credits
Dr. Michael Barnsley of the Georgia Institute of Technology originated this fractal type, and it was adapted for Winfract from the description in the book *Fractals Everywhere* by Dr. Barnsley.

BIFURCATION

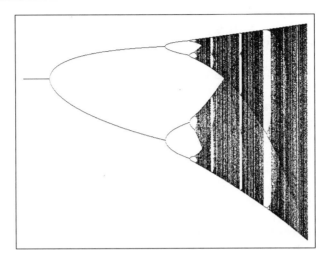

Fractal Category: Bifurcation

Formal Name: Verhulst Bifurcation

Fractal Type: bifurcation

Formula: $x' = x + rx(1 - x)$

Code

Routine type	Routine name	File
Fractal engine	Bifurcation()	CALCFRACT.C
Integer math orbit	LongBifurcVerhulst()	CALCFRACT.C
Floating-point orbit	BifurcVerhulst()	CALCFRACT.C

Parameter File Example

```
bifurcation {
   reset maxiter=20000 type=bifurcation
}
```

Description

This fractal models a very simplified abstract population growth. The variable x in the formula, which ranges from 0 to 1, represents the number of individuals in the population as a fraction of the total possible. As the points are plotted from left to right, the value of r, or the population's growth rate, is continually increased from 1.9 to 3.0 for the initial screen. Changes in the value of r can produce stable populations or chaotic ones.

The behavior of the population numbers is plotted on the vertical *y*-axis, which is scaled from zero to 1.34.

For relatively low values of *r* the population remains steady. Raising the population growth *r* creates a "boom and bust" oscillation pattern, similar to many population oscillations occurring in the real world. The population will rise to a peak then crash to a low, cycling between two constant levels. This is where you see the line split in two, or *bifurcate*.

At some rate beyond this point, the oscillations split again, into a 4-level oscillation pattern. Higher still, and they split into 8- and 16-level oscillations. Then you reach the point of chaos. The population level never settles out into a regular pattern or steady level when the growth rate is at these levels. It constantly fluctuates to unpredictable levels. Two populations with the same growth rate but with populations that differ in number by only one individual will have wildly different populations several generations later. Furthermore, you can't predict ahead of time which one will be higher!

At still higher levels of *r*, pockets of stability appear at odd period levels. The first is a 3-level oscillation. This splits into a 6-level oscillation, then 12-level, 24-level, and at some higher level chaos reappears. This alternating pattern of chaos and stability continues on for all higher growth rates.

Related fractal types are biflambda, bif+sinpi, and bif=sinpi.

Parameters: Filter cycles   1000.00

  Seed population   0.66

Filter cycles (default 1000) is the number of iterations to be done before plotting population values. This gives the iteration time to settle into the characteristic bifurcation branching patterns, and results in a clean-looking plot.

Seed population is the initial population value from which all others are calculated. For filtered maps, the final image is independent of seed population value in the valid range between 0.0 and 1.0.

Explorer
Try zooming in and finding the exact transition from stable oscillations to chaos. Just when you think you've found it, switch to a higher iteration level and a higher screen resolution. Surprise—there is no transition point! With each zoom you will find higher and higher periods between the stable and chaotic regions. Chaos and stability are kept separate by an infinite period.

Try different parameter values. Seed population becomes effective in unfiltered maps. Try setting filter cycles to 1 (unfiltered) and seed population to 0.001. This results in a map overlaid with interesting curves. Each seed population value results in a different set of curves. Then try increasing filter cycles with the values 1, 5, 10, 20, and 40, and watch the filtering action remove extra curves and reveal the original bifurcation shape.

History and Credits
This equation was originally studied by P. F. Verhulst in 1845. It was later studied by Robert May in 1971. The coding for this fractal originally came from Phil Wilson and was later revised by Kev Allen.

BIFURCATION LAMBDA

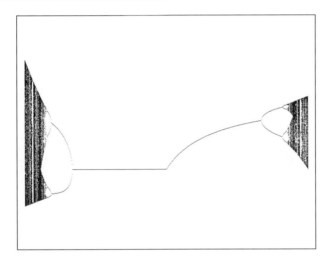

Fractal Category: Bifurcation

Formal Name: Robert May bifurcation

Fractal Type: biflambda

Formula: $x' = rx(1 - x)$

Code

Routine type	Routine name	File
Fractal engine	Bifurcation()	CALCFRACT.C
Integer math orbit	LongBifurcLambda()	CALCFRACT.C
Floating-point orbit	BifurcLambda()	CALCFRACT.C

Parameter File Example
```
biflambda {
   reset maxiter=20000 type=biflambda
}
```

Description

The bifurcation lambda formula differs from the bifurcation formula by the deletion of a single *x* term. The result is to make a two-headed bifurcation image that has a reflection of the original plot on the left. The plot of the fractal looks like a lower branch is missing, but the code is correct; that's just the way this fractal looks. See the description of the bifurcation fractal type for more information about this type, since most of the discussion applies to this type.

Parameters: Filter cycles   1000.00
                 Seed population   0.66

Filter cycles (default 1000) is the number of iterations to be done before plotting population values. This gives the iteration time to settle into the characteristic bifurcation branching patterns, and results in a clean-looking plot.

Seed population is the initial population value from which all others are calculated. For filtered maps the final image is independent of seed population value in the valid range between 0.0 and 1.0.

Explorer

Try turning off the filtering action with the following parameters:

Filter cycles   1.00
Seed population   0.01

This adds some additional curves to the plot. Varying seed population changes these extra curves.

History and Credits

This equation was originally studied by P. F. Verhulst in 1845. It was later studied by Robert May in 1971. The coding for this fractal originally came from Phil Wilson and was later revised by Kev Allen.

The behavior of the population numbers is plotted on the vertical *y*-axis, which is scaled from zero to 1.34 (−1.0 to 2.0 for biflambda).

BIFURCATION SINEPI

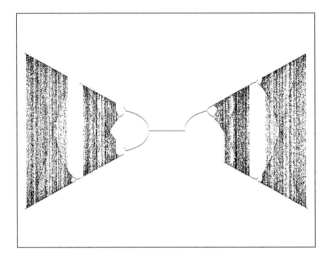

Fractal Category: Bifurcation

Formal Name: None

Fractal Type: bif=sinpi

Formula: $x' = r\sin(x)$

Code

Routine type	Routine name	File
Fractal engine	Bifurcation()	CALCFRACT.C
Integer math orbit	LongBifurcSetSinPi()	CALCFRACT.C
Floating-point orbit	BifurcSetSinPi()	CALCFRACT.C

Parameter File Example

```
bifurcation_equal_sinepi {
  reset maxiter=20000 type=bif=sinpi
}
```

Description

This fractal looks very similar to the Robert May Bifurcation fractal (see the bifurcation lambda fractal type), but it is based on an entirely different formula. It has the same basic shape, including the mysterious, missing lower branch on the right side. The reason is that recursive iterated functions have a universal relationship similar to the way circles are related to . The number   is the ratio of the circumference of a circle to its diameter. Iterated functions have a similar ratio:

$$(r_n - r_{n-1})/(r_{n+1} - r_n) = 4.66920160$$

where r_n is the value of x that produces a maximum value of $y = f(x)$ for a function $f(x)$. In other words, the ratio of the difference between successive parameters that produce a maximum is equal to a constant, known as *Feigenbaum's Number*.

This is true whether the function used is $rx(1 - x)$, $r\sin(\_ \times x)$, or any other function that has a single differential maximum. Feigenbaum's Number appears in all types of situations ranging from fluid-flow turbulence to electronic oscillators to chemical reactions and even to the Mandelbrot set. As a matter of fact, the budding of the Mandelbrot set along the negative x-axis occurs at intervals of Feigenbaum's Number.

Other related fractal types are bif+sinpi, biflambda, and bifurcation.

Parameters: Filter cycles   1000.00

Seed population   0.66

Filter cycles (default 1000) is the number of iterations to be done before plotting population values. This gives the iteration time to settle into the characteristic bifurcation branching patterns, and results in a clean-looking plot.

Seed population is the initial population value from which all others are calculated. For filtered maps, the final image is independent of seed population value in the valid range between 0.0 and 1.0.

Explorer
Try turning off the filtering action with the following parameters:

Filter cycles   1.00

Seed population   0.01

This adds some additional curves to the plot. Varying seed population changes these extra curves.

History and Credits
Mitchell Feigenbaum discovered this universal number in 1976 while investigating the maximum points in Robert May's bifurcation formula (see the biflambda fractal type) at Los Alamos National Laboratory in New Mexico. The computer he used for the study was extremely slow, so to save time he guessed at the values using his HP-65 hand-held calculator. As time progressed, the constant he was using to guess became more accurate and more closely matched the numbers returned by the computer. When he changed from a bifurcation formula to one based on the sine function and came up with the same constant, he realized he was on to something big.

BIFURCATION STEWART

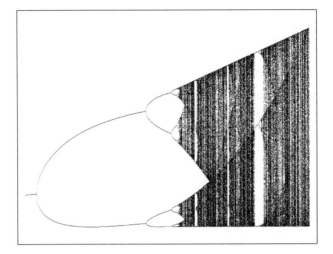

Fractal Category: Bifurcation

Formal Name: None

Fractal Type: bifstewart

Formula: $x' = rx^2 - 1$

Code

Routine type	Routine name	File
Fractal engine	Bifurcation()	CALCFRACT.C
Integer math orbit	LongBifurcStewart()	CALCFRACT.C
Floating-point orbit	BifurcStewart()	CALCFRACT.C

Parameter File Example

```
bifurcation_Stewart{
  reset maxiter=20000 type=bifstewart
}
```

Description

The bifurcation: Stewart fractal looks very much like the bifurcation fractal. A different poulation growth model is used, but the result is similar. When filtering is turned off, differences become apparent—see the Explorer section.

Parameters: Filter cycles   1000.00

Seed population   0.66

Filter cycles (default 1000) is the number of iterations to be done before plotting population values. This gives the iteration time to settle into the characteristic bifurcation branching patterns, and results in a clean-looking plot.

Seed population is the initial population value from which all others are calculated. For filtered maps, the final image is independent of seed population value in the valid range between 0.0 and 1.0.

Explorer
Try turning off the filtering action with the following parameters:

Filter cycles   1.00
Seed population   0.01

This adds some additional curves to the plot. Varying seed population changes these extra curves. With these values a fascinating web connects the opposing strands of the bifurcation.

BIFURCATION SUMMATION SINEPI

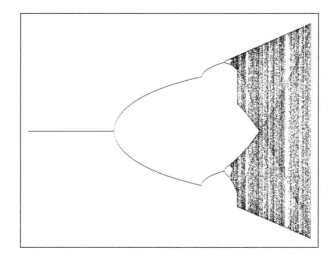

Fractal Category: Bifurcation

Formal Name: None

Fractal Type: bif+sinpi

Formula: $x' = x + r\sin(\pi x)$

Code

Routine type	Routine name	File
Fractal engine	Bifurcation()	CALCFRACT.C
Integer math orbit	LongBifurcAddSinPi()	CALCFRACT.C
Floating-point orbit	BifurcAddSinPi()	CALCFRACT.C

Parameter File Example

```
bifurcation_plus_sinepi {
  reset maxiter=20000 type=bif+sinpi
}
```

Description

This fractal looks much like the bifurcation fractal, with the puzzling difference that the lower branch is missing from the second bifurcation branching (as you can see in the screen dump at the head of this section). As with the other bifurcation types, further differences emerge if the filtering action is turned off.

Parameters: Filter cycles   1000.00

Seed population   0.66

Filter cycles (default 1000) is the number of iterations to be done before plotting population values. This gives the iteration time to settle into the characteristic bifurcation branching patterns, and results in a clean-looking plot.

Seed population is the initial population value from which all others are calculated. For filtered maps, the final image is independent of seed population value in the valid range between 0.0 and 1.0.

Explorer

Try turning off the filtering action with the following parameters:

Filter cycles   1.00

Seed population   0.01

This adds some additional curves to the plot. Varying the seed population adds extra curves that look like a web connecting the original branches of the plot.

CIRCLE

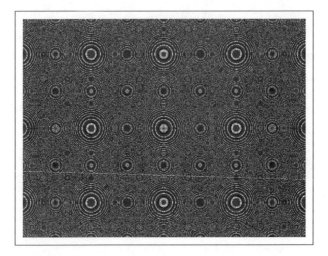

Fractal Category: Moire Pattern

Formal Name: Circle

Fractal Type: circle

Formula: c = integer part of $a \times (x^2 + y^2)$
$color = c$ modulo(number of colors)

Code

Routine type	Routine name	File
Fractal engine	StandardFractal()	CALCFRACT.C
Floating-point orbit	CirclefpFractal()	FRACTALS.C

Parameter File Example

```
circle {
  reset type=circle params=20000
}
```

Description

The circle fractal type is a family of fascinating moire patterns formed by calculating the square of the distance of each point from the origin and truncating the resulting number to an integer. Strictly speaking, this type is not a fractal at all because all detail disappears when you zoom in; true fractals have endless detail at smaller and smaller scales. However, as you zoom *out* the interference patterns created by the circle pattern become more detailed. Unlike most fractals, the appearance of images made with the circle algorithm change with resolution. Try both high and low resolution video modes.

Parameters: Magnification   200000

Increasing the magnification parameter has the same effect as zooming out, allowing you to effectively zoom out past the normal limits of approximately from –32 to 32.

Explorer
You can get a lot of insight into the nature of the circle fractal by making a sequence of images with different magnifications. Try multiples of 100 starting with 1.

Concentric circles

Magnification   1

Concentric rings—start of moire pattern

Magnification   100

Nine different concentric centers, with moire patterns between them

Magnification   10000

Very intricate moire patterns

Magnification   1000000

Special Effects
If you zoom in to your circle images, or use small magnification parameters, you will find that the detail stops, and the image resolves into discrete bands. But if you zoom out, or increase the magnification parameter, you find a rich tapestry of detailed moire patterns. This effect suggests that the circle fractal type may be a true fractal after all, but has somehow been turned inside out. You can invert your circle images using the inversion radius parameter under the extended options (Ⓨ) screen. Set the inversion radius to auto and make another sequence of images using magnification values of 1, 100, 10000, and 1000000. The result is a sequence of images that zoom into an isolated fractal circle swimming in a sea of blue. With inversion turned on, increasing the magnification parameter has the same effect as zooming in, the opposite as before. Inversion collapses the whole complex plane outside the inversion radius into the center of your image.

History and Credits
The circle fractal type is from A. K. Dewdney's "Computer Recreations" column in *Scientific American*. Dewdney attributes it to John Connett of the University of Minnesota.

COMPLEX MARK'S JULIA

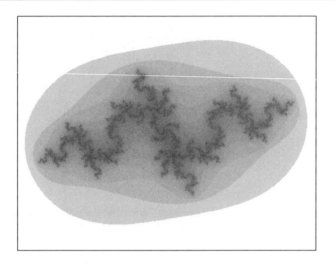

Fractal Category: Escape-time fractal

Formal Name: Complex Mark's Julia

Fractal Type: cmplxmarksjul

Formula: Initialize: $z = zpixel$
  Iterate: $z^2 c^{(p-1)} + c$

Code

Routine type	Routine name	File
Fractal engine	StandardFractactal()	CALCFRACT.C
Floating-point initialization	juliafp_per_pixel()	FRACTALS.C
Floating-point orbit	MarksCplxMand()	FRACTALS.C

Parameter File Example

```
cmplexmarksjul {
  reset maxiter=20000 inside=255 logmap=-1 type=cmplxmarksjul
}
```

Description

These fractals are the Julia sets associated with the different points from Complex Mark's Mandelbrot. As with other Julia set families, there are an infinite number of complex Julia sets.

Parameters:

Real part of parameter	0.3
Imaginary part of parameter	0.6
Real part of degree	1
Imag part of degree	0
Bailout value (0 means use default)	0

The real and imaginary parameters define the value of c in the formula. The value of z is initialized to the coordinates of the pixel color being calculated. The real and imaginary parts of the degree are used to set the complex value of p in the formula.

Explorer

With an infinite number of sets to choose from, a complete exploration of this fractal type is not possible. Fortunately, the cmplxmarksmand fractal is a catalog of all the different Julia sets associated with this formula. Find an interesting spot in cmplxmarksmand and use the right mouse button to toggle to the Julia set associated with the point in the center of the screen.

History and Credits

Mark Peterson originated the fractal formula and added the marksjulia fractal to Winfract. In a later version, he added the code allowing the period to be complex.

COMPLEX MARK'S MANDELBROT

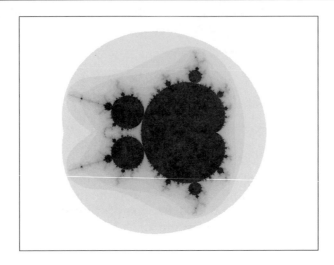

Fractal Category: Escape-time fractal

Formal Name: Complex Mark's Mandelbrot

Fractal Type: cmplxmarksmand

Formula: Initialize: $c = z = zpixel$
Iterate: $z^2 c^{(p-1)} + c$

Code

Routine type	Routine name	File
Fractal engine	StandardFractactal()	CALCFRACT.C
Floating-point initialization	MarksCplxMandperp	FRACTALS.C
Floating-point orbit	MarksCplxMand()	FRACTALS.C

Parameter File Example

```
cmplexmarksmand {
  reset maxiter=20000 inside=255 logmap=-1 type=cmplxmarksmand
}
```

Description

This fractal uses the traditional Mandelbrot fractal formula as a base for an even more interesting fractal. As can be seen by the formula, with the period variable *p* equal to (1, 0), the formula reduces to the traditional Mandelbrot set, as follows:

$$z^2 c^{(p-1)} + c = z^2 c^{[(1+i0)-1]} + c$$
$$= z^2 c^0 + c$$
$$= z^2 + c$$

As with the traditional Mandelbrot set, the initial value of z for each pixel calculation is zero. Other integer real values for p draw multiple Mandelbrot sets extending outward from the origin. Using imaginary and negative periods produce some rather unexpected results. No matter how bizarre the initial drawing, however, you can always find a tiny, undistorted Mandelbrot set somewhere in the drawing.

The cmplxmarksjul fractals are the Julia sets associated with each point on the drawing. The fractal type marksmandel is a faster but less generalized version of this fractal.

Parameters:		
Real perturbation of Z(0)		0
Imaginary perturbation of Z(0)		0
Real part of degree		1
Imag part of degree		0
Bailout value (0 means use default)		0

The real and imaginary perturbations warp the drawings. For exploration, we'd recommend using zeros for these parameters. The real and imaginary degree values are used to set the complex value of p in the fractal formula. The default settings produce the same old boring Mandelbrot set. Changing the real and imaginary portions of the degree gets some action going.

Real part of degree   1.1

Using a degree with a real value greater than 1 (such as 1.1 and above) splits the negative "tail" of the Mandelbrot set in two. Continue drawing sets with higher values of the real part and the two tails move towards vertical. At 2.0 they are both straight up and down. Go beyond 2.0 and a new negative tail begins to form.

Real part of degree   0.8

Use real values for the degree of less than one and the Mandelbrot set folds in on itself. First the negative tail of the set is absorbed into the body of the set, and knobs around the set move steadily towards the negative x-axis. At the above settings, the knobs that were at the top and bottom of the set have moved to 45 degree angles off the negative x-axis.

Real part of degree   0.55

At these values, the two knobs have merged into one, forming a new negative tail. This drawing looks like a miniature version of the original

Mandelbrot set. Progressively lowering the real value of the degree causes more and more of the set to absorb itself. At a value of zero there is only a point in the center of the screen.

Real part of degree   −0.6

With negative values for the real portion of the degree, the set is turned inside out. Using progressively more negative values causes more of the set to grow out of the negative x-axis.

Real part of degree   1.0

Imag part of degree   0.1

Using imaginary values as part of the degree causes the Mandelbrot set to skew into imaginary planes outside of the two-dimensional drawing. With degrees having a nonzero imaginary component, there is always a split along the negative x-axis. The set grows smaller as you move around the circumference in a counterclockwise direction if the imaginary values are positive. With negative imaginary values, the set grows larger in this direction.

Explorer

Whatever way you prefer to view the regular Mandelbrot set will also work well with this set. We would recommend setting Inside color to 0 in the FRACTALS / BASIC OPTIONS menu to distinguish the inside of the set from the outside. This is especially important with negative real values or when the degree is part imaginary.

Setting the FIRESTRM.MAP color map (COLORS / LOAD COLOR-MAP menu) with Log Palette set to −1 and MAXIMUM ITERATIONS set to 31000 (FRACTALS / BASIC OPTIONS menu) also produces excellent drawings. The small amount of extra time needed to draw the image at the higher iteration value is well worth the wait.

History and Credits

Mark Peterson originated the fractal formula and added the marksmandel fractal to Winfract. In a later version, he added the code allowing the period to be complex.

COMPLEX NEWTON

Fractal Category: Escape-time fractal

Formal Name: Newton

Fractal Type: complexnewton

Formula: $z' = [(n - 1)z^n + r]/[nz^{(n-1)}]$

Code

Routine type	Routine name	File
Fractal engine	StandardFractactal()	CALCFRACT.C
Floating-point initialization	otherjuliafp_per_pixel()	FRACTALS.C
Floating-point orbit	ComplexNewton()	MPMATH_C.C

Parameter File Example

```
complex_newton {
   reset maxiter=20000 inside=255 logmap=-1 params=10/3/1/0
   type=complexnewton
}
```

Description

This fractal is identical to the fractal type complexbasin except the colors represent the number of iterations Winfract required to find the solution. As with complexbasin, the iteration formula above is a generalization of Newton's method for finding solutions to $z^n - r = 0$, where z, n, and r are complex numbers. See the description for the complexbasin fractal type, which has a detailed explanation of Newton's method.

Parameters: Real part of degree   3

Imag part of degree   0

Real part of root   1

Imag part of root   0

The default parameters tell Winfract to look for the solutions to the equation $z^3 - 1 = 0$. The real part of degree and imag part of degree set the value of n in the formula. The parameters real part of root and imag part of root set the value of r in the formula. An odd integer value for the degree produces one fractal arm along the negative x-axis and $n - 1$ evenly spaced arms extending outward from the origin.

The effects of variations on the parameters for the complexnewton are identical to those for the complexbasin.

Explorer
Zoom in on any section of a Newton fractal and you will find a repetition of the same overall pattern in different colors. Higher zooms may require the use of higher maximum iteration levels and the use of logarithmic color to prevent overflowing the number of colors available on your machine.

History and Credits
The actual fractal characteristics of Newton's method for roots was first discovered by John Hubbard in Orsay, France. The first fractal types Newton and newtbasin were coded into Winfract by Tim Wegner. Lee Crocker wrote a more efficient algorithm using FPU-specific assembly language. Mark Peterson wrote the complexnewton and complexbasin fractal type variations.

COMPLEX NEWTON'S BASIN

Fractal Category: Escape-time fractal

Formal Name: Newton's basin

Fractal Type: complexbasin

Formula: $z' = [(n-1)z^n + r]/[nz^{(n-1)}]$

Code

Routine type	Routine name	File
Fractal engine	StandardFractactal()	CALCFRACT.C
Floating-point initialization	otherjuliafp_per_pixel()	FRACTALS.C
Floating-point orbit	ComplexBasin()	MPMATH_C.C

Parameter File Example

```
complex_basin {
  reset type=complexbasin params=10/3/1/0
  maxiter=20000
}
```

Description

Many colors in this fractal exist next to each other, but no color actually touches another. At every color boundary an intricately beautiful pattern forms, gently separating the two. The pattern itself is made of many colors and not one of these touches another. Each color of the pattern is kept separate by the pattern itself.

There are regions where colors may appear to touch when the value of n has an imaginary component. Then the fractal skews into imaginary complex planes along the negative x-axis that are not shown by Winfract. The skewing also appears in the smaller copies. Where the colors appear to touch, the fractal actually continues on into other complex planes.

Near the origin, and other points on the fractal, the colors seem to merge into a region of blue or black. This is where Winfract reached the maximum allowed number of iterations and gave up trying to determine the color. In this situation, Winfract assigns the inside color as a way of saying, "I don't know what the solutions are here. Your guess is as good as mine." Setting a higher iteration level will push back, but not entirely remove, the "unknown" regions.

The Newton fractal types, which include complexbasin, complexnewton, newton, and newtbasin, use Newton's method for finding the roots of the polynomial $z^n - r$ (the values of z satisfying the equation $z^n - r = 0$). Newton's method involves successive iterations of the equation $z' = z - p(z)/p'(z)$ to find better and better approximations of the roots to the polynomial, where p(z) is the polynomial whose roots we are seeking and p'(z) is the derivative of the polynomial. Each iteration of the equation improves the "guess" and rapidly converges to a correct solution to the equation.

If $n > 1$, there is always more than one root of the polynomial $z^n - r$. If the initial guess is near one of the roots, Newton's method will converge to that root. But if the initial guess is between several of the roots, Newton's method has trouble deciding which root to converge to. This indecision gives rise to chaotic behavior that can be used to generate beautiful fractals.

The initial value, or "guess," of z is the screen coordinate for the pixel color being calculated. This guess is plugged into the generalized formula. The result from this calculation is used as the next value of z and run through the equation again. With each iteration, Winfract determines whether the value of $p(z)$ is less than a predetermined threshold. When this happens, Winfract determines which root was found and displays the corresponding color. The value of n can also be a complex number.

The fractal type complexnewton is similar to this fractal except it displays the number of iterations performed rather than the solution. The fractal types Newton and newtbasin are faster versions of this fractal that work strictly with the integer roots of the number 1.

Parameters:

Real part of degree	3
Imag part of degree	0
Real part of root	1
Imag part of root	0

The default parameters tell Winfract to look for the solutions to the equation $z^3 - 1 = 0$. The real part of degree and imag part of degree set the value of n in the formula. The parameters real part of root and imag part of root set the value of r in the formula. An odd integer value for the degree produces one fractal arm along the negative x-axis and $n - 1$ evenly spaced arms extending outward from the origin. The actual solutions to $z^3 - 1 = 0$ are $(1,0)$, $(-1/2 + i[(-3)/2])$, and $(-1/2 - i[(-3)/2])$.

The fractal arms are always found between the actual solutions to the equation.

Real part of degree	3
Imag part of degree	0
Real part of root	10
Imag part of root	0

These parameters tell Winfract to look for solutions to $z^3 - 10 = 0$. Raising the value of the real portion of the root enlarges the fractal arms.

Real part of degree	3
Imag part of degree	0
Real part of root	1
Imag part of root	1

These parameters set the equation to $z^3 - (1 + i) = 0$. Adding an imaginary component to the root rotates the fractal arms slightly in the counterclockwise direction.

Real part of degree	3.5
Imag part of degree	0
Real part of root	1
Imag part of root	0

These parameters instruct Winfract to find the values of z that satisfy the equation $z^{3.5} - 1 = 0$. Fractional values above an odd integer split the arm along the negative x-axis and rotate the other arms towards the positive x-axis.

Real part of degree	4

Real even integers for the degree produce n evenly spaced arms extending out from the origin with no arm on the negative x-axis.

Real part of degree	4.75

Raising the real part of degree to fractional real values above an even integer causes a new fractal arm to form along the negative x-axis. The fractal arms above and below the negative x-axis are rotated toward the positive x-axis.

Real part of degree	10
Imag part of degree	3
Real part of root	1
Imag part of root	0

These parameters tell Winfract to look for values of z that satisfy $z^{(10+i3)} = 1$. The hitch is there are an *infinite* number of solutions! These solutions fall along an exponential spiral around the origin. This is best seen in the drawing of the complexnewton fractal using the same parameters. The blue areas of the complexnewton fractal surround the actual solutions to the equation. If the imaginary portion of the degree is positive, the spiral is counterclockwise. Negative imaginary portions produce a clockwise exponential spiral of solutions.

Winfract clips the solutions to those existing on the imaginary plane based between − and +. The spiral of solutions both above and below the negative axis continue on in other imaginary complex planes based on positive and negative multiples of 2. The remaining solutions are skewed into other complex planes.

Real part of degree   −5

Negative real values for the degree effectively turn the fractal inside out.

Explorer
Zoom in on any section of a Newton fractal and you will find a repetition of the same overall pattern. No matter how high the zoom level, the pattern will repeat itself if you stay within the accuracy limits of the Winfract calculation algorithm.

Warnings
This fractal is very slow if your machine does not have a floating-point coprocessor.

History and Credits
The actual fractal characteristics of Newton's method for roots was first discovered by John Hubbard in Orsay, France. The first fractal types Newton and newtbasin were coded into Winfract by Tim Wegner. Lee Crocker wrote a more efficient algorithm using FPU-specific assembly language. Mark Peterson wrote the complexnewton and complexbasin fractal type variations.

DIFFUSION LIMITED AGGREGATION

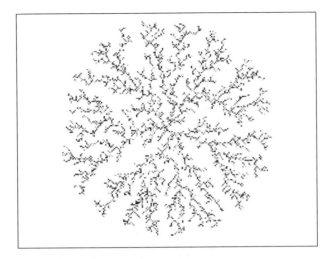

Fractal Category: Random fractal

Formal Name: None

Fractal Type: diffusion

Code

Routine type	Routine name	File
Fractal engine	diffusion()	CALCFRACT.C

Parameter File Example
```
diffusion {
   reset type=diffusion params=1
}
```

Description
This fractal type begins as a single point in the center of the screen. Winfract then randomly generates points around the pixel until it finds a point adjacent to a point already assigned a color, at which time its location is fixed and the next sequential color is assigned. This process continues until the edges of the screen are reached.

Parameters: Border size   10

The border size limits how far the point is allowed to wander away from the colored pixel region. Lowering the number reduces the generation time but results in more densely packed branches. Higher numbers take much longer to generate but result in more delicate structures.

Alternate Color Maps
Continuous palette maps, such as FIRESTRM.MAP or GREY.MAP, work best with this fractal type.

History and Credits
Diffusion was inspired by a *Scientific American* article a few years back. Adrian Mariano provided the code and documentation for Winfract.

FUNCTION VARIABLE FRACTALS

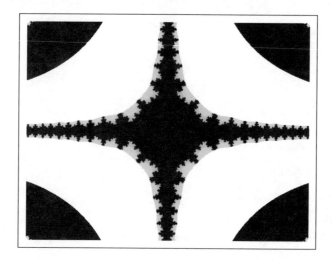

Fractal Category: Escape-time fractal

Formal Name: None

Fractal Types: fn(z*z), fn*fn, fn*z+z, fn+fn, fn(z)+fn(pix), sqr(1/fn), sqr(fn)

Formulas: fn(z^2)
  fn(z)fn(z)
  fn + fn
  $p_1$fn(z) + $p_2 z$
  $p_1$fn(z) + $p_2$fn(z)
  $p_1$fn(z) + $p_2$fn(*pixel*)
  $1/$fn(z)^2
  fn(z)^2

where fn(z) is one of conj, cos, cosh, cosxx, cotan, cotanh, exp, flip, ident, log, recip, sin, sinh, sqr, tan, or tanh.

Code

These fractals all use the StandardFractal() fractal engine in CALCFRACT.C. There are many different orbit routines for these types in the file FRACTALS.C. Each type has both an integer-math and a floating-point version. These orbit functions call other functions for certain special cases that were separately coded in an effort to achieve the best possible performance.

Fractal type	Floating point orbit routine	Integer math orbit routine
fn(z)+fn(pix)	Richard8fpFractal()	Richard8Fractal()
fn(z*z)	TrigZsqrdfpFractal()	TrigZsqrdFractal()
fn*fn	TrigXTrigfpFractal()	TrigXTrigFractal()
fn*z+z	ZXTrigPlusZfpFractal()	ZXTrigPlusZFractal()
fn+fn	TrigPlusTrigfpFractal()	TrigPlusTrigFractal()
sqr(1/fn)	Sqr1overTrigfpFractal()	Sqr1overTrigFractal()
sqr(fn)	SqrTrigfpFractal()	SqrTrigFractal()

Parameter File Example

```
function_type {
   reset maxiter=20000 inside=255 logmap=-1 type=fn(z*z)
function=sin
}
```

Description

When Winfract's formula compiler was first released, several people went on a creative rampage of generating new fractal types. The Stone Soup Group was getting so many different fractal types from these people that names could not be created quickly enough! So we lumped them all together here, and generalized the formulas so that one type could accomodate many new formulas.

The short list of eight different types is deceptive. For example, consider the fn*fn fractal type. The orbit routine consists of multiplying two functions together, and each of these two functions can be any of 16 different functions. That one fractal type alone is actually 240 different types in disguise! Toss in changes in the two parameters and the number of variations is mind-boggling.

Parameters:	
Real coefficient first function	1
Imag coefficient first function	0
Real coefficient second function	1
Imag coefficient second function	0
First function	sin

Second function	sqr
Bailout value (0 means use default)	0

The real coefficient and imag coefficient of the first four parameters refer to the complex variables p_1 and p_2 of the formulas. The first function and second function accept one of the following function names:

conj, cos, cosh, cosxx, cotan, cotanh, exp, flip, ident, log, recip, sin, sinh, sqr, tan or tanh

Most of these function variable values refer to the transcendental function commonly known by the same name. For example, "sin" refers to the familar sine function from high school trigonometry, while "sinh" refers to the somewhat less familiar hyperbolic sine. Several of these functions have no common name or are peculiar to Winfract.

The function cosxx is the complex conjugate of the correct cosine function. Earlier versions of Winfract had a sign error in the code for the cosine function. Fractals made with the earlier cos can be reproduced using cosxx instead of cos.

The ident function is the identity function. It is defined by ident(z) = z.

The flip function swaps the real and imaginary parts of a complex number. Hence, flip(x + iy) = y + ix.

Finally, the recip function calculates the reciprocal, so recip(z) = 1/z.

All of these functions are generalizations of the corresponding functions you might have studied in a high school math class because they operate on complex numbers instead of the more familiar real numbers. If you have no idea what these functions are, you can still discover fractals just as well as a math PhD! Just experiment with different values of the parameters.

The bailout value is the variable that determines when Winfract should stop the formula iteration and assign the pixel a color. The default value is 4.

History and Credits
These fractal types were contributed to Winfract by Scott Taylor, Lee Skinner, and Jm Richard-Collard. Tim Wegner programmed the types into Winfract and developed the function variable scheme.

GINGERBREAD MAN

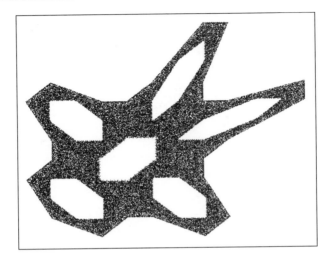

Fractal Category: Orbital fractal

Formal Name: Gingerbreadman

Fractal Type: gingerbreadman

Formula: Initialize: x,y = parameters
 Iterate: $x' = 1 - y + |x|$
  $y' = x$

Code

Routine type	Routine name	File
Fractal engine	orbit2dfloat()	LORENZ.C
Floating-point orbit	gingerbreadfloatorbit()	LORENZ.C

Parameter File Example

```
gingerbreadman {
   reset type=gingerbreadman maxiter=20000
}
```

Description

Hot from the mathematical oven—a cookie fractal. We tried to think of something intelligent to say about this fractal type, but it's hard to be serious about a fractal that looks like something you'd find in your Christmas stocking. The orbit traces out a gingerbread man lying on his side. Just when you think he is finished baking, you will see some new pixels being added to his outline. Don't wait for him to finish—he bakes forever!

Explorer
Zoom in on the "skin" section of the gingerbread man and you'll find smaller copies of the fellow.

History and Credits
The gingerbread man is from Robert L. Devaney's description in *The Science of Fractal Images.*

HENON FRACTALS

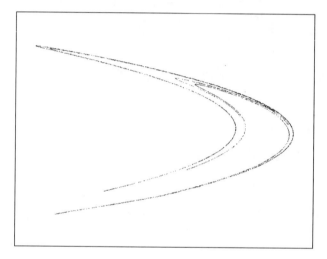

Fractal Category: Orbital fractal

Formal Name: Henon

Fractal Type: henon

Formula: Initialize: $x = y = 1$
Iterate: $x' = 1 + y - ax^2$
$y' = bx$

Code

Routine type	Routine name	File
Floating-point fractal engine	orbit2dfloat()	LORENZ.C
Floating-point orbit	henonlongorbit()	LORENZ.C
Integer math fractal engine	orbit2dlong()	LORENZ.C
Integer math orbit	henonfloatorbit()	LORENZ.C

Parameter File Example
```
Winfract type=henon maxiter=20000
```

Description
This fractal type, named after its founder, Michael Henon, came from an investigation into the orbits of astronomical objects. The Henon fractal is an example of a very simple dynamic system that never settles into a stable, periodic cycle. With each iteration of the two equations, the new x and y positions are plotted. The orbit tracings form a characteristic banana shape. On closer inspection of any line, you will find it composed of many thinner lines. Each of these lines is made up of even thinner lines. Every line in the fractal is composed of a cluster of infinitely thin lines. The fractional dimension of the henon fractal type is somewhere between 1.0 and 2.0.

Parameters: a   1.4
b   0.3

The a and b parameters are used as the constants in the formula. Changing them to other values will usually result in the iterations falling into a periodic loop.

Explorer
Zoom in on any line section and you'll see a collection of thinner lines. You may have to wait a considerable time at high zooms for enough of the iteration points to fall inside your zoom box and form the lines.

History and Credits
Michael Henon, of Nice Observatory in France, discovered this fractal in 1976.

HOPALONG

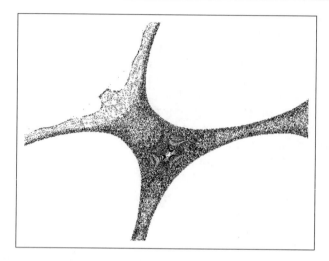

Fractal Category: Orbital fractal

Formal Name: None

Fractal Type: hopalong

Formula: Initialize: $x = y = 0$:
Iterate: $x' = y - \text{sign}(x)\text{sqrt}(\text{abs}(bx - c))$
$y' = a - x$

(The function "sign()" returns 1 if the argument is positive, −1 if argument is negative.)

Code

Routine type	Routine name	File
Floating-point fractal engine	orbit2dfloat()	LORENZ.C
Floating-point orbit	hopalong2dfloatorbit()	LORENZ.C

Parameter File Example

```
hopalong             { ; looks like an ape
  reset type=hopalong corners=-0.318669/0.450611/-0.025523/0.611877
  params=0.3/0.3 float=y
  }
```

Description
The hopalong orbital fractal has the fascinating property that it traces out certain patterns, apparently indefinitely, then suddenly leaps out to a

new area and paints new shapes. Don't wait for it to complete because it has been programmed to run forever. You might try running it overnight to see if any new surprises await!

Parameters: a   0.4

b   1

c   0

The parameters *a, b,* and *c* are the numbers used in the calculation of the new *x* and *y* values (see the previous formula).

Explorer
Because this fractal type keeps developing, you can have fun watching it grow and mutate. Try zooming in to interesting areas. Keep in mind that unlike escape-time fractals, the actual calculation does not change as you zoom in; you just see a smaller piece of the same orbit. As you zoom in, it is interesting to note how certain areas are continually missed by the orbit, and others are traced over and over again. Try tweaking the parameters slightly to see what happens. You may find that you have to zoom out to see the whole fractal as you try different parameters. Here are some experiments that we tried. You can invent your own just as easily—just plug in different numbers.

Three loops

a   0.3

b   .3

c   0

Chain-link necklace

a   3

b   .3

c   0

Flower

a   3

b   .3

c   2

Diamond made of circles

a   .3

b   .3

c   −6

Another exotic flower

a   10

b   .3

c   2

History and Credits
These fractal types are from A. K. Dewdney's "Computer Recreations" column in *Scientific American*. They are attributed to Barry Martin of Aston University in Birmingham, UK.

ITERATED FUNCTION SYSTEMS

Fractal Category: Iterated Function Systems (IFS)

Formal Name: Iterated Function Systems

Fractal Type: ifs

Formula:
$$\begin{bmatrix} x' \\ y' \end{bmatrix} = \begin{bmatrix} a & b \\ c & d \end{bmatrix} \begin{bmatrix} x \\ y \end{bmatrix} + \begin{bmatrix} e \\ f \end{bmatrix}$$

$$\begin{bmatrix} x' \\ y' \\ z' \end{bmatrix} = \begin{bmatrix} a & b & c \\ d & e & f \\ h & i & j \end{bmatrix} \begin{bmatrix} x \\ y \\ z \end{bmatrix} + \begin{bmatrix} k \\ l \\ m \end{bmatrix}$$

Code

Routine type	Routine name	File
Fractal engine	ifs()	LORENZ.C

Parameter File Example

```
fern {
  reset type=ifs ifsfile=fractint.ifs ifs=fern
}
```

Description

IFS is another Winfract universe disguised as a humble fractal type. There is no limit to the variety of fractals you can make with this type alone. Iterated Function Systems are directly inspired by the idea of self-similarity. Self-similarity is the quality an object possesses when its parts are miniatures of the whole (see Chapter 1). Each IFS fractal is defined by several equations that specify different self-similarities that exist in the fractal. You can change those equations and create new fractals by editing .IFS files that contain the IFS parameters.

An example of an IFS fractal is a delicately curved fern. You can generate the fern by selecting the IFS fractal type from the FRACTALS / FRACTAL FORMULA menu, selecting the file FRACTINT.IFS, and then selecting the fern. There are four transformations that define this fern. (There is a figure depicting these transformations in the Chapter 1 discussion of IFS.) The first transformation isn't what you would really think of as self-similarity—it maps the whole fern to the stem at the bottom. The second transformation maps the whole fern to the fern that remains after cutting off the bottom two fronds. This transformation is the source of the curling fern tip. The third transformation maps the whole fern to the bottom left-hand branch. The last transformation maps the bottom left-hand branch with the bottom right-hand branch.

Winfract uses the random form of IFS generation. This means that any point can be used to start, and each point is plotted and then transformed by the random choice of one of the transformations. You will see a collection of points appearing on the screen like raindrops on a window which slowly build up to the fractal shape. When new colors start to overlap older points, the next sequential color in the palette is assigned.

Parameters

There are no regular Winfract parameters associated with this fractal type, so when you reach the standard Winfract parameters screen after selecting an IFS fractal, just click on OK. The IFS parameters are stored in .IFS files, which you can edit using the Windows Notepad application. An example of a set of IFS parameters from the file FRACTINT.IFS is:

```
fern   {
      a          b          c          d          e          f          probablility
      0.0        0.0        0.0        0.16       0.0        0.0        0.01
      0.85       0.04       -0.04      0.85       0.0        1.6        0.85
      0.2        -0.26      0.23       0.22       0.0        1.6        0.07
      -0.15      0.28       0.26       0.24       0.0        0.44       0.07
   }
```

These are the parameters which define a fern. The line containing a, b, c, d, e, f, and probability labels the numbers to show you how they fit into the matrix equation. Each line of numbers provides the values for the matrix equation:

$$\begin{bmatrix} x' \\ y' \end{bmatrix} = \begin{bmatrix} a & b \\ c & d \end{bmatrix} \begin{bmatrix} x \\ y \end{bmatrix} + \begin{bmatrix} e \\ f \end{bmatrix}$$

The first four numbers are the the elements a, b, c, and d of the matrix. These numbers control how much the transformation rotates and shrinks. The next two numbers are the elements e and f making up a vector that shifts the transformation in two dimensions. The last number is a probablility that tells Winfract how often to apply that transformation.

Each numeric line of the IFS entry defines an affine transformation that maps the whole fern to a part of itself. (An affine transformation can rotate, shrink, or shift an object, but preserves its shape and proportions.) These are the four self-similarities, or transformations from the whole fern to its parts, that we discussed above.

Explorer

It is tricky to figure out what these parameters do, but you can make headway by experimenting. FRACTINT.IFS has four copies of the fern entry discussed above, named ferna, fernb, fernc, and fernd. In ferna, the probability number at the end of the row has been set to zero, effectively neutralizing the first transformation. In fernb, the second line has zero probability, in fernc the third line, and in fernd the fourth. When you render these "snipped ferns," you will get an idea about what each line does by what is missing in the image.

Ferna has no stem, but otherwise looks normal. The first transformation mapped the whole fern to the stem. With that transformation disabled, the stem is missing.

Fernb looks rather nondescript, not like a fern at all. That is because the second transformation provides the magic that copies the bottom two fronds to the infinitely many miniatures higher up on the fern. Without that transformation, all that is left are the stems of the bottom two branches.

Fernc consists of only the stem. The missing transformation of the whole fern to the bottom left branch is what makes the fern fronds project from the stem. With this disabled, only the stem remains.

Finally, fernd has the right-hand ferns missing because the fourth transformation which copies the left fronds to the right is missing.

Try this experiment. In the original fern entry, the b and c values are .04 and –0.04. These values control the fern curl. Try bumping them up to .06 and –0.06 to increase the curl. (You can edit FRACTINT.IFS using the WIndows Notepad to do this.)

There are quite a number of other IFS example files on the disk. To try them out, select the IFS fractal type using FRACTALS / FRACTAL FORMULA, select the file FRACTINT.IFS, and then select the desired IFS fractal.

Winfract can also handle more complex IFS fractals that can be viewed in 3D. Try the IFS fractals in FRACTINT.IFS that have 3D in their name. To control the 3-D viewing, use the FRACTALS / 3D PARAMS menu.

Alternate Color Maps

Try the map file GREEN.MAP to color the fern green. When viewing the fern, you can load the map file using COLORS / LOAD COLOR-MAP.

History and Credits

The originator of Iterated Function Systems is Michael Barnsley. His book *Fractals Everywhere* is an excellent reference. Many of the sample IFS files provided with this book came from the program Fdesign, by Doug Nelson, a freeware IFS fractal generating program that works well with Winfract.

JULIA SETS

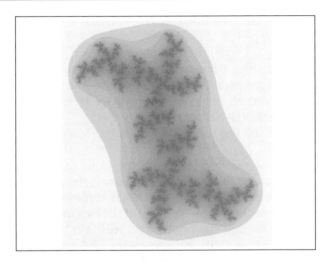

Fractal Category: Escape-time fractal

Formal Name: Julia set

Fractal Type: julia

Formula: Initialize: $z = zpixel$
        Iterate: $z^2 + c$

Code

Routine type	Routine name	File
C fractal engine	StandardFractactal()	CALCFRACT.C
ASM integer math fractal engine	calcmand()	CALCMAND.ASM
ASM floating point fractal engine	calcmandfp()	CALMANFP.ASM
Integer math initialization	julia_per_pixel()	FRACTALS.C

Integer math orbit	JuliaFractal()	FRACTALS.C
Floating-point initialization	juliafp_per_pixel()	FRACTALS.C
Floating-point orbit	JuliafpFractal()	FRACTALS.C

Parameter File Example
```
Julia {
   reset maxiter=20000 inside=255 logmap=-1 type=julia
}
```

Description

"You obtain an incredible variety of Julia sets: some are a fatty clouds, others are a skinny bush of brambles, some look like the sparks which float in the air after a firework has gone off. One has the shape of a rabbit, lots of them have sea-horse tails."—Adrien Douady, *Julia Sets and the Mandelbrot Set*, p. 161.

For every x, y point on the Mandelbrot set, you can generate a unique Julia set. And since there are an infinite number of points, there is an infinity of Julias. Each Julia is different and yet eerily the same. All are symmetrical and all have a self-symmetry that gives an overall pattern repeated in infinitely smaller scale.

Julia sets use the same formula as the Mandelbrot set, only in a different way. The Mandelbrot set uses a different value of c for each pixel and starts every iteration loop with the value of z equal to zero. The Julia sets, on the other hand, are calculated using the same value for c throughout the drawing and varying the initial value of z with each pixel. Julia sets have an overall symmetry around the origin. If you cut the set in half at any angle through the origin, you will find that each half is a reverse image of the other. This self-symmetry and reversed symmetry are the signatures of a Julia set.

Julia sets are not limited to the classic formula described in this fractal type. *Any* complex function that is differentiable (analytic) has a Julia set. And whenever there is a collection of Julia sets where the derivative of the formula can be set to zero, there is one associated Mandelbrot set for the whole collection.

Parameters:		
Real part of parameter	0.3	
Imaginary part of parameter	0.6	
Bailout value (0 means use default)	0.0	

The real part of parameter and the imaginary part of parameter are used to set the real and imaginary portion of the variable c in the formula. The bailout value is the variable that determines when Winfract should stop the iterations and assign the pixel a color. The default value is 4.

Explorer

Starting with the Mandelbrot set is the best method of finding interesting Julia sets. It is, after all, a catalog of Julia sets. Whatever colorful pattern you find in the Mandelbrot set will be the self-symmetrical pattern drawn in the associated Julia set. Generate the default Mandelbrot set (fractal type mandel under FRACTALS / FRACTAL FORMULAS), point at an area near the lake with the mouse, and click the right mouse button.

Some sets to view include the following:

Real part of parameter	0.28261
Imaginary part of parameter	–0.01077
Real part of parameter	0.16894
Imaginary part of parameter	–0.65747
Real part of parameter	–0.74527
Imaginary part of parameter	0.2475

If the Julia set variable c is close to the Mandelbrot lake, large areas of blue will be splotched in various places on the screen. If the value of c isn't actually in the Mandelbrot lake, there is more to see inside that blue! Set the iteration level higher (select it from the FRACTALS / BASIC OPTIONS menu) and drive the blues back into the lake from whence they came. If the iteration level exceeds the number of colors available on your machine, you should try using a logarithmic color map (set the LOG PALETTE option under FRACTALS / BASIC OPTIONS to –1 or 1.)

Special Effects

Continuous potential produces good viewing. You will find potenial under the FRACTALS / EXTENDED OPTIONS menu. Try setting POTENTIAL MAX COLOR to 255, SLOPE to 500, and BAILOUT to 200. For best results with continuous potential, turn the floating-point switch on using the FLOATING-PT MATH check box on the FRACTALS / BASIC OPTIONS menu.

Alternate Color Maps

All the color maps will work well with the Julia sets. Try loading FIRESTM.MAP using the COLORS / LOAD COLOR-MAP menu.

History and Credits

Julia sets are named after the mathematician Gaston Julia. With the aid of Pierre Fatou, Julia studied complex dynamic systems for fifteen years between 1910 and 1925. Unfortunately, there were no computers around at the time, making the calculations arduous and extremely time-consuming. We had to wait until 1979 for Dr. Mandelbrot to revive Fatou's and Julia's work and, with the aid of modern computers, create a science out of chaos.

JULIBROT

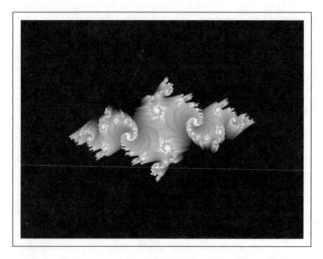

Fractal Category: Four-dimensional escape-time fractal

Formal Name: Julibrot

Fractal Type: julibrot

Formula: $z^2 + c$

Code

Routine type	Routine name	File
Fractal engine	Std4dFractal()	JULIBROT.C
Integer math initialization	jb_per_pixel()	JULIBROT.C
Integer math orbit	JuliaFractal()	FRACTALS.C

Parameter File Example

```
julibrot        {
  reset type=julibrot corners=-2.0/2.000012/-1.500014/1.5
  params=-0.83/-0.83/0.25/-0.25 colors=@altern.map
  }
```

Description

The Mandelbrot set is a catalog of all the various Julia sets. Every point on the two-dimensional drawing of the Mandelbrot set intersects with a unique two-dimensional Julia set. Thought of as a whole, the Mandelbrot and Julia depictions are different aspects of a single four-dimensional mathematical object called the *Julibrot*. If you were to draw a vertical line on the Mandelbrot depiction and draw all the Julia sets that intersect with that line, layered one on top of another, you would have a snapshot of a moment in the life of a Julibrot. Move the line horizontally in the negative direction along the x-axis and you move backward in time. Move the line in the positive direction and you move forward in time. The 3-D transformations in Winfract generally take a two-dimensional fractal and plot the iteration levels as the third dimension. These three-dimensional fractals are hollow and similar to a relief drawing stamped out of a sheet of copper. If you turn over the copper, all you see is the underside of the same drawing.

Julibrots are solid. They have Julia fractal characteristics in both the horizontal and vertical directions and Mandelbrot fractal characteristics along their depth. Peel away the outer layers like an onion and reveal different fractals underneath.

Julibrots are really four-dimensional objects. In order to visualize a four-dimensional Julibrot, think of it as a solid 3-D crystal changing with time, where time dimension is the Mandelbrot x-axis (see the parameters below). You can show the Julibrot changing with time by generating a sequence of Julibrot images and changing the Mandelbrot x parameter a little with each image. Some Julibrots are born, live hectic lives, then die. Others are reincarnated again and again in an endless cycle. They even have fractal characteristics along their time lines—they *behave* like fractals! Winfract is the *only* program that allows you to explore the existence of this dynamic, solid fractal type.

Some people feel that because the Julibrot is an abstract object, any of the four axes can be used as the time axis. This is not the case. Consider using either the Julia x- or y-axis for time. If you depict the Julibrot at a particular point before time zero, you will find a mirror image of the Julibrot at the same point on the other side of time zero. Using the Mandelbrot y-axis as the time axis produces a similar situation, but the images before and after time zero are identical instead of mirrored. Any one of these three axes used for time produces a symmetry of Julibrots about time zero. Time, however, is not symmetrical. Objects from the past cannot suddenly appear as mirrored or identical images in the future. Use of the Mandelbrot x-axis as time prevents this from happening—all objects along the time-line are then unique.

Any mathematical formula that has both a Mandelbrot set and a family of Julia sets can be displayed as a Julibrot. However, Winfract currently draws the Julibrot based on the equation $z^2 + c$ only. This Julibrot, though, has a fascinating existence. Born out of the void as a single speck of dust, it grows slowly at first in spits and sputters, alternating between expansions and sudden explosive contractions. With each spurt of growth, it is larger than before. Soon it starts curling in on itself. Eddies form into massive swirling vortexes. In one final heave, it coagulates into a twisting, wriggly mass. Then, like a star going supernova, it collapses one last time and explodes into fragments. The fragments themselves explode into smaller fragments and these explode in turn, again and again, until only the void remains.

Parameters

The Julibrot fractal type does not use the normal Winfract parameters screen. You will see the parameters screen after selecting type Julibrot from the FRACTALS / FRACTAL FORMULAS menu, but the parameters boxes will be marked N/A (for not applicable). Click on OK, and then you will see a Fractint-style screen that lets you enter the Julibrot parameters. Use the arrow keys to move from field to field, and press (ENTER) when you have finished altering values. The mouse does not work with this screen. The default parameters are:

Julibrot Parameters

Julia from x	1.99999
Julia to x	−2
Julia from y	1.5
Julia to y	−1.49999
Mandelbrot from x	−0.83
Mandelbrot to x	−0.83
Mandelbrot from y	0.25
Mandelbrot to y	−0.25
Number of z pixels	128
Penetration level	30
Location of z origin	8
Depth of z	8
Screen height	7
Screen width	10
Distance to screen	24
Distance between eyes (0 for Grayscale)	0
Blue:Red ratio (0 for Grayscale)	0

The default parameters for the Julibrot provide an absolutely gorgeous view of the Julibrot just before it reaches its maturity and turns into a wriggly lump. The first four Julia parameters set the corners of the drawing. Changing the Julia parameters zooms in or out of the drawing. Using the mouse or keyboard zoom box will automatically change these parameters for you and keep the aspect ratio of the image proportional.

Figure 5-1 shows part of the Julibrot's relationship to the Mandelbrot set. The shading of this figure is somewhat different than the rendering of the Julibrot in Winfract. The darker shades of the Mandelbrot set in the upper right-hand corner correspond to the darker shades of the Julibrot. The line through the Mandelbrot set is the z-axis of the Julibrot. The x-axis of the Mandelbrot set corresponds to the time, or t-axis, of the Julia set. This drawing is shown at t = −1.098. Moving the line in the positive direction along the Mandelbrot x-axis shows the Julibrot at later points in time.

The Mandelbrot parameters form the end points for a line of Julia sets. The two "from" parameters draw the Julia set associated with the Mandelbrot point in the foreground. The Julia set associated with the "to" Mandelbrot point is drawn at the rear. Winfract draws the foremost Julia sets in the brightest shades with progressively dimmer shades used to the rear. The dimmest shade is used to draw the Julia set associated with the "to" endpoint of the Mandelbrot line.

Remember that we are thinking of the Mandelbrot x parameter as a time dimension. To keep each level of the Julibrot display in the same time reference, the two Mandelbrot x parameters should be identical. Then each Julibrot image is a snapshot of the Julibrot at time x. Setting the Mandelbrot "from x" parameter different from the Mandelbrot "to x" parameter will

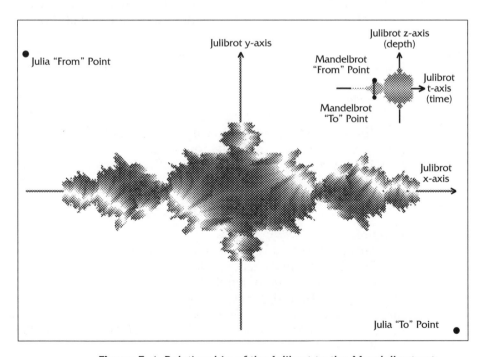

Figure 5-1 Relationship of the Julibrot to the Mandelbrot set

skew the depiction along the time line, and make the time metaphor break down. Each layer of Julia sets would then be in a different time frame. Skewing the time frame produces some interesting effects, though! It amounts to slicing the 4-D Julibrot with the knife at a different angle. Setting the Mandelbrot y parameters equal and varying the x parameters depicts the evolution of a cross section over time. In this case, the z-axis of the drawing represents time rather than depth. The deeper levels of the drawing show the cross section at later points in time (or earlier if you draw the Mandelbrot line from a positive x to a negative x).

The Number of z pixels parameter determines how many Julia sets will be layered. With the above settings, 128 of the Julia sets along the Mandelbrot line will be layered to make up the drawing. Setting this number higher will give the drawing better depth resolution. Because there are only 256 shades of gray available, depth resolutions above 256 provide little improvement in the quality of the image.

The Penetration level parameter is equivalent to the Maximum Iteration parameter used for the Mandelbrot and Julia set fractals. Setting the Maximum Iteration higher in these fractals sharpens the areas closest to the lakes (areas where the orbit never escapes). With the Julibrots, as the name Penetration level implies, the higher values take you deeper into the Julibrot and remove the outer layers to let you see what lies beneath. The deeper layers of the Julibrot have more details but take much longer to draw.

The Screen height and Screen width parameters are used to determine the aspect ratio of the drawing and also provide a frame of reference for other parameters. You can use any units of measure you want—inches, feet, meters, and so on—so long as you use the same units for all parameters requiring a distance measure.

If you want the Julibrot drawn for viewing without the red/blue 3-D glasses, then set the parameters for distance between eyes and blue:red ratio both to zero. Winfract will automatically load the GREY.MAP file to use for drawing. For grayscaled drawings the remaining parameters are not used.

Explorer

You can zoom in on any of the Julibrot drawings—even the ones in red/blue 3D! This has the effect of looking at the Julibrot through a 3-D magnifying glass. You should definitely try at least one zoom and experience it for yourself. To find the more interesting Julibrots, you should use the Mandelbrot set as a guide. Pick a straight line anywhere on the Mandelbrot set that looks interesting and plug the end points into Mandelbrot *x* and *y* parameters.

Special Effects

Setting the blue:red ratio parameter to a value other than zero will instruct Winfract to load the GLASSES1.MAP file to use for drawing. This map draws alternating blue and red pixels needed for use with the red/blue glasses. These are called *anaglyph* 3-D drawings. Because the eye is more sensitive to blue light than red, the anaglyph would appear on the bluish side if equal intensities for red and blue were used to draw the image. The blue:red ratio determines how much brighter the red image will be than the blue. A good setting for the blue:red ratio is 0.8. If the image appears on the reddish side then use a higher number. Likewise, if the drawing appears bluish in the glasses you are using, the number should be lowered.

Anaglyphic drawings need more information than the grayscaled drawings to place the image at the proper depth in the monitor and draw it with an accurate perspective. The distance-between-eyes parameter should be a measure of the distance between your pupils. For most people, three inches is a good number. Another parameter used as a reference is distance to the screen. This should be a measure of how far your eyes are from the screen.

The Location-of-z origin parameter determines how far beyond the screen into the monitor the center of the image will appear to the viewer. Setting this value to a negative distance will place the center of the image in front of the screen out in open space. Many 3-D enthusiasts consider this practice of "breaking the viewing plane" as vulgar, but others get quite a kick out of it. Try it both ways and see which one you prefer!

The final parameter, Depth of *z*, determines how thick the image will appear. If you use the default settings of location of *z* origin and depth of *z* (both equal to 8), then the front part of the image will appear four inches into the monitor (8 − 8/2) and the rear edge of the image will appear at 12 inches into the monitor (8 + 8/2).

Warnings

With this particular fractal, the screen may be blank for a period of time before anything is actually drawn on it. Also, Winfract will only attempt to draw the fractal in 256 colors. Trying to use 16 colors simply does not provide adequate depth resolution for the 3-D effect. If you are running on an EGA or CGA machine, you will have to use a disk video option with 256 colors.

It takes a *long* time to draw a portion of the Julibrot, even using Winfract on a 386! Indeed, for a 320 x 200 with a *z* resolution of 128 it may take as long as an hour to draw. The amount of time required is directly proportional to the resolution product of all three axes. If it takes one hour to draw a 320 x 200 x 128 image, then it would take 15 hours to draw an 800 x 600 x 256 image. You can reduce the amount of time by keeping the penetration level to a reasonably low number.

Alternate Color Maps
The only color maps available for the Julibrot are GREY.MAP and GLASSES1.MAP, both of which are loaded automatically when needed. However, many grayscale images look terrific when using colorful maps, and the Julibrot is no exception. Use the COLORS / LOAD COLOR-MAP menu to load CHROMA.MAP or FIRESTM.MAP. Then try color cycling ((·) key) to really show off your Julibrot jewel!

History and Credits
The Julibrot algorithm and code were both originated by Mark Peterson. Mark coined the name Julibrot by combining "Juli-a" with "Mandel-brot." At about the same time Mark developed the Julibrot algorithm, Dr. Pickover independently published an article on an identical fractal type, which he referred to as "Repeller Towers" in *Computers in Physics*, "A Note on Rendering Chaotic Repeller Distance Towers," May/June 1988 (Vol. 2 No. 3).

KAM TORUS

Fractal Category: Orbital fractal

Formal Name: Kam Torus

Fractal Type: kamtorus and kamtorus3d

Formula: Initialize: $x = y = 0$
Iterate: $x' = x\cos(a) + (x^2 - y)\sin(a)$
$y' = x\sin(a) - (x^2 - y)\cos(a)$

Code

Routine type	Routine name	File
2-D floating point fractal engine	orbit2dfloat()	LORENZ.C
2-D integer math fractal engine	orbit2dlong()	LORENZ.C
3-D floating point fractal engine	orbit3dfloat()	LORENZ.C
3-D integer math fractal engine	orbit3dlong()	LORENZ.C
Floating-point orbit	kamtorusfloatorbit()	LORENZ.C
Integer math orbit	kamtoruslongorbit()	LORENZ.C

Parameter File Example

```
Kam Torus {
  reset type=kamtorus
}
```

Description

Initially this fractal generates concentric circles. As it progresses, smaller concentric circles are generated inside the outer edges of the previous circles. When the fractal reaches maturity, it grows "whiskers" extending outward perpendicular to the radius. These whiskers eventually curl in on themselves.

At the start of each orbit calculation, the initial values of x and y are set to the orbit level divided by 3 (the number 3 is hard-coded into Winfract). As the fractal is drawn, a point is plotted at the screen coordinates given by the values of x and y. After the calculations reach a stop value, the orbit level is incremented and a new set of initial values for x and y are calculated.

Parameters:
Angle (radians)	1.30
Step size	0.05
Stop value	1.50
Points per orbit	150

The angle parameter is used as the setting for the variable a in the formula. Lowering this value will create a smaller fractal and cause it to enter the mature "whisker" stage more quickly.

The step-size parameter is used as the increment for the orbit. Lower values will generate tighter concentric circles. Higher values produce more widely spaced circles.

The stop-value parameter determines when to stop the fractal generation and call it quits. Higher values produce larger, more detailed fractals.

The points-per-orbit parameter determines how many points will be plotted before Winfract moves on to the next orbit. High values produce more solid circles. Lower values produce a scattering of points in the circle. Some of the lower values produce some interesting interference patterns when they overlap.

Explorer:

Angle (radians)	0.5
Step size	0.01
Stop value	1.5
Points per orbit	500

These settings will produce a fractal "eye." Try to use a high screen resolution around 800 x 600 pixels.

Angle (radians)   4.712

Changing the value of the angle to half of   (approximately 1.571) will produce a four-legged starfish.

Special Effects
The 3-D variant of this fractal type is kamtorus3d. This fractal plots each new orbit as occurring at a different depth.

History and Credits
The term "KAM" is from the three people who studied this equation: Kalmogorov, Arnold, and Moser. The code used by Winfract came from Stone Souper Scott Taylor, who found it in E. Reitman's book *Exploring the Geometry of Nature*. The 3-D representation was coded by Tim Wegner.

L-SYSTEM FRACTALS

Fractal Category: L-System fractal

Formal Name: None

Fractal Type: lsystem

Parameter File Example
```
bush {
   reset type=lsystem params=4 lname=bush
}
```

Description
See the User-Defined Fractals section in this chapter.

LAMBDA

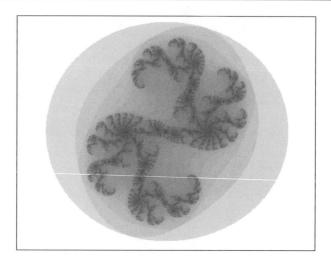

Fractal Category: Escape-time fractal

Formal Name: The Logistic Equation

Fractal Type: lambda

Formula: Initialize: $z = zpixel$
Iterate: $cz (1 - z)$

Code

Routine type	Routine name	File
Fractal engine	StandardFractactal()	CALCFRACT.C
Integer math initialization	julia_per_pixel()	FRACTALS.C
Integer math orbit	LambdaFractal()	FRACTALS.C
Floating-point initialization	juliafp_per_pixel()	FRACTALS.C
Floating-point orbit	LambdaFPFractal()	FRACTALS.C

Parameter File Example
```
lambda {
  reset maxiter=20000 inside=255 logmap=-1 type=lambda
}
```

Description
This fractal type calculates the Julia sets for the Lambda formula $cz (1 - z)$, where the variable c is the *lambda* of the equation. (We have used c rather than the Greek letter lambda because the letter used to designate

the variable that connects the Mandelbrot and Julia variants is traditionally the letter c.)

The fractal type mandellambda is the Mandelbrot set associated with this Julia family. Clicking the right mouse button toggles to the mandellambda fractal type. Clicking the right mouse button from the mandellambda fractal type toggles to the Julia set associated with the point in the center of the screen.

Parameters: Real part of parameter   0.85

Imaginary part of parameter   0.6

Bailout value (0 means use default)   0.0

The real and imaginary portions of the parameter are used to set the value of the variable c in the formula. At the start of each pixel's iteration loop, the value of z is initialized to the coordinates associated with the pixel's location.

Explorer
Since this fractal type produces a family of Julia sets, the best way to find the most interesting sets is to use the mandellambda fractal type as your guide. Zoom in on an interesting section of the mandellambda fractal type and then click the right mouse button to toggle to this fractal type.

Some places to try are the following:

Real part of parameter   0.2393
Imaginary part of parameter   1.0507

Real part of parameter   −0.6091
Imaginary part of parameter   0.8117

```
map=firestrm logmap=-1 params=-0.2393/1.0507 type=lambda
maxiter=20000 inside=150
map=firestrm logmap=-1 params=-0.6091/0.8117 type=lambda
maxiter=20000 inside=150
```

Special Effects
Several settings on the FRACTALS / BASIC OPTIONS menu work well with the Lambda fractal. Try setting MAXIMUM ITERATIONS to 20000, INSIDE COLOR to 150, and LOG PALETTE to 1.

Alternate Color Maps
Try loading FIRESTRM.MAP or CHROMA.MAP using the COLORS / LOAD COLOR-MAP menu.

History and Credits
The lambda equation comes from the same population modeling equation used in bifurcation and is discussed on pages 139 and 211 of *The*

Science of Fractal Images. Tim Wegner wrote the code for this fractal type and the corresponding Mandelbrot mapping, fractal type mandellambda.

LAMBDA FUNCTION FRACTALS

Fractal Category: Escape-time fractal

Formal Name: None

Fractal Type: lambdafn

Formula: Initialize: $z = zpixel$
Iterate: $c$fn(z),

where fn(z) is one of conj, cos, cosh, cosxx, cotan, cotanh, exp, flip, ident, log, recip, sin, sinh, sqr, tan or tanh.

Code

Routine type	Routine name	File
Fractal engine	StandardFractactal()	CALCFRACT.C
Integer math initialization	long_julia_per_pixel()	FRACTALS.C
Integer math orbit	LambdaTrigFractal()	FRACTALS.C
Floating-point initialization	otherjuliafp_per_pixel()	FRACTALS.C
Floating-point orbit	LambdafpFractal()	FRACTALS.C

Paramter File Example

```
lambda_function {
  reset maxiter=20000 inside=255 logmap=-1
  type=lambdafn function=sin
}
```

Description

These are variants of the classic Julia set families. Instead of the traditional z^2, we've substituted a transcendental function multiplied by c. As with all Julia sets, a Mandelbrot set is associated with any of the function fractals (see the mandelfn fractal type).

Parameters:		
	Real perturbation of $z(0)$	0
	Imaginary perturbation of $z(0)$	0
	First function	sin
	Bailout value (0 means use default)	0

Setting the real perturbation of $z(0)$ and the imaginary perturbation of $z(0)$ to a nonzero value will warp the original fractal. The first function parameter accepts any one of these function names to generate a fractal:

> conj, cos, cosh, cosxx, cotan, cotanh, exp, flip, ident, log, recip, sin, sinh, sqr, tan or tanh

Most of these function variable values refer to the transcendental function commonly known by the same name. For example, "sin" refers to the familar sine function from high school trigonometry, while "sinh" refers to the somewhat less familiar hyperbolic sine. Several of these functions have no common name or are peculiar to Winfract.

The function cosxx is the complex conjugate of the correct cosine function. Earlier versions of Winfract had a sign error in the code for the cosine function. Fractals made with the earlier cos can be reproduced using cosxx instead of cos.

The ident function is the identity function. It is defined by $\text{ident}(z) = z$.

The flip function swaps the real and imaginary parts of a complex number. Hence $\text{flip}(x + iy) = y + ix$.

Finally, the recip function calculates the reciprocal, so $\text{recip}(z) = 1/z$.

The bailout value is the variable that determines when Winfract should call it quits on the iterations and assign the pixel a color. The default value is 4.

Explorer

For feathery, nested spirals of the LambdaSine (first function set to sin) and the frost-on-glass patterns of the LambdaCosine (first function set to cos), make the real part of c equal to 1 and the imaginary part anywhere ranging from 0.1 to 0.4. The best patterns are closer to 0.4. For the tongue and blobs of LambdaExponent (first function set to exp), try a real part of 0.379 for *c* and an imaginary part of 0.479.

Warnings
Winfract can calculate the transcendental functions with Mark Peterson's fast integer routines that do not require a math coprocessor. There is a trade-off, though, between speed and accuracy. After a couple of maximum zooms, you will exceed the accuracy range of the integer math. Then Winfract will automatically switch to floating-point math. If you don't have an 80387 or an 80486, take a long vacation. The drawing may be finished by the time you come back!

History and Credits
Mark Peterson wrote the code for the trigonometric fractals, and Tim Wegner coded the exponential and logarithmic fractals.

LORENZ FRACTALS

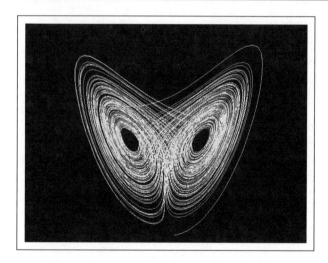

Fractal Category: Orbital fractals

Formal Name: Lorenz

Fractal Types: lorenz, lorenz3d, lorenz3d1, lorenz3d3, lorenz3d4

Formulas
lorenz /lorenz3d
  Intitialize: $x' = x - (ax + ay)dt$
      $z = y = z = 1$

Iterate: $y' = y + (bx - y - zx)dt$
$z' = z - (cz + xy)dt$

lorenz3d1
Initialize: $n = \text{sqrt}(x^2 + y^2)$
$z = y = z = 1$
Iterate: $x' = x + (-ax - x + ay - by + n - an + yz)dt$
$y' = y + (bx - ax - ay - y + bn + an - xz - nz\ )dt$
$z' = z + (y/2 - cz)dt$

lorenz3d3
Initialize: $n = \text{sqrt}(x^2 + y^2)$
$z = y = z = 1$
Iterate: $x' = x + [(-ax - x + ay - by + yz)/3 + n^2 - an^2$
$(2xyn/3)(b + a - z)]dt$
$y' = y + [(bx - ax - zx - ay - y)/3 + 2axy - 2xy +$
$(b + a - z)(x^2 - y^2)/3n]dt$
$z' = z + (3x^2y - y^3)/2 - czdt$

lorenz3d4
Initialize: $n = \text{sqrt}(x^2 + y^2)$
$z = y = z = 1$
Iterate: $x' = x + [-ax^3 + (2a + b - z)x^2y + axy^2 - 2xy^2 +$
$(zy^3 - by^3)/(2x^2 + 2y^2)]dt$
$y' = y + [bx^3 - zx^3 + ax^2y - 2x^2y + (-2a - b + z)xy^2$
$-ay^3/(2x^2 + 2y^2)]dt$
$z' = z + (2x^3y - 2xy^3 - cz)dt$

Code

Routine type	Routine name	File
2-D floating point fractal engine	orbit2dfloat()	LORENZ.C
2-D integer math fractal engine	orbit2dlong()	LORENZ.C
3-D floating point fractal engine	orbit3dfloat()	LORENZ.C
3-D integer math fractal engine	orbit3dlong()	LORENZ.C
Floating-point orbit	lorenz3dfloatorbit()	LORENZ.C
Floating-point orbit	lorenz3d1floatorbit()	LORENZ.C
Floating-point orbit	lorenz3d3floatorbit()	LORENZ.C
Floating-point orbit	lorenz3d4floatorbit()	LORENZ.C
Integer math orbit	lorenz3dlongorbit()	LORENZ.C

Parameter File Example

```
lorenz {
   reset type=lorenz
}
```

Description

A single-point loop draws the path of two double spirals, cocked at an angle of a butterfly's wings in flight. The point spirals for a time in one loop, then unexpectedly jumps to the other loop. If you let it spiral for an eternity, it will never return to any spot where it has already been as it travels on its journey through its private infinity.

This fractal originally came from three simultaneous equations to describe the motion of a water wheel. The three variables, x, y, and z, completely describe the motion of the dynamic system from one point in time to the next. Water flows directly into the buckets on top of the water wheel. The buckets themselves have holes in them that drain the water. This creates a chaotic, dynamic system where the water wheel continually changes speed and sporadically changes direction.

The original Lorenz fractal traces out a two-lobe orbit in three dimensions. The fractal types lorenz3d1, lorenz3d3, and lorenz3d4 are variations of the original fractal with one, two, and four lobes respectively.

Parameters:

Time step	0.02
a	5
b	15
c	1

The time step variable is used to set the value of *dt* in the formula. The smaller this value is, the slower the plotting, but you will get more detail. Higher values will plot more quickly, but the image can look rather chunky.

The variables a, b, and c change the corresponding variables in the formula. Higher values of a and c tend to collapse the spirals into circles. Higher values of b make the fractal larger.

Explorer

Another good set of variables to try is twice the default values:

Time step	0.02
a	10
b	30
c	2

Special Effects

The lorenz family of fractals trace their orbits in three dimensions. The fractal type lorenz gives you a fixed view, projecting the 3-D orbit onto your two-dimensional screen from one direction only. The fractal type lorenz3d is the same set of equations, but with the added twist of showing the orbits using Winfract's perspective 3-D routines. These routines can be used with the red/blue glasses that come with this book. They plot a red and blue point for each orbital position so as to fool the brain into thinking the point is positioned in three-dimensional space.

The default perspectives values ($x = 60, y = 30, z = 0$) are not the best ones to use for fun viewing. Try other angles, such as 20/0/0 and 40/0/0. While you're at it, try setting the perspective parameter to a value less than 100 and view the fractal from *inside* the orbits.

History and Credits

Edward Lorenz originally described this fractal (though it wasn't *called* a fractal at the time) in an article entitled "Deterministic Non-Periodic Flow," which was published in the *Journal of the Atmospheric Sciences* in 1963. Unfortunately, there were not too many mathematicians or physicists who read that particular journal, so it was quite a while before Lorenz's work became widely known.

The one, two, and four lobe formulas were developed by Rick Miranda and Emily Stone.

LYAPUNOV

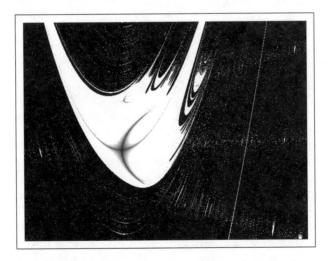

Fractal Category: Bifurcation

Formal Name: Lyapunov

Fractal Type: lyapunov

Formula: $x' = rx(1 - x)$

Code

Routine type	Routine name	File
Fractal engine	lyapunov()	CALCFRACT.C
Floating-point orbit	BifurcLambda()	CALCFRACT.C

Parameter File Example

```
Swallow      { ; The swallow from Scientific American
  reset type=lyapunov
  corners=3.8066559/3.8798065/3.809082/3.8639221
  params=0/0.5 maxiter=15 colors=@lyapunov.map
}
```

Description

The Bifurcation fractal illustrates what happens in a simple population model as the growth rate increases. The Lyapunov fractal expands that model into two dimensions by letting the growth rate vary in a periodic fashion between two values. Each pair of growth rates is run through a logistic population model and a value called the Lyapunov Exponent is calculated for each pair and is plotted. The Lyapunov Exponent is calculated by adding up log |r – 2rx| over many cycles of the population model and dividing by the number of cycles. Negative Lyapunov exponents indicate a stable periodic behavior and are plotted in color. Positive Lyapunov exponents indicate chaos and are colored black.

Parameters:		
	Order (integer)	0
	Population seed	0.5
	Filter cycles	0

Each possible periodic sequence yields a two-dimensional space to explore. The order parameter selects a sequence that determines how the Lyapunov calculation oscillates between the two growth rate values. Let *a* represent the first growth value and *b* the second. The default value 0 represents the sequence *ab* which alternates between the two values of the growth parameter. The order parameter can be calculated for any desired sequence. Take your sequence of *a*s and *b*s and arrange it so that it starts with at least 2 *a*s and ends with *b*. It may be necessary to rotate the sequence or swap *a*s and *b*s. Strike the first *a* and the last *b* off the list and replace each remaining *a* with a 1 and each remaining *b* with a 0. Interpret this as a binary number and convert it into decimal.

As an example of this, you can actually derive the order parameter from a sonnet! A sonnet is a poem with fourteen lines that has the following rhyming sequence: *abba abba abab cc*. Ignoring the rhyming couplet at the end, let's calculate the order parameter for this pattern.

abbaabbaabab	Doesn't start with at least 2 as.
aabbaabababb	Rotate it.
1001101010	Drop the first and last, replace with 0s and 1s.

512+64+32+8+2 = 618

An order parameter of 618 gives the Lyapunov equivalent of a sonnet. "How do I love thee, let me count the ways...."

The population seed is the intial value used to start the population model. When two parts of a Lyapunov overlap, which spike overlaps the other is strongly dependant on the initial value of the population model. Any changes from using a different starting value between 0 and 1 may be subtle.

Explorer
Try the different Lyapunov examples stored in the parameter file LYAPUNOV.PAR.

History and Credits
A. K. Dewdney, "Mathematical Recreations," *Scientific American*, September 1991. Algorithm coded by Roy Murphy.

MAGNETISM FRACTAL TYPES

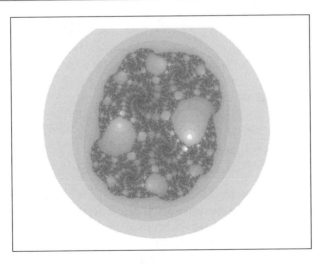

Fractal Category: Escape-time fractals

Formal Name: Magnetism Model Type I & II

Fractal Types: magnet1j, magnet2j, magnet1m, and magnet2m

Formula: Type I $\dfrac{[z^2 \times c - 1]^2}{[2z \times c - 2]^2}$

Type II $\dfrac{[z^3 + 3(c-1)z + (c-1)(c-2)]^2}{[3z^2 + 3(c-2)z + c^2 - 3c + 3]^2}$

Code

Routine type	Routine name	File
Fractal engine	StandardFractactal()	CALCFRACT.C
Floating-point initialization	mandelfp_per_pixel()	FRACTALS.C
Floating-point initialization	juliafp_per_pixel()	FRACTALS.C
Floating-point orbit	Magnet1Fractal()	FRACTALS.C
Floating-point orbit	Magnet2Fractal()	FRACTALS.C

Parameter File Example

```
magnet {
  reset params=0.35/1.3 maxiter=20000 logmap=-1
  inside=255 type=magnet1j
}
```

Description

These fractals are a descriptive model of the phase transition of a ferromagnetic material from a magnetic state to a nonmagnetic state as its temperature is raised. The derivation of the formulas is well beyond the scope of this book, but an in-depth discussion of the topic can be found in *The Beauty of Fractals*, pages 129–146.

These magnet1j and magnet2j fractal types form the family of Julia sets associated with the formulas. The magnetm1 and magnetm2 fractal types are the associated Mandelbrot sets.

Parameters:
Real part of parameter	0.3
Imaginary part of parameter	0.6
Bailout value (0 means use default)	0.0

The real part of parameter and imaginary part of parameter are used to set the real and imaginary portion of the variable c in the formula for the Julia fractal types, magnet1j and magnet2j. The bailout value is the variable that determines when Winfract should stop iterating and assign the pixel a color. The default value is 4.

Real perturbation of $z(0)$	0.0
Imaginary perturbation of $z(0)$	0.0

The real perturbation of $z(0)$ and imaginary perturbation of $z(0)$ have a warping effect on the magnet1m and magnet2m fractal types when they are nonzero.

Explorer
Miniature copies of the classical Mandelbrot sets are located at these settings:

Set fractal type (FRACTALS / FRACTAL FORMULA) to magnet1m.
Set parameters (FRACTALS / FRACTAL PARAMS) to:

| Xmin | 1.81 | Xmax | 2.27 |
| Ymin | 1.46 | Ymax | 1.81 |

Set fractal type (FRACTALS / FRACTAL FORMULA) to magnet2m.
Set parameters (FRACTALS / FRACTAL PARAMS) to:

| Xmin | 1.9176 | Xmax | 1.9713 |
| Ymin | 0.8829 | Ymax | 0.9276 |

Generate a spiral using these parameters:

Set fractal type (FRACTALS / FRACTAL FORMULA) to magnet1m.
Set parameters (FRACTALS / FRACTAL PARAMS) to:

| Xmin | 1.2793 | Xmax | 1.3023 |
| Ymin | 0.9639 | Ymax | .9811 |

Try setting Log palette to 1 or −1 and using a high Maximum Iterations (FRACTALS / BASIC OPTIONS menu).

Since the magnet1m and magnet2m fractal types are the Mandelbrot sets for the formulas, they are actually a map of all the various Julia sets. These are your best guides to the most interesting Julia sets associated with the magnet1j and magnet2j fractal types. Starting with magnet1m or magnet2m, point the mouse cursor to turbulent areas and click the right mouse button to generate the Julia variants.

Alternate Color Maps
Smooth color maps, such as ALTERN.MAP and FIRESTRM.MAP, work well with this fractal type.

History and Credits
This fractal was adapted from the description in *The Beauty of Fractals*, by H. O. Peitgen and P. H. Richter, pages 129–146. Kevin Allen of Australia contributed the code.

MANDELBROT SET

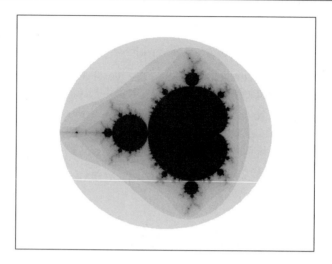

Fractal Category: Escape-time fractal

Formal Name: Mandelbrot Set

Fractal Type: mandel

Formula: Initialize: $c = z = zpixel$
Iterate: $z^2 + c$

Code

Routine type	Routine name	File
C fractal engine	StandardFractactal()	CALCFRACT.C
ASM integer math fractal engine	calcmand()	CALCMAND.ASM
ASM floating point fractal engine	calcmandfp()	CALMANFP.ASM
Integer math initialization	mandel_per_pixel()	FRACTALS.C
Integer math orbit	MandelFractal()	FRACTALS.C
Floating-point initialization	mandelfp_per_pixel()	FRACTALS.C
Floating-point orbit	MandelfpFractal()	FRACTALS.C

Parameter File Example

```
mandelbrot {
   reset maxiter=20000 inside=255 logmap=-1 type=mandel
}
```

Description

The Mandelbrot set is the most famous fractal of them all, an incredibly complex shape based on a simple iterated formula. See Chapter 1 for a complete discussion of the Mandelbrot set and how it is genetrated.

Parameters: Real perturbation of $z(0)$ 0

Imaginary perturbation of $z(0)$ 0

Bailout value (0 means use default) 0

The real perturbation of $z(0)$ and imaginary perturbation of $z(0)$ have a warping effect on the Mandelbrot set when they are nonzero. The bailout value is the variable that determines when Winfract should call it quits on the iterations and assign the pixel a color. The default value is 4. Clicking the right mouse button toggles the fractal type to the Julia set. Winfract uses the point in the center of the screen as the c value when it makes the switch. Clicking the right mouse button again toggles back to the Mandelbrot set. This feature is disabled if you are using perturbation parameters.

If you are in a hurry and want to bypass the zoom boxes, set the center-mag= parameter and go directly to the spot you want at correct magnification.

Explorer

The most interesting places in the Mandelbrot set are in the nooks and crannies of the spheroids. You can try these examples using the FRACTALS / FRACTAL PARAMS.

Delicate flowers bloom within the crease of the heart:

Xmin	0.279742	Xmax	0.285477
Ymin	−0.008619	Ymax	−0.012920

Spiral whirlpools:

Xmin	−0.171606576	Xmax	−0.166273182
Ymin	−0.655470068	Ymax	−0.659469929

Mandelbrot buds:

Xmin	−0.749721533	Xmax	−0.740832543
Ymin	0.1280884	Ymax	0.121421594

Extending from the tips of the spheres are more straight-line images. Sword blades lash out of the negative tail:

Xmin	−1.5167	Xmax	−1.4833
Ymin	0.0125	Ymax	−0.0125

For speed, use the default setting of Maximum Iterations (FRACTALS / BASIC OPTIONS) of 150 to draw the image. Much of the image at the higher magnification levels will appear blue, meaning either the area is part of the Mandelbrot lake or the iteration limit was exceeded before Winfract could determine the color. Try setting Maximum Iterations to around 1,000 or so. This will also sharpen the image. Some people frequently use settings as high as 30,000. Winfract can handle iteration levels in the tens of thousands with only a moderate increase in calculation time through the use of its periodicity-checking and solid guessing algorithms.

Whenever the iteration level exceeds the available number of colors, an "overflow" occurs creating a jumbled mish-mash of disjointed colors. When this happens, try setting the Log palette to 1 if you are using the default palette, or −1 if you are using a continuous palette such as FIRESTRM.MAP. You can set these on the FRACTALS / BASIC OPTIONS menu.

Special Effects

Try the different values of the Inside parameter in the FRACTALS / BASIC OPTIONS menu to see structure inside the Mandelbrot lake.

The Mandelbrot set has tendrils emanating out of its bays. They are normally too thin to show. You can make them visible with the distance estimator method. First select 2 colors using the VIEW / IMAGE SETTINGS menu. Then set DISTANCE ESTIMATOR to 1 on the FRACTALS / EXTENDED OPTIONS menu. For best results, you may also want to disable solid guessing, which can accidently snip some of these tendrils. To do that, push the 1-PASS radio button at the top of the FRACTALS BASIC / OPTIONS menu.

To get continuously varying colors instead of strips, use the Continuous potential parameters. You will find potenial under the FRACTALS / EXTENDED OPTIONS menu. Try setting POTENTIAL MAX COLOR to 255, SLOPE to 500, and BAILOUT to 200. For best results with continuous potential, turn the floating-point switch on using the FLOATING-PT MATH check box on the FRACTALS / BASIC OPTIONS menu. Make sure the number of colors is set for 256 under VIEW / IMAGE SETTINGS.

Warnings

Mandelbrot exploration is highly addictive! People have been known to lock themselves behind closed doors for days on end feverishly searching for that perfect fractal. Have a friend check on you occasionally just to remind you what time it is. But don't let your friend look at the screen— he or she might get caught up in it also!

History and Credits
Benoit B. Mandelbrot (b.1924) is credited with the discovery of this fractal. In 1979 he created a catalogue of Julia sets which he planned to use as a guide in exploration of Julia sets. The Mandelbrot set is that catalog. Bert Tyler, the original author of Winfract, wrote the high-speed generation algorithm, which has subsequently been enhanced by the other Stone Soup Group members.

MANDELBROT LAMBDA

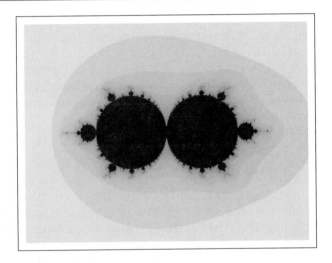

Fractal Category: Escape-time fractal

Formal Name: None

Fractal Type: mandellambda

Formula: Initialize: $c = z = zpixel$
Iterate: $cz(1 - z)$

Code

Routine type	Routine name	File
Fractal engine	StandardFractactal()	CALCFRACT.C
Integer math initialization	mandel_per_pixel()	FRACTALS.C
Integer math orbit	LambdaFractal()	FRACTALS.C
Floating-point initialization	mandelfp_per_pixel()	FRACTALS.C
Floating-point orbit	LambdaFPFractal()	FRACTALS.C

Parameter File Example

```
mandellambda {
  reset maxiter=20000 inside=255 logmap=-1
  type=mandellambda
}
```

Description

This is the Mandelbrot map of the lambda fractal type. You should note that this fractal type uses the same formula as lambda; however, the fractal is generated to produce a Mandelbrot set rather than a Julia set. In the lambda fractal, which produces a family of Julia sets, the value of the variable c is kept constant and the initial value of z is changed from pixel to pixel to correspond with the associated Cartesian coordinates. Since the Mandelbrot lambda is a Mandelbrot set, the initial value of z is kept constant at 0.5, a *critical point* for the formula, and the value of c is changed from pixel to pixel to correspond with the Cartesian coordinates. For information on determining a formula's critical point, refer to *The Science of Fractal Images,* 1988, page 156.

Parameters: Real perturbation of $z(0)$　　　　0

Imaginary perturbation of $z(0)$　　0

Bailout value (0 means use default)　0

The real perturbation of $z(0)$ and imaginary perturbation of $z(0)$ have a warping effect on the set when they are nonzero. During normal generation of the fractal, a new value of c is used for each pixel. The value of the variable p (*perturbation*), however, is kept constant throughout the drawing.

The bailout value is the variable that determines when Winfract should stop iterating and assign the pixel a color. The default value is 4.

Clicking the right mouse button toggles the fractal type to the Julia set. Winfract uses the point in the center of the screen as the c value when it makes the switch. Clicking the right mouse button again toggles back to the Mandelbrot set. This feature is disabled if you are using a nonzero value for the perturbation parameters.

Explorer

You can try these examples using the FRACTALS / FRACTAL PARAMS menu. These settings will show you one of the local spirals:

Xmin　1.91439　　Xmax　1.93662

Ymin　1.05123　　Ymax　1.03457

And these will show you the source of the commotion nearby—a tiny Mandelbrot set:

Xmin	1.93233	Xmax	1.93422
Ymin	1.03954	Ymax	1.04096

History and Credits

The lambda equation comes from the same population modeling equation used in bifurcation and is discussed on pages 139 and 211 of *The Science of Fractal Images*. Tim Wegner wrote the code for this fractal type and the corresponding Mandelbrot-mapping fractal type mandellambda.

MANDELBROT LAMBDA FUNCTION

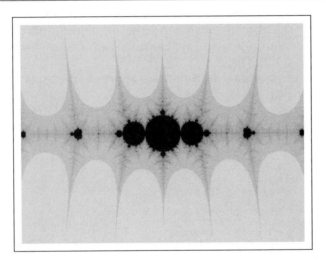

Fractal Category: Escape-time fractal

Formal Name: None

Fractal Type: mandelfn

Formula: Initialize: c = z = *zpixel*
                      Iterate: *c*fn(z).

where fn(z) is one of conj, cos, cosh, cosxx, cotan, cotanh, exp, flip, ident, log, recip, sin, sinh, sqr, tan, or tanh.

Code

Routine type	Routine name	File
Fractal engine	StandardFractactal()	CALCFRACT.C
Integer math initialization	long_mandel_per_pixel()	FRACTALS.C
Integer math orbit	LambdaTrigFractal()	FRACTALS.C
Floating-point initialization	othermandelfp_per_pixel()	FRACTALS.C
Floating-point orbit	LambdafpFractal()	FRACTALS.C

Parameter File Example

```
mandelfn {
   reset maxiter=20000 inside=255 logmap=-1
   type=mandelfn
}
```

Description

These are variants of the classic Mandelbrot set. Instead of the traditional z^2, we've substituted a transcendental function multiplied by c. As with all Mandelbrot sets, associated with any of the function fractals is an entire family of Julia sets.

The trigonometric functions appear rather spiky. This is because Winfract watches only the real portion of z rather than checking the modulus of z. The Formula Compiler (see type formula) can be used to view these fractals with a modulus bailout check. A formula for the Mandelbrot fractal based on the sine function would look like this:

```
MandelSine = {
   z = pixel:
      z = pixel * sin(z),
   |z| < 32
}
```

The lambdafn fractal types are the Julia sets associated with each of the functions.

Not all the default fractals are really Mandelbrot sets, however, because the initial value of z is always set to zero. To obtain a real Mandelbrot fractal, the initorbit= parameter must be set to the fractal's critical point. The *critical point* is defined as the point where the derivative of the function is equal to zero.

Parameters:		
	Real perturbation of $z(0)$	0
	Imaginary perturbation of $z(0)$	0
	First function	sin
	Bailout value (0 means use default)	0

Using a nonzero value for the real perturbation of $z(0)$ and the imaginary perturbation of $z(0)$ will warp the original fractal. The first function parameter accepts any one of these function names to generate a fractal:

conj, cos, cosh, cosxx, cotan, cotanh, exp, flip, ident, log, recip, sin, sinh, sqr, tan, or tanh

Most of these function variable values refer to the transcendental function commonly known by the same name. For example, "sin" refers to the familar sine function from high school trigonometry, while "sinh" refers to the somewhat less familiar hyperbolic sine. Several of these functions have no common name or are peculiar to Winfract.

The function cosxx is the complex conjugate of the correct cosine function. Earlier versions of Winfract had a sign error in the code for the cosine function. Fractals made with the earlier cos can be reproduced using cosxx instead of cos.

The ident function is the identity function. It is defined by $\text{ident}(z) = z$.

The flip function swaps the real and imaginary parts of a complex number. Hence $\text{flip}(x + iy) = y + ix$.

Finally, the recip function calculates the reciprocal, so $\text{recip}(z) = 1/z$.

The bailout value is the variable that determines when Winfract should call it quits on the iterations and assign the pixel a color. The default bailout value is 4.

Explorer
Even though the initial value of the cosine fractal is off, there is still a tiny copy of the Mandelbrot set located at these coordinates:

First function	cos		
Xmin	4.68	Xmax	4.76
Ymin	−0.03	Ymax	0.03

You can set these parameters using the FRACTALS / FRACTAL PARAMS menu.

Special Effects
Like almost all the fractals in Winfract, these can be redrawn in 3D, transformed onto a sphere, or made into a starfield.

Warnings
After a few zooms, these fractals can be very slow without a coprocessor.

History and Credits
Mark Peterson wrote the code for the trigonometric fractals, and Tim Wegner coded the exponential and logarithmic fractals.

MANOWAR

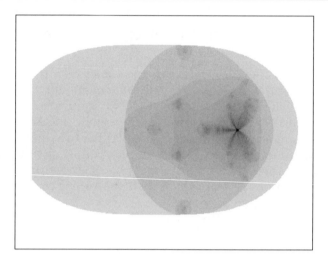

Fractal Category: Escape-time fractal

Formal Name: None

Fractal Types: manowar, manowarj

Formulas: Initialize: $c = m = z = zpixel$ (Mandelbrot variant)
Initialize: $m = z = zpixel$ (Julia variant)
Iterate: $z' = z^2 + m + c;$
$m' = z;$

Code

Routine type	Routine name	File
Fractal engine	StandardFractactal()	CALCFRACT.C
Integer math initialization	mandel_per_pixel()	FRACTALS.C
Integer math initialization	julia_per_pixel()	FRACTALS.C
Integer math orbit	ManOWarFractal()	FRACTALS.C
Floating-point initialization	mandelfp_per_pixel()	FRACTALS.C
Floating-point initialization	juliafp_per_pixel()	FRACTALS.C
Floating-point orbit	ManOWarfpFractal()	FRACTALS.C

Parameter File Example
```
Winfract maxiter=20000 inside=255 logmap=-1 type=manowar
```

Description

This fractal looks like an oblong tube with several fractal spots, including one main chaotic area on the right-hand side. Clicking the right mouse button will toggle from the Mandelbrot mapping of the formula to the Julia sets.

Parameters

These are the parameters for the manowar fractal type

Real perturbation of $z0$)	0.0
Imaginary perturbation of $z(0)$	0.0
Bailout value (0 means use default)	0.0

As with other Mandelbrot types, the real and imaginary perturbation parameters warp the image by perturbing the initial orbit value.

For the manowarj fractal type the parameters are as follows:

Real part of parameter	0.0
Imaginary part of parameter	0.0
Bailout value (0 means use default)	0.0

The values for the real and imaginary part of parameter are used to set the value of the variable c in the formula.

Explorer

Negative values of the real parameter result in the manowarj fractal breaking up into two globules when the imaginary parameter is 0. Try these values:

Real part of parameter	−1.9
Imaginary part of parameter	0.0

As you slowly make the real parameter less negative, the two globules will merge. The value when they just touch is −1.75.

History and Credits

The original formula is from Art Matrix. Tim Wegner added the Julia version.

MARK'S JULIA

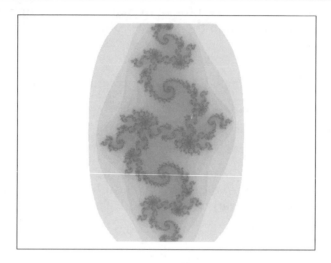

Fractal Category: Escape-time fractal

Formal Name: Mark's Julia

Fractal Type: marksjulia

Formula: Initialize: $z = zpixel$
Iterate: $z^2 c^{(p-1)} + c$

Code

Routine type	Routine name	File
Fractal engine	StandardFractactal()	CALCFRACT.C
Integer math initialization	julia_per_pixel()	FRACTALS.C
Integer math orbit	MarksLambdaFractal()	FRACTALS.C

Parameter File Example

```
marksjulia {
  reset maxiter=20000 inside=255 logmap=-1
  type=marksjulia
}
```

Description

These fractals are the Julia sets associated with the different points from Mark's Mandelbrot. Clicking the right mouse button toggles back to Complex Mark's Mandelbrot.

Parameters:	Real part of parameter	0.1
	Imaginary part of parameter	0.9
	Parameter exponent (>0)	0.0
	Bailout value (0 means use default)	0.0

The real and imaginary parameters define the value of c in the formula. The value of z is initialized to the coordinates of the pixel color being calculated. The parameter exponent is used to set the complex value of p in the formula.

Explorer

With an infinite number of sets to choose from, exploration of this fractal type could take a while. Fortunately, the marksmand fractal is a catalog of all the different Julia sets associated with this formula. Find an interesting spot in marksmand and toggle to the Julia set associated with the point in the center of the screen.

History and Credits

See Complex Mark's Mandelbrot.

MARK'S MANDELBROT

Fractal Category: Escape-time fractal

Formal Name: Mark's Mandelbrot

Fractal Type: marksmandel

Formula: Initialize: $c = z = zpixel$
Iterate: $z^2 c^{(p-1)} + c$

Code

Routine type	Routine name	File
Fractal engine	StandardFractactal()	CALCFRACT.C
Integer math initialization	mandel_per_pixel()	FRACTALS.C
Integer math orbit	MarksLambdaFractal()	FRACTALS.C

Parameter File Example

```
marksmandel {
  reset maxiter=20000 inside=255logmap=-1 type=marksmandel
}
```

Description

Mark's Mandelbrot is a faster version of Complex Mark's Mandelbrot. By restricting the variable p to real integers greater than 1, the fractal algorithm can be calculated much more quickly.

The marksjulia fractal draws the Julia sets associated with each point on this fractal. Cmplxmarksmand is a slower version of this fractal that allows the value of the variable p to be complex.

Parameters:

Real perturbation of $z(0)$	0
Imaginary perturbation of $z(0)$	0
Parameter exponent (>0)	1
Bailout value (0 means use default)	0

The real and imaginary perturbations warp the drawings. For exploration we recommend using zeros for these parameters. The parameter exponent is used to set the complex value of p in the fractal formula. These default settings draw a traditional Mandelbrot set. Using a value of 2 for the exponent draws a double Mandelbrot set. A value of 3 draws a triangular Mandelbrot set. A setting of 4 draws a square Mandelbrot.

History and Credits

Mark Peterson originated the fractal formula and added the marksmandelbrot fractal to Winfract.

MARK'S MANDELPOWER

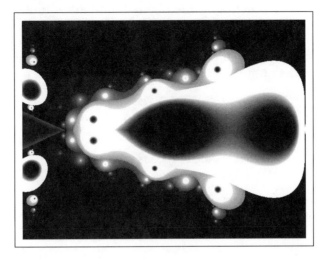

Fractal Category: Escape-time fractal

Formal Name: None

Fractal Type: marksmandelpwr

Formula: Initialize: $z = z_{pixel}, c = z^{z-1}$
              Iterate: $z' = c\,\mathrm{fn}(z) + pixel;$

Code

Routine type	Routine name	File
Fractal engine	StandardFractactal()	CALCFRACT.C
Integer math initialization	marks_mandelpwr_per_pixel()	FRACTALS.C
Integer math orbit	MarksMandelPwrFractal()	FRACTALS.C
Floating-point intialization	marks_mandelpwrfp_per_pixel	FRACTALS.C
Floating-point orbit	MarksMandelPwrfpFractal()	FRACTALS.C

Parameter File Example

```
Injector  { ; Lee Skinner
  reset type=marksmandelpwr function=tan
  corners=-0.949173/0.822122/-0.664236/0.664232
  maxiter=1024
  inside=maxiter logmap=yes potential=256/511/0
  colors=@injector.map
  }
```

Description

Marksmandelpwr uses a modification of the traditional Mandelbrot algorithm. In each iteration, the iterated function is multiplied by $c = z^{z-1}$, where z is the initial orbit value. Originally, the function variable in the formula used the square function. The example above uses the tangent function, and also applies the continuous function option which makes the colors smoothly flow from one to the other in a pseudo 3-D effect.

Parameters: Real perturbation of $z(0)$ 0

                Imaginary perturbation of $z(0)$ 0

                First function   sin

                Bailout value (0 means use default)   0
                   (marksmandelpwr default is 4)

The first two parameters are the normal, mandelbrot-style pertubations of the initial iterated value. You can use these to mutate the image; they are normally 0. The formula has been generalized using a function variable.

Explorer

Try different values of the function variable.

A Turtle

Real perturbation of $z(0)$	0
Imaginary perturbation of $z(0)$	0
First function	recip
Bailout value (0 means use default)	0
(marksmandelpwr default is 4)	

A Flower Pistil

Real perturbation of $z(0)$	0
Imaginary perturbation of $z(0)$	0
First function	tanh
Bailout value (0 means use default)	0
(marksmandelpwr default is 4)	

History and Credits

This fractal type was discovered by Mark Peterson, then coded and generalized by Tim Wegner.

MARTIN

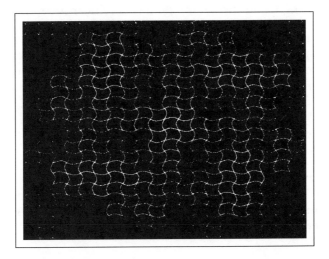

Fractal Category: Orbital fractal

Formal Name: None

Fractal Type: martin

Formula: Initialize: x = y = 0:
Iterate: x' = y − sin(x)
y' = a − x

Code

Routine type	Routine name	File
2-D floating point fractal engine	orbit2dfloat()	LORENZ.C
Floating-point orbit	martin2dfloatorbit()	LORENZ.C

Parameter File Example

```
martin {
  reset type=martin params=3.14159
}
```

Description

This orbit fractal makes a crazy-quilt pattern of interlinked shapes that are traced over and over. The color is incremented each time a pixel is retraced.

Parameters: *a*   3.14

The parameter a is the number used in the calculation of the new y value (see the previoius formula). The chaotic behavior of the orbit is the most interesting when the parameter a is very near the number (3.14159...).

Explorer

Try making a sequence of images using parameter values that straddle the value of . When $a = 3.0$, the orbit traces a single link of the chain-fence pattern. Then you can increment a by a small amount such as .02, and redraw the fractal with $a = 3.02, 3.04, 3.08, 3.10, 3.12, 3.14$, and finally 3.14159. You might try even smaller increments near . As the parameter value comes closer and closer to , the chain-link pattern expands and covers more and more of the plane.

History and Credits

These fractal types are from A. K. Dewdney's "Computer Recreations" column in *Scientific American*. They are attributed to Barry Martin of Aston University in Birmingham, UK.

NEWTON

Fractal Category: Escape-time fractal

Formal Name: Newton

Fractal Type: newton

Formula: $z' = [(n - 1)z^n + r]/(nz^{n-1})$

Code

Routine type	Routine name	File
Fractal engine	StandardFractactal()	CALCFRACT.C
MPC math initialization	MPCjulia_per_pixel()	FRACTALS.C
MPC math orbit	MPCNewtonFractal()	FRACTALS.C
Floating-point initialization	otherjuliafp_per_pixel()	FRACTALS.C
Floating-point orbit	NewtonFractal2()	NEWTON.ASM

Parameter File Example

```
Newton {
  reset type=newton center-mag=0/0/1.5 params=4 logmap=-1
  maxiter=750 map=firestrm.map
}
```

Description

Strings of fiery pearls flung from the core of a hot dwarf sun. This fractal is a faster version of complexnewton. The iteration formula above is a generalization of Newton's method for finding solutions to $z^n - 1 = 0$, where z is a complex number and n is a positive integer greater than or equal to 3. The fractal description for complexbasin has a detailed explanation of Newton's method.

The newtbasin is the same fractal, except the color displayed represents the solution obtained by Newton's method rather than the number of iterations required. The complexnewton and complexbasin are slower, but they allow any complex value to be used for n.

Parameters: Polynomial degree (>2)   3

The default parameters tell Winfract to look for the solutions to the equation $z^n - 1 = 0$. The polynomial degree parameter sets the value of n in the formula. An odd integer value for the degree produces one fractal arm along the negative x-axis and $n - 1$ evenly spaced arms extending outward from the origin. The fractal arms are always found between the actual solutions to the equation.

Polynomial degree (> 2)   4

The polynomial degree determines how many fractal arms will appear in the image. In this case, four evenly spaced fractal arms extend outward from the origin. If the polynomial degree is odd, one of the arms will be along the negative x-axis.

Explorer

The Newton fractals are similar to Julia sets in that the images on the smaller scales are copies of the overall image. Large zooms out from the origin create a tunnel effect with the fractal arms shrinking in size as they approach the origin.

Alternate Color Maps
As with other escape-time fractals, a smooth color palette is a good variation. These palettes are best used with a logarithmic color option.

History and Credits
The actual fractal characteristics of Newton's method for roots was first discovered by John Hubbard in Orsay, France. The first fractal types Newton and newtbasin were coded into Winfract by Tim Wegner. Lee Crocker wrote a more efficient algorithm using FPU-specific assembly language.

NEWTON'S BASIN

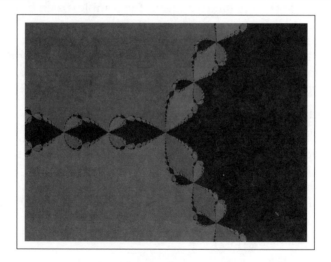

Fractal Category: Escape-time fractal

Formal Name: Newton's Basin

Fractal Type: newtbasin

Formula: $z' = [(n - 1)z^n + r]/(nz^{n-1})$

Code

Routine type	Routine name	File
Fractal engine	StandardFractactal()	CALCFRACT.C
MPC math initialization	MPCjulia_per_pixel()	FRACTALS.C
MPC math orbit	MPCNewtonFractal()	FRACTALS.C
Floating-point initialization	otherjuliafp_per_pixel()	FRACTALS.C
Floating-point orbit	NewtonFractal2()	NEWTON.ASM

Parameter File Example

```
newtbasin {
   reset type=newtbasin params=3
}
```

Description

This fractal is identical to the fractal type Newton except the colors represent the solution itself rather than the number of iterations Winfract required to find the solution. See the description of the Newton fractal type for more information.

PICKOVER ATTRACTOR

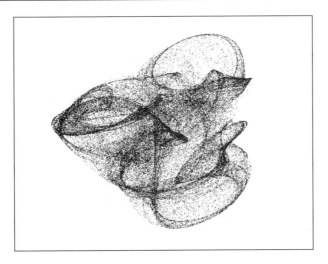

Fractal Category: Orbital fractal

Formal Name: None

Fractal Type: pickover

Formula: Initialize: $x = y = z = 1$

Iterate:
$$x' = \sin(ax) - z\cos(bx)$$
$$y' = z\sin(cx) - \cos(dy)$$
$$z' = \sin(x)$$

Code

Routine type	Routine name	File
Floating-point fractal engine	orbit3dfloat()	LORENZ.C
Floating-point orbit	pickoverfloatorbit()	LORENZ.C

Parameter File Example

```
pickover {
  reset maxiter=20000 type=pickover
}
```

Description

This fractal forms a three-dimensional wispy cloud of points as they orbit through the iterations. A majority of the points collect along the fractal's strange attractors.

Parameters: a   2.24

b   0.43

c   −0.65

d   −2.43

The parameters a, b, c, and d correspond to the applicable variables in the formula. Changing these will produce an entirely different fractal.

Special Effects

Because this fractal is three-dimensional, we've included an option in Winfract for viewing with the red/blue 3-D glasses. Select the FRACTALS / 3D PARAMS menu. At the bottom of the 3D PARAMETERS dialog box, press the SUPERIMPOSE radio button.

History and Credits

This fractal type was developed by Clifford A. Pickover of IBM's Thomas J. Watson Research Center.

PICKOVER M/J FRACTALS

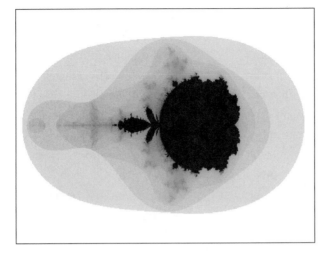

Fractal Category: Escape-time fractal

Formal Name: Mandelbrot and Julia sets

Fractal Types: manzpower, julzpower
manzzpwr, julzzpwr
mandel4, julia4
manfn+zsqrd, julfn+zsqrd
manfn+exp, julfn+exp

Formulas: $z^m + c$
$z^z + z^m + c$
$z^4 + c$
$fn(z) + z^2 + c$
$fn(z) + e^z + c$

where $fn(z)$ is one of conj, cos, cosh, cosxx, cotan, cotanh, exp, flip, ident, log, recip, sin, sinh, sqr, tan, or tanh.

Code

Routine type	Routine name	File
Fractal engine	StandardFractactal()	CALCFRACT.C
Integer math initialization	long_julia_per_pixel()	FRACTALS.C
Integer math initialization	long_mandel_per_pixel()	FRACTALS.C
Floating-point initialization	otherjuliafp_per_pixel()	FRACTALS.C

Floating-point initialization	othermandelfp_per_pixel()	FRACTALS.C
Integer math orbit	longZpowerFractal()	FRACTALS.C
Floating-point orbit	floatZpowerFractal()	FRACTALS.C
Integer math orbit	LongTrigPlusExponentFractal()	FRACTALS.C
Floating-point orbit	FloatTrigPlusExponentFracta()	FRACTALS.C
Floating-point orbit	floatZtozPluszpwrFractal()	FRACTALS.C
Integer math orbit	Mandel4Fractal()	FRACTALS.C
Floating-point orbit	TrigPlusZsquaredfpFracta()	FRACTALS.C
Integer math orbit	TrigPlusZsquaredFracta()	FRACTALS.C
Floating-point orbit	floatTrigPlusExponentFractal()	FRACTALS.C
Integer math orbit	LongTrigPlusExponentFractal()	FRACTALS.C
Floating-point orbit	floatZtozPluszpwrFractal()	FRACTALS.C
Integer math orbit	Mandel4Fractal()	FRACTALS.C

Parameter File Example

```
manfn+zsqrd {
  reset maxiter=20000 inside=255 logmap=-1 type=manfn+zsqrd
}
```

Description

This is another collection of variations of the classical Mandelbrot and Julia sets. The last two types allow any one of six functions to be used to generate the fractal. As with all Mandelbrot/Julia set combinations, there is only one Mandelbrot set associated with a complete family of Julia sets. Each point on the Mandelbrot set corresponds to a unique Julia set.

The fractal types starting with the "man" prefix generate the Mandelbrot set associated with the formula. The fractal types with the "jul" prefix are used to generate the Julia sets for the formula. No matter how bizarre the overall Mandelbrot set may look, there are always tiny copies of the classic Mandelbrot set scattered throughout the fractal.

The manzpower fractal is another periodic Mandelbrot set similar to the marksmandel fractal. With the manzpower fractal type, subtracting one from the value of m is the period. For example, the default settings use a value of 2, which is $z^2 + c$, or the classic Mandelbrot set with a period of 1. A value for m of 3 produces a double Mandelbrot set, or a period of $3 - 1 = 2$. The mandel4 fractal type is a faster version of manzpower using a parameter of 4 for m.

Explorer

Set the Biomorph option in FRACTALS / BASIC OPTIONS menu to 0 and create organic-looking fractals. Try the manfn+sqrd fractal type with all the default parameters except with Biomorph set to 0, and you will see a big biomorph digesting little biomorphs!

History and Credits
These types have been explored by Clifford A. Pickover of IBM's Thomas J. Watson Research Center.

PLASMA CLOUDS

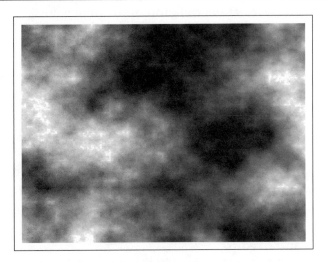

Fractal Category: Random fractal

Formal Name: Midpoint Displacement

Fractal Type: plasma

Formula: Variant of the midpoint displacement algorithm

Code

Routine type	Routine name	File
Fractal engine	plasma()	CALCFRACT.C

Parameter File Example
```
plasma {
  reset type=plasma
}
```

Description
Plasma clouds are generated using a recursive algorithm that randomly picks the four corner colors, picks a color for the center, and then recursively quarters the four new rectangles. Random colors are averaged with

those of the outer rectangles so the small adjacent points differ only slightly, creating a smoothed-out, cloudlike effect. The more colors your video mode is capable of, the better. The images can be saved and viewed in a 3-D mode as a fractal landscape. Your clouds are transformed into mountains!

Using the starfield feature, Plasma Clouds can be used as a template for generating realistic starfields if your video mode supports at least 256 colors. The starfield default settings work best in an 800 x 600 video mode. See the Starfields section for details on the different parameters.

Color cycling for this fractal is required for all Winfract users! The result is an eye-catching cauldron of writhing colors!

Parameters: Graininess factor (.1 to 50, default is 2)

The graininess factor determines how abruptly the colors change from one pixel to the next. A value of .5 yields the smoothest clouds, while 50 yields the grainiest.

Special Effects
These fractals make excellent landscapes using the LANDSCAP.MAP color palette file. They also make excellent planets with spherical projection!

Explorer
Zooming does not work with this fractal because the image is randomly created each time. See the guided tour in Chapter 2 for an example of how to create a landscape from a plasma image.

History and Credits
The midpoint displacement algorithm was first used by Archimedes as a method for constructing parabolas. Later, around 1900, the number theorist Teiji Takagi used a variation on the method to create a fractal curve between two points that had an infinite length. The algorithm in Winfract was adapted from Pascal code written by Bret Mulvey.

POPCORN FRACTALS

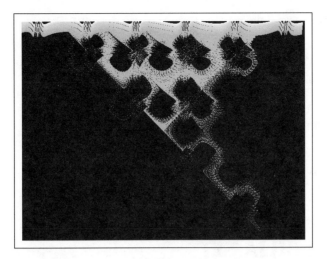

Fractal Category: Orbital fractal

Formal Name: None

Fractal Type: Popcorn

Formula: Initialize: $x = x_{zpixel}$, $y = y_{zpixel}$,
Iterate: $x' = x - 0.05 \sin(y) + \tan(3y)$
$y' = y - 0.05 \sin(x) + \tan(3x)$

Code

Routine type	Routine name	File
Fractal engine	StandardFractactal()	CALCFRACT.C
Integer math initialization	long_julia_per_pixel()	FRACTALS.C
Integer math orbit	LPopcornFractal()	FRACTALS.C
Floating-point initialization	otherjuliafp_per_pixel()	FRACTALS.C
Floating-point orbit	PopcornFractal()	FRACTALS.C

Parameter File Example

```
Popcorn {
   reset maxiter=20000 inside=255 type=popcorn
}
```

Description

This fractal is called "popcorn" because it looks like a bowl of popped popcorn. The screen coordinates are used as the initial values for the variables x and y. With each iteration, the new x and y positions are plotted to the screen. Each new iteration cycle is plotted in the next sequential color from the current color palette.

Parameters: Bailout value (0 means use default)   0

Winfract uses the bailout value as one of the criteria to stop the iterations. Winfract will stop the iterations when the value of $x^2 + y^2$ is greater than or equal to the bailout value. The default value is 4. To increase the number of iterations, raise the value of Maximum Iterations using the FRACTALS / BASIC OPTIONS menu or use the command-line parameter maxiter=.

History and Credits

Clifford A. Pickover of IBM's Thomas J. Watson Research Center originated this fractal type.

POPCORN JULIA SET

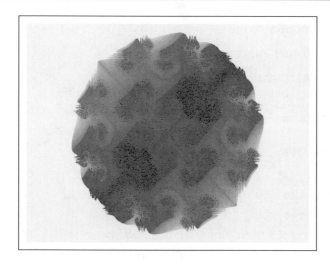

Fractal Category: Escape-time fractal

Formal Name: None

Fractal Type: popcornjul

Formula: Initialize: $x = x_{zpixel}$, $y = y_{zpixel}$,
Iterate: $x' = x - 0.05 \sin(y) + \tan(3y)$
$y' = y - 0.05 \sin(x) + \tan(3x)$

Code

Routine type	Routine name	File
Fractal engine	StandardFractactal()	CALCFRACT.C
Integer math initialization	long_julia_per_pixel()	FRACTALS.C
Integer math orbit	LPopcornFractal()	FRACTALS.C
Floating-point initialization	otherjuliafp_per_pixel()	FRACTALS.C
Floating-point orbit	PopcornFractal()	FRACTALS.C

Parameter File Example

```
PopcornJulia {
   reset maxiter=20000 inside=255 logmap=-1 type=popcornjul
}
```

Description

This fractal is the Julia set associated with the popcorn fractal type. Recall that the Julia set uses the screen coordinates for the corresponding pixel as the initial values for the variables x and y. The iterations continue until the value of $x^2 + y^2$ becomes higher than the bailout value, the orbits become periodic, or the maximum allowable number of iterations is reached. The pixel's color is assigned according to the number of iterations Winfract performed.

Pressing the ⊛ key will toggle on the orbits plotted in the popcorn fractal type. Color cycling works well with this fractal.

Parameters: Bailout value (0 means use default)   0

The default bailout is 4.

Explorer

Unlike most of the Julia fractal types in Winfract that have an entire family of sets, this fractal type has only one Julia set associated with the formula. Zooming in on any section of the fractal will show the same overall pattern only at higher iteration levels.

Alternate Color Maps

Smooth color maps, such as FIRESTRM.MAP, used at high maximum iteration levels work best with this fractal type. If the maximum iteration level exceeds the number of colors available on your screen, turn on the logarithmic color mapping using the FRACTALS / BASIC OPTIONS menu or set the command-line parameter logmap= to 1 or –1.

History and Credits

Clifford A. Pickover of IBM's Thomas J. Watson Research Center originated the popcorn fractal type.

ROSSLER THREE D

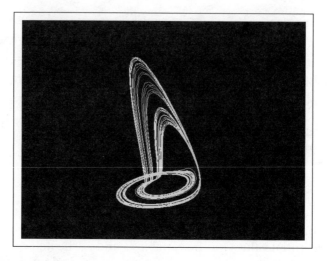

Fractal Category: Orbital fractal

Formal Name: Rossler

Fractal Type: rossler3d

Formula: Initialize: $x = y = z = 1$
Iterate: $x' = x - (y - x)dt$
$y' = y + (x + ay)dt$
$z' = z + (b + xz - cz)dt$

Code

Routine type	Routine name	File
Floating-point fractal engine	orbit3dfloat()	LORENZ.C
Floating-point orbit	rosslerlongorbit()	LORENZ.C
Integer math fractal engine	orbit3dlong()	LORENZ.C
Integer math orbit	rosslerfloatorbit()	LORENZ.C

Parameter File Example

```
rossler3d  {
  reset type=rossler3d
}
```

Description

Named after its originator, Dr. Otto Rossler, this fractal is very similar to
the Lorenz fractal. The three variables, x, y, and z, plot a position in three-
dimensional space. The dt term is the time increment.

Dr. Rossler describes the fractal as "a sausage in a sausage in a sausage in a sausage. Take it out, fold it, squeeze it, put it back." Dr. Rossler takes a very philosophical view of this fractal, which he imagines as a wind sock in an airfield: "an open hose with a hole in the end, and the wind forces its way in. Then the wind is trapped. Against its will, energy is doing something productive, like the devil in medieval history. The principle is that nature does something against its own will and, by self-entanglement, produces beauty." (James Gleick, *Chaos—Making a New Science*, pages 141–142.)

Parameters: Time step   0.04
	a	0.2
	b	0.2
	c	5.7

The time step parameter is used as the *dt* term in the formula. Higher values generate the fractal more quickly but produce many sharp corners. Lower values take longer and smooth out the curves.

The parameters *a*, *b*, and *c* are used for the corresponding variables in the formula. Changing the values of *a* and *b* will generally destroy the fractal. Changing the value of *c* will alter the fractal's size.

Special Effects
Since this fractal is inherently three-dimensional, it is possible to generate it as an anaglyph for viewing with the red/blue glasses. You can access the 3-D options using the FRACTALS /3D PARAMS menu.

History and Credits
This fractal was discovered by Otto Rossler, a nonpracticing medical doctor in Germany. Dr. Rossler became interested in chaos through his studies of chemistry and theoretical biology.

SIERPINSKI

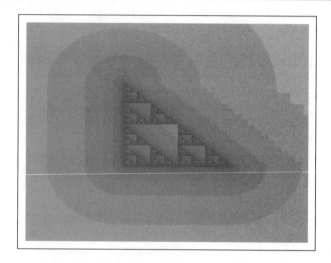

Fractal Category: Escape-time fractal

Formal Name: Sierpinski's Gasket

Fractal Type: sierpinski

Formula: Initialize: $x = x_{zpixel}, y = y_{zpixel}$
Iterate:
$$x' = 2x - 1 \quad \text{if } x > .5$$
$$x' = 2x \qquad\;\; \text{if } x <= .5$$
$$y' = 2y - 1 \quad \text{if } y > .5$$
$$y' = 2y \qquad\;\; \text{if } y <= .5$$

Code

Routine type	Routine name	File
Fractal engine	StandardFractactal()	CALCFRACT.C
Integer math initialization	long_julia_per_pixel()	FRACTALS.C
Integer math orbit	SierpinskiFractal()	FRACTALS.C
Floating-point initialization	otherjuliafp_per_pixel()	FRACTALS.C
Floating-point orbit	SierpinskiFPFractal()	FRACTALS.C

Parameter File Example

```
Sierpinski  {
  reset maxiter=20000 inside=255 logmap=-1 type=sierpinski
}
```

Description

This fractal, named after its mathematician originator, is full of so many holes that there is nothing left of it. The overall shape is that of a triangle. Cut out of the triangle are successively smaller triangles carried on into infinity. Imagine a Swiss cheese where there are only holes remaining and no cheese. That's the way Sierpinski acts, except the holes are triangles.

The reason there is "no cheese" is because the fractal exists between the first and second dimensions. One-dimensional objects are lines which have a length. Two-dimensional objects are planes which have a length and width that can be used to calculate the object's circumference and surface area. The Sierpinski fractal has a circumference but no surface area. It is more than a line and yet less than a plane. It exists in a fractional dimension between the two.

Parameters: Bailout value (0 means use default)   0

The bailout value determines at what level the iterations should cease. The default value is 4. Lower values are ignored. Changing this parameter to higher values alters the overall color of the fractal but otherwise has no appreciable effect.

Explorer

Zoom in and you will find smaller and smaller triangles.

History and Credits

The original mathematical concept of the fractal came from a mathematician named Sierpinski in the early twentieth century. The fractal code was obtained from a BASIC program in *Fractals Everywhere* by Michael Barnsley (page 251).

SPIDER

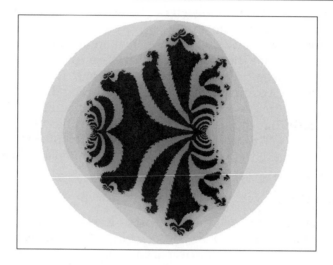

Fractal Category: Escape-time fractal

Formal Name: None

Fractal Type: spider

Formula: Initialize: $z = c = z_{pixel}$
Iterate: $z' = z^2 + c$
$c' = c/2 + z'$

Code

Routine type	Routine name	File
Fractal engine	StandardFractactal()	CALCFRACT.C
Integer math initialization	mandel_per_pixel()	FRACTALS.C
Integer math orbit	SpiderFractal()	FRACTALS.C
Floating-point initialization	mandelfp_per_pixel()	FRACTALS.C
Floating-point orbit	SpiderfpFractal()	FRACTALS.C

Parameter File Example

```
Spider  {
  reset maxiter=20000 inside=255 logmap=-1 type=spider
    }
```

Description
The name tells it all—this type looks like a spider!

Parameters
As with other Mandelbrot types, the parameters warp the image by perturbing the initial orbit value.

Explorer
Try zooming in on the area where the legs appear to be converging.

History and Credits
This fractal type came from the program *Fractal Magic*. It was sent to us as a Fractint formula type by Lee Skinner.

TETRATION FRACTAL

Fractal Category: Escape-time fractal

Formal Name: None

Fractal Type: tetrate

Formula: Initialize: $z = c = z_{pixel}$
            Iterate: $z' = c^z$

Code

Routine type	Routine name	File
Fractal engine	StandardFractactal()	CALCFRACT.C
Floating-point initialization	othermandelfp_per_pixel()	FRACTALS.C
Floating-point orbit	TetratefpFractal()	FRACTALS.C

Parameter File Example

```
Tetrate {
  reset type=tetrate maxiter=1023 potential=255/511
  inside=255 corners=1.58675/2.77/3.22225/4.10550
}
```

Description

This fractal type orginated from an investigation into the properties of the generalized Ackerman exponential. Winfract initializes the variables z and c to the complex value corresponding to the screen pixel color being evaluated. By successively raising the variable c in the fractal formula to the z power with each iteration, Winfract is performing a *tetration* of z, hence the name.

The following examples show the wide range of images that the tetration type can produce. The fractal named "The Tunnel" has smoothly varying colors that seem to form the sides of a cavern. The smooth colors come from the use of the continuous potential option, which turns bright stripes into blending hues. The other examples have more of a crazy-quilt appearance with solid colored patches.

Parameters:	
Real part of parameter	0
Imaginary part of parameter	0
Bailout value (0 means use default)	0

The real part of parameter and imaginary part of parameter are added to the initial value of z for each pixel calculation. Winfract compares the bailout value parameter to the modulus of z with each iteration. When the modulus is greater than or equal to the bailout value, Winfract stops iterating and assigns a color to the pixel.

Explorer

Here are a few places to visit and start you on your explorations. Try the following commands :

The Land

Using the FRACTALS / BASIC OPTIONS menu, set:

Maximum Iterations   1023

Using the FRACTALS / FRACTAL PARAMS menu, set:

Xmin	−6	Xmax	6
Ymin	−4.5	Ymax	4.5

The Tunnel

Using the FRACTALS / BASIC OPTIONS menu, set:

    Maximum Iterations   1023

Using the FRACTALS / EXTENDED OPTIONS menu, set:

    Potential Max Color   255
    Slope   511

Using the FRACTALS / FRACTAL PARAMS menu, set:

    Xmin 1.58675   Xmax 2.77
    Ymin 3.22225   Ymax 4.10550

Circles

Using the FRACTALS / FRACTAL PARAMS menu, set:

    Xmin −0.32/   Xmax 0.15
    Ymin −0.18   Ymax 0.18

The Star Spiral

Using the FRACTALS / FRACTAL PARAMS menu, set:

    Xmin −1.59911   Xmax 1.58942
    Ymin   0.584366   Ymax 0.591539

Warnings

Every iteration of this fractal requires a complex power calculation. If you do not have a floating-point coprocessor this fractal type will take a very long time to generate.

History and Credits

This fractal type was created by Lee Skinner from Albuquerque, New Mexico.

TIM'S ERROR

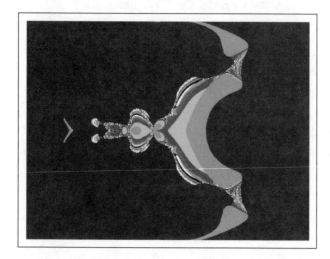

Fractal Category: Escape-time fractal

Formal Name: None

Fractal Type: tim's_error

Formula: Initialize: $z = z_{pixel}, c = z^{z-1}$
            Iterate: $tmp = fn(z)$
                       $real(tmp) = real(tmp) * real(c) - imag(tmp) * imag(c);$
                       $imag(tmp) = real(tmp) * imag(c) - imag(tmp) * real(c);$
                       $z' = tmp + pixel;$

Parameter File Example

```
pterodactyl {
  reset type=tim's_error function=sqr
  corners=-2.5/3.0/-2.0/2.0
  }
```

Description

One of your authors was attempting to code the marksmandelpower fractal
as a built-in fractal type, but made a programming error. The result was
sufficiently interesting that it was left in the program with a name im-
mortalizing both the errant programmer and the serendipitous error.

The tim's_error fractal looks like a pterodactyl straight from the age
of dinosaurs, swooping through the air with giant reptile wings.

Parameters: Real perturbation of $z(0)$ 0

            Imaginary perturbation of $z(0)$ 0

First function	sin
Bailout value (0 means use default)	0

The first two parameters are the normal Mandelbrot-style pertubations of the initial iterated value. You can use these to mutate the image; they are normally 0. The formula has been generalized using a function variable. The pterodactyl image occurs when this variable is set to the *sqr* function. The default bailout value is 4.

Explorer
Try warping the pterodactyl using the first parameter. You can get an image that looks more like a giant insect than an ancient flying reptile.

Three loops

Real perturbation of $z(0)$	0.3
Imaginary perturbation of $z(0)$	0.0
First function	sqr

History and Credits
This fractal type was discovered and coded by Tim Wegner.

UNITY

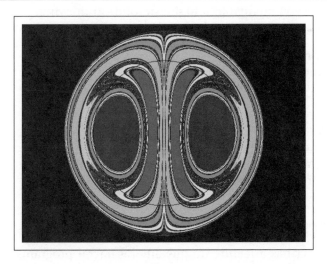

Fractal Category: Escape-time fractal

Formal Name: Unity

Formula: Initialize: $x = x_{zpixel}$, $y = y_{zpixel}$
Iterate: $One = x^2 + y^2$
$y' = (2 - One)*x;$
$x' = (2 - One)*y';$

Parameter File Example

```
Unity {
  reset type=unity logmap=-1 maxiter=20000
    }
```

Description

Circles in circles and lines within lines.
Zoom in closer and see what you find.
Patterns pertaining to a search, you'll see,
Of x chasing y to Unity.

The Unity fractal is based on a round-about approximation of the number 1. The first line of the formula is the equation for a unit circle. From there, the next y is calculated based on how far it deviated from the correct answer. The next x is based on how far the y' variable deviates from the correct answer. As soon as the variable *One* approximates the real number 1 to within one pixel width, the iterations top and the number of iterations required to that point are displayed to the screen as a color.

This is the only fractal where the bailout criterion is based on the width of a pixel on the screen. This creates some interesting effects. As you zoom in to the fractal, some lines expand while others become smaller. Also, if you change to a higher-resolution drawing, more lines develop. In all of the drawings, the line of the unit circle is always one pixel wide.

Explorer

The most interesting section is where both the x- and y-coordinates are close to the square root of two.

History and Credits

Mark Peterson originated this fractal and adapted it to Winfract. At the time he was intrigued by Newton's fractal, which approximates complex roots, and wondered if other approximation algorithms would also produce fractals. In this case, one did.

USER-DEFINED FRACTALS

Winfract has a feature unique among fractal programs. It lets you enter your own fractal formulas, and then it generates the corresponding image on the screen. You can thus explore your own ideas and create previously unknown fractals. You use the formula, lsystem, and IFS fractal types to explore these new fractal formulas. Zoom into unexplored depths—translate to dazzling 3D—the only limit is your own imagination!

The Formula Compiler

The formula compiler interprets algebraic expressions defining escape-time fractals into a series of program instructions. These instructions are then turned over to the powerful Winfract engine, which quickly generates the corresponding fractal. All the resources available to other fractal types in Winfract can also be used with your own formulas.

To compile a formula, select the formula fractal type. Winfract will ask you which text file you would like it to use. You can select the default FRACTINT.FRM or another formula file. (You can create your own file containing fractal formula experiments.) Winfract will scan the text file and create a list of the available formulas from which to choose. Select the formula you'd like to use. As you will see, you can add your own formulas to this file.

If you are running in the batch mode, you can bypass the queries from Winfract by setting formulafile= to the text file containing the list of formulas and also setting formulaname= to the name of the formula you want to run. Winfract will then skip the queries and go straight to work.

Formula Files

The formula compiler reads and compiles formulas from a DOS text file, such as the supplied file FRACTINT.FRM. (You can view and edit the file FRACTINT.FRM using the Windows Notepad application. Do this now, and follow along as you read about the formula parser.) Operationally, the formula compiler is divided into three major sections. The first section separates the formula names from the actual formula to create the list of names. Once you tell Winfract which formula will be used, it passes the formula information to an internal interpreter section called the *Parser*. The Parser compiles the formula into a set of instructions that are then executed by Winfract.

Formula Names and Comments

The formula compiler distinguishes names from formulas by looking for a set of curly brackets. It treats any text enclosed in curly brackets as a formula and the text immediately before the brackets as the name, as follows:

FormulaName = { _ Formula _ }

The "=" symbol is optional. Comments can also be placed in the file if they are named explicitly as "comments" and if the text is enclosed in the curly brackets:

```
comment = {
        Comments can be placed right before your fractal
        formulas. This is where you would describe all
        the wonderful properties of your formula, its
        history, or whatever. The comment section can
        take up as many lines as you like, provided they are
        enclosed within curly brackets.
}
```

Any number of comment sections can be placed in the formula file. The use of the "comment" name informs the compiler that the text in the enclosing brackets is not a formula and should be disregarded.

A second method of creating comments was added starting with Winfract version 16. The Parser ignores everything following a semicolon (;) up to the end of the line. An example of this method of adding comments is:

```
c = z = 1/pixel:  ; this is a comment
```

The Parser
The Parser looks for three distinct sections in every formula. The first section it looks for is the initial conditions. Generally, this section defines the values for your variables. The second section details the math operations performed on each iteration. The third section specifies the conditions under which the iterations should continue. There can be any number of math operations in each of the sections, provided the total number of characters between the curly brackets is fewer than 200. The Parser looks for each of the sections to be separated by a different punctuation marking:

MyFractal { Initial Condition: Iteration, Condition }

The full colon separates the initial conditions from the iterations. The comma separates the iterations from the conditionals. Multiple math statements should be separated by commas or else be placed on separate lines.

These three sections can be placed on separate lines for clarity, but the required punctuation must be used.

MyFractal { $c = z = 1/pixel : z = $ sqr $(z) + c, |z| <= 4$ }

or

```
MyFractal {              ; name of fractal and start of formula block
c = z = 1/pixel:         ; initial conditions (once per pixel)
        z = sqr (z) + c, ; iterated formula
|z| <= 4                 ; bailout condition
}                        ; end of formula block
```

Let's walk through this example and say what each part of this formula does. "MyFractal" is the name that will appear in the list of formula types loaded from your .FRM file. The variable *pixel* always refers to the complex number mapped to the screen pixel color being calculated. The calculation is repeated for all the values of the variable *pixel* needed to cover the screen. The line $c = z = 1/pixel$ defines two variables c and z and initializes them to $1/pixel$. This initialization is done once for each pixel calculation. The formula $z = sqr(z) + c$ is the calculation that is iterated over and over. In this case, in each iteration, z is changed to be the sum of the square root of the previous z and c. The last formula, $|z| <= 4$, is true. When this condition fails to be true, the iteration is halted. If periodicity checking is enabled, the default condition and then the iterations are halted when the successive values of z fall into a periodic loop.

Note that either upper- or lowercase may be used. The entry

$z = a + \sin(z\ pixel\text{\textasciicircum}z)$

is the same as:

$Z = A + SIN(Z \times PIXEL\text{\textasciicircum}Z)$

Precedence

If you've never written computer programs, you may be unfamiliar with the term *precedence*, although you are probably familiar with the concept. If you were to calculate the expression $a + 4bc^3$, where $a = 7$, $b = 2$ and $c = 3$, you know you need to cube the value of c before multiplying by $4b$; and you need to perform the multiplication before the addition to a. This way the expression evaluates to 223. Powers are performed before multiplication because they have a higher *precedence*. Likewise, multiplication and division are performed before addition or subtraction. An expression suitable for the formula compiler equivalent to $a + 4bc^3$ would be:

$a + 4 \times b \times c\text{\textasciicircum}3$

If, on the other hand, you wanted 4 added to a before multiplying and then you wanted to cube the entire expression, you would write the expression as $[(a + 4)bc]^3$. Here you are overriding the normal precedence of the expression by enclosing the portion you'd like calculated first within parentheses. The Parser equivalent in this case would be:

$[(a + 4) \times b \times c]\text{\textasciicircum}3$

The chart below shows the precedence rules that are in effect when your formula is parsed and interpreted. These rules govern the order in which operations are performed if not explicitly determined with parentheses. The lower-numbered precedence level operations are done before the higher-numbered ones. Table 5-2 lists all the formula parser operators according to precedence.

Precedence Level 1	
2.34543	Convert from a real constant to a complex real constant
(1.32, −7.64)	Convert from a Cartesian constant to a complex constant
MyVariable	Creation of automatic complex variable
Abs ( )	Converts both real and imaginary components to positive numbers
Conj ( )	Complex Conjugate
Cos ( )	Complex Cosine
Cosh ( )	Complex Hyperbolic Cosine
Cosxx ( )	Complex Conjugate of Cosine
Cotan ( )	Complex Cotangent
Cotanh ( )	Complex Hyperbolic Cotangent
Exp ( )	Complex Exponential
Flip ( )	Swap real and imaginary parts
Fn1 ( )	First function variable
Fn2 ( )	Second function variable
Fn3 ( )	Third function variable
Fn4 ( )	Fourth function variable
Imag ( )	Replaces the real component with the imaginary component, then sets the imaginary portion to zero, creating a pure real number
Log ( )	Complex Logarithm

Table 5-2 The formula parser operator precedence levels

Real ( )	Zeros the imaginary component, creating a pure real number	
Sin ( )	Complex Sine	
Sinh ( )	Complex Hyperbolic Sine	
Sqr ( )	Complex Square	
Tan()	Complex Tangent	
Tanh()	Complex Hyperbolic Tangent	
Precedence Level 2		
–	Complex Negation	
^	Complex Power	
Precedence Level 3		
*	Complex Multiplication	
/	Complex Division	
Precedence Level 4		
+	Complex Addition	
–	Complex Subtraction	
Precedence Level 5		
=	Assignment	
Precedence Level 6		
<	Real Component Comparison (Less than)	
<=	Real Component Comparison (Less than or equal to)	
>	Real Component Comparison (Greater than)	

Table 5-2 The formula parser operator precedence levels (continued)

>=	Real Component Comparison (Greater than or equal to)
==	Complex Comparison (Equal to)
!=	Complex Comparison (Not equal to)
Precedence Level 7	
&&	Logical AND
||	Logical OR

Table 5-2 The formula parser operator precedence levels (continued)

These are the operations and functions supported by the formula compiler. The formula compiler also supports nested parentheses of an unlimited depth (well, in reality it's limited by the size of the computer's stack space) and a modulus squared operator | |.

The functions fn1(...) to fn4(...) are variable functions. When used, the user is prompted at run time to specify one of cos, cosh, cosxx, cotan, cotanh, exp, ident, log, recip, sin, sinh, sqr, tan, or tanh, in exactly the same way as with the built-in function variable fractal types discussed earlier in this chapter.

The rand predefined variable is changed with each iteration to a new random number with the real and imaginary components containing a value between zero and 1. Use the srand() function to initialize the random numbers to a consistent random number sequence. If a formula does not contain the srand() function, then the formula compiler will use the system time to initialize the sequence. This could cause a different fractal to be generated each time the formula is used depending on how the formula is written.

Predefined Variables

The formula compiler uses several predefined variables (see Table 5-3) as an aid in interfacing with the rest of Winfract. The most important among these is the predefined variable z. The Winfract fractal engine performs an occasional check on the value of z to determine whether iterations of the equation have fallen into a periodic loop. By maintaining the value of z current with the results of the iteration, Winfract will use this periodicity check to speed the drawing of your fractal.

Another important predefined variable is *pixel*. This variable is updated by Winfract as it calculates the color of each pixel on the screen. It sets the value of *pixel* to the complex number equivalent to the current

Predefined Variables (x, y)	
z	Used for periodicity checking
p1	Parameters 1 and 2
p2	Parameters 3 and 4
pixel	Screen coordinates
LastSqr	Modulus from the last sqr() function
rand	Complex random number

Table 5-3 The formula parser predefined variables

position on the screen relative to the values of the screen corners. For example, if you started Winfract with

Xmin −4   Xmax   4
Ymin −3   Ymax   3

then the value of *pixel* for the upper left-hand corner of the screen would be −4 + i3 and the upper right-hand corner would be 4 + i3.

Two other useful variables are $p1$ and $p2$. These variables are set by the formula compiler as each color is calculated using the values entered from the FRACTALS / FRACTAL PARAMS menu or with the params= command. The variable $p1$ is composed of the first two parameters in params=, and $p2$ is composed of the second two. If you set params=1/2/3/4, or enter the values 1 through 4 for the first four parameters of the FRACTAL PARAMS menu, then Winfract will set $p1$ equal to 1 + i2 and $p2$ equal to 3 + i4.

Parser Errors

As the Parser compiles a formula it looks for syntax errors. These are errors in the formula that make no mathematical sense. If you were to try compiling:

Bogus1 { $z = 0$: $z = z + * 2$, $|z| <= 4$}

the Parser would tell you

```
Error(0):   Should be an Argument
    z = 0:   z = z + * 2; |z| <= 4
                        ^
    ...Press any key to continue...
```

meaning the Parser was expecting you to try adding something to *z* before multiplying by 2. After you press a key, Winfract will return to the Fractal Types list. Table 5-4 is a complete list of Parser errors.

After the Parser has completed compiling a formula without encountering any errors, it passes the set of instructions to Winfract's fractal engine for immediate execution.

Formula Examples

The diagram in Figure 5-2 breaks down the different sections of the formula for the traditional Mandelbrot set. After compiling the formula, the Parser will give Winfract a set of instructions which read, "When drawing

Number	Error	Explanation
Error(0)	Should be an Argument	An operator was found when the Parser was expecting a variable, constant, or the value returned by a function.
Error(1)	Should be an Operator	An argument was found when the Parser was expecting an operator.
Error(2)	')' needs a matching '('	There are more closed parentheses than open parentheses.
Error(3)	Needs more ')'	There were more open parentheses than closed parentheses.
Error(4)	Undefined Operator	An operator was used, such as '!' or '%', that is not supported by the Parser. The "Precedence Level" chart in Table 5-2 lists all supported operators.
Error(5)	Undefined Function	A function was used, such as tan(. . .), that is not supported by the Parser. The "Precedence Level" chart in Table 5-2 lists all supported operators.
Error(6)	More than one ','	There can be only one comma in a formula. This separates the iteration portion from the conditional. If more than one statement is required, use a semicolon.

Table 5-4 Parser errors

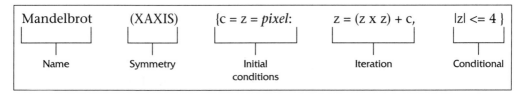

Figure 5-2 Different sections of the formula for the traditional Mandelbrot set

the screen, assume the fractal is symmetrical about the x-axis. For each pixel on the screen set z equivalent to the Cartesian coordinate on the screen and set the automatic variable c equal to z. Then successively perform the iterations until the conditional is false (z is not less than 4), the maximum limit to the number of iterations is reached, or the value of z falls into a periodic loop."

Winfract will execute the instructions using the currently set math mode and each pixel on the screen will be colored according to the number of iterations performed. If the maximum allowable number of iterations was performed or z went into a periodic loop, the color is set to the value of the variable *inside*.

Formula Compiler Hints

There are a few things to consider when using the formula compiler. Specify a symmetry only after you are sure the fractal is symmetrical; otherwise, Winfract will draw a false picture. Second, remember that integer mathematics, which is the default math mode, has a limited range. The range is fine for additions, subtractions, and multiplications, but when the formulas involve powers or trigonometric functions, the range of this math mode is easily exceeded. When this happens, the iterations stop and Winfract draws however many iterations it took before the overflow occurred. This also creates false pictures that are not real fractals. They are not *real* fractals because the drawing is based on the limitations of the integer mathematics rather than the mathematics described in the formula. You should always try drawing the fractal using floating-point math at one time or another to see if it matches the integer drawing. This way you can be sure you are looking at the real McCoy.

With your text editor (or the Windows Notebook application) you can modify or create any formula that comes to mind.

```
Mandel3 = {
     z = pixel, c = sin(z):
          z = (z * z) + c
          z = z * 1/c,
     |z| <= 4
}
```

Don't be bashful. There is a fractal out there with your name on it.

L-Systems

L-systems were developed in 1968 by A. Lindenmayer as a method for modeling the growth of living organisms. A. R. Smith and P. Prusinkiewicz both applied the system to computer graphics. This drawing system enables drawing not only lifelike trees and plants, but also abstract fractals such as the Koch curve and the classic Sierpinski gasket. More important, Winfract will run the L-system definitions you create using your text editor! The L-system definitions are listed in Table 5-5.

Command	Function
nn	Specifies a number. The number *nn* can be prefixed by "I" to mean 1/*nn*, by "Q" to mean *nn*, or by a combination of the two.
Angle *nn*	Specifies the primary turning angle in fractions of a circle (360/*nn* degrees).
Axiom *string*	Character string containing the initial turtle drawing instructions.
c = string	Instructs Fracting to recursively replace each occurrence of *c* in this and all other strings with *string*.
F	Move forward, and draw a line.
G	Move forward, but don't draw a line.
+	Instructs the turtle to turn left (counterclockwise) using the primary angle.
−	Instructs the turtle to turn right (clockwise) using the primary angle.
nn	Creates a secondary angle which is *nn* degrees higher than the primary angle.
/*nn*	Creates a secondary angle which is *nn* degrees lower than the primary angle.
D	Turn using the secondary angle, move forward, and draw a line.

Table 5-5 L-systems definitions

Command	Function
M	Turn using the secondary angle, move forward, but do not draw a line.
C*nn*	Set the drawing color to color number *nn*.
< *nn*	Add *nn* to the drawing color number.
> *nn*	Subtract *nn* from the drawing color number.
/	Toggles the use of negative angles for instructions "+", "−", "\", and "/", but note "D" or "M'.
@ *nn*	Multiply the line segment by *nn*.
[	Save the current state of the turtle (position, primary and secondary angles) and continue drawing.
]	Restore the previously saved state of the turtle.
;;	Designates a comment line.

Table 5-5 L-systems definitions (continued)

You write L-system definitions in a text file in a format similar to the one used by the fractal type formula. If you are within the Winfract program and select the lsystem fractal type, Winfract will prompt you for the file you want to use containing the L-systems definitions. It will then scan the file and create a list of names from which to choose from. This selection process can also be done using lfile= to specify the definition text file and lname for the name of the L-system definition that Winfract is to run.

The L-system definition consists of a name followed by the definition enclosed in curly brackets, as follows:

MyLSystemName { . . . L-system Definition . . . }

The use of curly brackets helps Winfract separate the definition names from the actual definitions. Using a definition name of "Comment" tells Winfract to ignore whatever text is enclosed within the curly brackets. Text lines within an L-system definition beginning with ";;" also designate comments.

```
Comment {
        This text, and the name "Comment," is completely ignored
by Winfract.
}

BogusDefinition {
        ;; These are comment lines within an L-system definition
        ;; since they begin with ;;.
}
```

Winfract interprets the instructions within the definition via a Logo-like turtle graphics interpreter. Winfract uses a "turtle," which follows simple instructions, such as "Draw a line" and "Turn left," to draw the L-system fractal. These instructions are contained within the string declared by the keyword *Axiom*.

Initially, the turtle is pointed directly towards the right side of the screen. The F and G characters instruct the turtle to move in the direction it is pointing. For the F command, the turtle moves forward in the direction it is pointing and draws a line between the new point and where it was before it moved. The G command instructs the turtle to move forward in the direction it is pointing and not draw a line.

The + and – characters are turning instructions. Somewhere in the definition, the turning angle is specified by the keyword *Angle* followed by a number. Note that all numbers can be prefixed by I, Q, or both to mean the inverse of the number or the square root of the number, respectively. Declaring Angle 6 tells the turtle to turn one-sixth of a full circle (360/6 degrees) whenever a turning instruction is used. The + character turns the turtle to the left, and the – character turns the turtle to the right.

Creating a Koch curve using these instructions is a snap:

```
KochCurve {
        Angle 6
        Axiom F
        F=F+F -- F+F
}
```

The Angle 6 instruction declares a turning angle of one-sixth of a circle, or 60 degrees. The axiom is to simply draw a line. The definition of a straight line, however, is modified to have a triangular hump in the middle. This is done by declaring F = F+F –– F+F, which reads as "draw a line forward, turn left, draw a line forward, turn right twice, draw a line forward, turn left, draw a line forward."

Notice that the definition of a line, F =, uses line statement F. If Winfract is instructed to go only one level deep, it will go down one level and use the original definition of a straight line. When it returns to the previous level, the definition of a line has been modified to have the triangular hump. Instructing Winfract to go two levels deep creates a line with a triangular hump on the first level. On the second level a straight line is defined as a triangular hump drawn using lines with triangular humps. With each level the length of the lines used is increasingly smaller.

Other characters can be used as needed to define subaxioms. Here is an example:

```
DragonCurve {
        Angle 4
        Axiom X
        X=X-YF-
        Y=+FX+Y
}
```

Here the characters X and Y are used to define subaxioms.

```
Bush {
        Angle 16
        Axiom ++++F
        F=FF-[-F+F+F]+[+F-F-F]
}
```

Bushes and trees utilize the [and] symbols, which save and restore the turtle's position and angle. This enables the turtle to draw branches and sub-branches and still be able to return to the previous branch or trunk to continue the drawing. The Bush example consists of two [] pairs which create forked branches. This particular example creates a plant that looks like wind-blown sagebrush.

Parameters Options for Fractal Type Lsystem

Order   2

The order parameter determines how deeply Winfract will apply the character string substitutions. The deeper the level, the more detailed the image. With each level of depth the time required to generate the image is squared. If an image takes 10 minutes to draw at level 6 it will take 100 minutes to draw at level 7 and 10,000 minutes at level 8.

The L-system code is new to Winfract, so you're swimming in uncharted territory. Other L-systems to try are the following:

```
ColorTriangleGasket {
    Angle 6
    Axiom -- X
    X=++FXF++FXF++FXF>1
    F=FF
}
```

```
SierpinskiSquare {
    Angle 4
    Axiom F+F+F+F
    F=FF+F+F+F+FF
}
```

Winfract's Source Code

The complete source code for Winfract is included on your *Fractals for Windows* companion disk. This chapter will show you how to extract it from the distribution disk, rebuild (assuming you have an appropriate compiler) the executable file from the source code, and modify the source files to add your own fractal types.

Let's get the caveats out of the way first: The Winfract source code is not the best place to look if your goal is to learn how to build Windows applications. For one thing, Winfract's source code is massive. This is a huge program, including well over 1MB of C source. For another, Winfract's source code is the collective work of many programmers from around the world, with the wide variety of programming styles one would expect of such an effort. For a third, Winfract was originally developed as a Windows port of an MS-DOS-based program, and reflects that heritage. As such, it is not the best template to use for a design-it-from-scratch Windows application (as a port of an MS-DOS-based program, on the other hand, it's a far better reference). Finally, there are a number of other excellent reference books already in the marketplace that address the novice

Windows programmer's needs, with source code examples targeted for that audience. Having gotten the caveats out of the way....

If you are a programmer, you are probably curious about the coding magic in Winfract's innards. This chapter will give you directions about where to start exploring. It covers four topics. First, it describes the basic steps needed to extract the source code from the companion disk and rebuild Winfract using the popular Borland and Microsoft compilers. Next, it briefly describes the various source code files in an effort to help you find particular code segments that you may be interested in. Third, it describes the C language structure that contains the core information about all the different Winfract fractal types. Finally, it walks you through adding several different fractal types to Winfract.

EXTRACTING THE SOURCE FILES

The source code to Winfract is stored on your distribution floppy disk inside a file called WINSRC.EXE. WINSRC.EXE is a self-extracting archive file, a special type of MS-DOS program that contains other programs stored in compressed form inside it. To obtain Winfract's source code in a usable form, first set up an appropriate directory on your hard disk. This directory is referred to here as C:\WINSRC, although you can name it anything you like. Then make that new directory your current one, insert your Winfract distribution disk into your floppy disk drive, and run the WINSRC program from the DOS prompt. WINSRC will extract all of the appropriate source files from its innards and deposit them onto your current directory.

```
C:> MD \WINSRC(ENTER)
C:> CD \WINSRC(ENTER)
C:> A:\WINSRC(ENTER)
```

REBUILDING WINFRACT

You will need to have access to an appropriate C compiler in order to rebuild Winfract from its source files. Instructions for using several such compilers are in the next few paragraphs. Other environments may work as well, but we can't vouch for them. Although several of the source modules to Winfract are written in assembler, you don't need an assembler unless you intend to modify them. Current object files for all of the assembler modules have been included with the source files.

Microsoft C 7.0

(Alternately, you can use Microsoft C 6.0 along with either the Windows 3.0 or 3.1 Software Development Kit.) The source files include a

WINFRACT.MAK file that will rebuild Winfract for you and a short MAKEWIN.BAT file that invokes it. WINFRACT.MAK, as distributed, assumes that you are using Microsoft C 7.0 and the Windows 3.1 SDK. If you're using Microsoft C 6.0 and/or version 3.0 of the SDK, you will have to edit WINFRACT.MAK to activate the 'DEFINE' statements, (see the following code) for those products at the beginning of that file.

```
#
#  If you are using MSC 6.0 and/or the Windows 3.0 SDK,
#  un-comment one or more of the following:
#
# MSC6 = YES
# SDK30 = YES

# un-comment the following for debugging:
# DEBUG = YES
```

Microsoft's QuickC for Windows, Version 1.0

The source files include a QCWINFRA.MAK file that will rebuild Winfract using this product. Just start up QuickC for Windows, select the PROJECT / NEW option, use the DIRECTORIES box to select your C:\WINSRC directory, replace the *.MAK name in the FILE NAME entry with QCWINFRA.MAK, and then select PROJECT / BUILD. After the build has completed, either select RUN / GO to run Winfract directly from QuickC, or just run the executable file directly as you do all of the other WinApps you build using QuickC.

Note that, according to QuickC for Windows conventions, QCWINFRA.MAK builds a program called QCWINFRA.EXE. (The authors used this alternate name for the QuickC Makefile because we had already used the filename WINFRACT.MAK for the Microsoft C 7.0 development environment and wanted to avoid filename conflicts on the distribution disk.) Also, note that this process does not automatically build WINFRACT.HLP from the supplied WINFRACT.RTF. Microsoft's Help Compiler, which is distributed separately as an option to QuickC for Windows, performs that function. If you have purchased the help compiler option to QuickC for Windows, you can build WINFRACT.HLP using the command hc winfract.

Borland's C++ for Windows

The source files include a WINFRACT.PRJ file for this product. When you start up your copy of Borland's C++ for Windows using the source directory, it automatically will find the project file for you.

THE SOURCE FILES

Winfract was originally developed as a Windows port of the popular freeware MS-DOS fractal program, Fractint. The concept was to develop a Windows application that combined the power and speed of Fractint with the advantages of the Windows user interface and Windows' use of protected mode.

As such, the Winfract source code can be logically divided into four sections. These sections, and the routines that compose them, are:

• The Windows front-end (user interface) and back-end (display and printing) code. This code handles all of the user interaction and displays, handing off any actual fractal generating functions to the core fractal routines taken from Fractint.

• The "glue" logic, which binds the Fractint-for-DOS routines to the Windows front-end and back-end code.

• The fractal-generating engine code, taken straight from the DOS version of Fractint. Winfract and Fractint use identical source code for their fractal engines. Because of this code sharing, new versions of both programs can be released virtually simultaneously.

• The MS-DOS user interface code, also taken straight from Fractint. Much of this code was not in the original versions of Winfract, but was added later after the ability to display a 25 x 80 text-mode "pop-up" window was added to version 17.2 of Winfract for this purpose.

Figure 6-1 shows the interaction between these main sections of code.

The Windows Front- and Back-End Code

The Windows front-end and back-end routines consist of the following modules:

WINFRACT.RC, WINFRACT.DEF, MATHTOOL.RC, MATHTOOL.DEF, COORD.DLG, ZOOM.DLG

These are fairly standard resource control, definition, and dialog files. The only reason that the Winfract source has multiple resource control and dialog files is because Winfract is quite often being developed by several people at once, and this way the authors tend to trip over each other less frequently.

WINFRACT.C

This is the main routine. WINFRACT.C includes the routines that start up the program and handle the overall menu items. The main message loop is

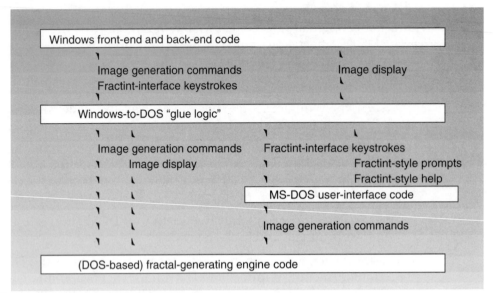

Figure 6-1 Winfract's basic structure

located in MainWndProc() in this module. After initializing its environment, the startup routines in WINFRACT.C invoke the fractint_main() module (found in MAINFRAC.C) to begin generating an initial fractal image.

WINFRACT.C communicates with the fractal engine from that point on using global variables. The time_to_restart flag, for instance, is used to order the fractal-generating routines to abandon their current calculations and begin a new image because the user has just done something major like select a new fractal type. The time_to_quit flag is used to order the fractal engine to shut down and return to the main routine which called it so that Winfract itself can terminate.

WINFRACT.C also handles updating the displayed fractal image (which is stored internally as a device-independent bitmap) whenever it receives a WM_PAINT request. Although this module sure *looked* complicated to its authors back when it was first written, it's really fairly standard WinApp code.

DIALOG.C, DIALOG2.C
These are the primary dialog functions. DIALOG.C is smaller and contains mostly file selection code based on the sample programs in the Windows 3.0 Software Development Toolkit. DIALOG2.C contains most of the fractal-specific (and Winfract-specific) dialogs.

As with WINFRACT.C, these routines are fairly standard WinApp code and communicate with the fractal-generation code by setting global variables. This communication is indirect. These routines are called by the main message loop in WINFRACT.C and return with a TRUE result if the user presses the OK button or FALSE if the user presses CANCEL. The code in WINFRACT.C then handles the actual communication with the fractal engine routines.

MATHTOOL.C
This module contains the zoom-box, window-sizing, and coordinate-display routines invoked when you specify the use of any of these options. As with the routines in DIALOG.C and DIALOG2.C, these routines communicate indirectly with the code in the fractal engine, leaving the direct communication with these routines to the code in WINFRACT.C.

SELECT.C
This module contains routines which select bitmap regions, and it is based on the sample programs provided as part of the Windows 3.0 Software Development Toolkit. It is used by the zoom-box logic to draw and update the zoom-box displays.

PROFILE.C
This module contains the routines which read and modify the Winfract-specific section of your SSTOOLS.INI file. The Fractint-specific section of SSTOOLS.INI is processed by CMDFILES.C. The initialization logic in WINFRACT.C calls the InitializeParameters() routine in this module to read the SSTOOLS.INI file, and calls the SaveParameters() and SaveParamSwitch() routines whenever a setting is changed and that file needs to be updated.

WINTEXT.C
This module contains routines that handle a special 25 x 80 text-mode pop-up window. WINTEXT.C is used to handle the text-mode help and prompting routines brought over from the MS-DOS code. This module was written so as to be easily extracted from the Winfract source and used by other Windows applications. The initialization code in WINFRACT.C calls the wintext_initialize() routine in this module once to set up the text window and calls the wintext_destroy() routine when Winfract is shutting down. All other interaction with this text window is handled by the glue-logic module WINDOS2.C.

WINFRACT.RTF, MATHTOOL.RTF
These routines contain the RTF (Rich Text Format) source used by the Help Compiler to generate the WINFRACT.HLP help file.

WINFRACT.H, DIALOG2.H, MATHTOOL.H
These are include files of common definitions. WINFRACT.H includes those definitions of interest to all of the Windows-specific modules, while the other two files include definitions of interest only to their respective C modules and the resource control files.

The Windows/Fractals Glue-Logic
The Windows glue-logic routines consist of the following modules:

MAINFRAC.C
The routines in this module are handled as subroutines by the startup code in WINFRACT.C, but look like the Main program to the fractal engine code taken from Fractint. The primary routine in this module is fractint_main(). Fractint_main() is called by WINFRACT.C as soon as that module has finished initializing its environment, and returns only when the Windows front-end code has indicated to it (by setting the time_to_quit global variable) that Winfract is shutting down.

Fractint_main() contains the main fractal engine control loop that initializes all the fractal variables and invokes the fractal engine logic taken from the MS-DOS-based Fractint code. The DOS-based fractal engine code returns to this control loop whenever a call to the keypressed() routine (described below) returns a nonzero value indicating to it that the (MS-DOS) user has pressed a key on the keyboard. The main control loop then takes the appropriate action based on the status of the time_to_... flags that have been set by the Windows front-end code, and then either resumes or restarts the fractal image.

Depending on the function to be performed, the routines in this module call either modules from Fractint (e.g., save-to-GIF) or Windows-specific code (e.g., save-to-BMP) to handle it.

WINDOS.C
This routine handles most of the service calls that the fractal engine code invokes to handle what it thinks of as the MS-DOS keyboard, screen, and printer activity. A great deal of the glue-logic magic is performed here.

The keypressed() routine is called periodically by the fractal engine code to see if what it thinks of as the MS-DOS user has pressed a key. In the MS-DOS-based Fractint program, this routine just checks the keyboard to see if any activity has occurred and returns either the keypress value or zero if there is no activity to report. The keypressed() routine in WINDOS.C calls PeekMessage() to check the Windows-interface code for any user activity, handles any such activity that exists, examines the state of the various time_to_... flags that result, and returns those results as keypresses to the calling programs. The getakey() routine performs the same function, but doesn't return until some such activity has occurred.

The fractal engine code writes and reads back what it thinks of as pixels on the MS-DOS user's screen by invoking the putcolor(), getcolor(), put_line(), and get_line() routines. In the MS-DOS-based Fractint program, that's just what happens. These routines in WINDOS.C actually perform these functions on a Device-Independent Bitmap, periodically ordering the main display routines in WINFRACT to update its image window using this DIB. This bitmap is used for the printing and clipboard routines as well.

There are a number of other glue-logic routines in WINDOS.C as well. The win_print() routine handles all printer access, while the win_cycle() routine handles the color cycling. Stopmsg() handles the messages from the fractal engine as Windows-style message boxes.

Finally, WINDOS.C also contains a number of do-nothing routines (such as the ..._overlay() routines that assist with Fractint-for-DOS's overlay structure) that allow the authors to copy over the Fractint-for-DOS modules as-is without editing them.

WINDOS2.C

This routine handles the interface between the DOS-based help and prompting routines and the 25 x 80 pop-up text window provided by WINTEXT.C. In the MS-DOS-based Fractint program, the setfortext() and setforgraphics() routines switch the screen from graphics to text mode and back, saving and restoring the graphics screen image as necessary. These routines in WINDOS2.C invoke appropriate routines in WINTEXT.C to pop up Winfract's 25 x 80 text window and bring it back down. Other routines such as movecursor() and putstring() perform their functions on that 25 x 80 text window rather than the MS-DOS screen.

WGENERAL.ASM

This is a small assembler module that includes the scaled 32-bit-integer multiply and divide routines. It is all that is left from a much larger set of assembler routines that handle the low-level physical activity of the MS-DOS world in the Fractint code.

The Fractal-Generating Code

The core fractal-generating routines are common to both Winfract and its MS-DOS-based cousin Fractint. These routines consist of the following modules:

FRACTINT.H

This is an include file of common definitions.

FRACTALP.C, FRACTYPE.H

FRACTALP.C contains a single, fractal-specific structure containing information about each of the fractal types included in Winfract—in fact, the only items that most of the other modules know about the fractal types in Winfract are contained in this structure. Because of its importance to the rest of the program, the fractal-specific structure is described in more detail in the next section.

CALCFRAC.C

CALCFRAC.C contains the code for the basic fractal engine and its general algorithms. Calcfract() is the fractal engine entry point called by the main fractal loop in MAINFRAC.C, and it oversees the remainder of the fractal engine code. Calcfract() scans the fractalspecific structure (described in the next section) for any fractal-specific information, initializes its pointers accordingly, and invokes whichever fractal routine that structure states should generate that image.

CALCFRAC.C also contains most of the routines that handle the core fractal types. StandardFractal(), for example, is the general escape-time fractal image generator and handles most of the options specific to escape-time fractals, such as the inside and outside options. Bifurcation() performs the same function for the various bifurcation fractals. Plasma() generates plasma cloud images.

CALCFRAC.C also contains the routines handling many of the general fractal-related algorithms. The solidguess(), boundary_trace(), and tesseral() routines are found here.

FRACSUBR.C

FRACSUBR.C contains service routines invoked by the startup fractal code in MAINFRAC.C and the core fractal code in CALCFRAC.C. It's actually an overflow module that was created when CALCFRAC.C grew too large for many of the popular MS-DOS-based compilers.

The most important routine by far in this module is calcfracinit(), which is called by MAINFRAC.C prior to starting any fractal image. Calcfracinit() determines whether or not an image has been zoomed too deep for its integer algorithm (and if so, switches to its floating-point equivalent algorithm), determines the actual image corners, fills up coordinate arrays determining the location of every pixel, and initializes a few coordinate-related variables.

FRACTALS.C

FRACTALS.C contains most of the fractal-specific code for the escape-time fractals. The fractal-specific functions for the Lambda fractal, (a standard escape-time fractal using the formula $z(n + 1) = Lambda \times z(n) \times (1 - n - z(n)\^2)$ are located in FRACTALS.C.

FRACSUBA.ASM

FRACSUBA.ASM contains several general service routines that have been moved into assembler for speed. Every routine in this module was at one time a small C routine in FRACTALS.C.

CALCMAND.ASM, CALMANFP.ASM

These are the Mandelbrot/Julia set routines, hand-tuned in assembler for the last ounce of speed. When folks compare the speed of various fractal programs, they're almost invariably discussing how fast those programs generate a Mandelbrot fractal. There are far more readable (but slower) C versions of these same fractal types in the core fractal engine.

NEWTON.ASM, LORENZ.C, JB.C, PARSER.C, TESTPT.C, LSYS.C, LSYSA.ASM

These routines handle the Newton, Lorenz, JuliBrot, Formula, test, and L-Systems fractal types respectively. These fractal types either didn't fit into the core fractal engine structure or, as with the Mandelbrot/Julia routines above, were hand-coded for speed.

MPMATH_C.C, MPMATH_A.ASM, MPMATH.H

These MP (Mark Peterson's) math routines handle floating-point mathematics using integer exponent/mantissa pairs.

FPU087.ASM, FPU387.ASM

These are customized floating-point math operations, written in assembler for speed.

The MS-DOS Interface Code

The MS-DOS interface routines are common to both Winfract and its MS-DOS-based cousin, Fractint. These routines, which are the MS-DOS-based routines not directly involved in the actual calculation of fractal images, consist of the following modules:

CMDFILES.C

The routines in this module handle startup parameters, as specified either on the startup command line, the fractint section of your SSTOOLS.INI file, or any parameter files being processed. The parameters in the Winfract section of that file are handled by the PROFILE.C routine.

HELP.C, HELPDEFS.H

This module and its include file handles Fractint's online help engine (which is different from the Winfract/Windows help engine, and is invoked when you press (CTRL)-(F1)).

PROMPTS.C

The routines in this module handle Fractint's full-screen prompting logic, and are invoked when you set the hotkey option to Fractint-style screens.

PLOT3D.C, 3D.C, LINE3D.C

The routines in these modules handle Winfract's 3-D capabilities as invoked by the 3-D and 3-D Overlay functions.

ENCODER.C, DECODER.C, LOADFILE.C, GIFVIEW.C, TGAVIEW.C, F16.C

The routines in these modules handle the GIF and TARGA file loading and saving capabilities of Winfract and Fractint. Winfract's Save-to-BMP capabilities are handled separately in WINDOS.C.

MISCRES.C, MISCOVL.C

The routines in these modules are routines from the Fractint-for-DOS program that literally didn't fit anywhere else. In fact, many of the routines in these modules are never called in the Winfract version of the program, but some of them are, and it is far easier to copy these modules from one environment to the other as-is, rather than reconvert them every time either program is updated.

THE FRACTAL-SPECIFIC STRUCTURE

The fractal-specific structure in FRACTALP.C contains all of the information most of the modules in Winfract need to know about fractals. Even the main fractal engine code uses that structure to access any routines that are specific to any fractal type.

The fractal-specific structure and the definitions of the flag bits that are included in it are located in the FRACTINT.H include file. Fractal types are added to Winfract simply by adding any new routines required to generate the fractal types to the basic fractal engine and then adding new entries to this structure describing the fractal types and pointing to the routines which generate them. In the next section, we'll go through this process, adding several new fractal types to Winfract.

Listing 6-1 shows the layout of the fractal-specific structure and its related flag values. Listing 6-2 shows the fractal-specific entries and related variables for the Mandelbrot/Julia family of fractals.

Listing 6-1 Winfract's fractal-specific structure and related flags

```
struct fractalspecificstuff
{
    char  *name;                /* name of the fractal */
    char  *param[4];            /* name of the parameters */
    float paramvalue[4];        /* default parameter values */
```

```
    int    helptext;              /* helpdefs.h HT_xxxx, -1 for none */
    int    helpformula;           /* helpdefs.h HF_xxxx, -1 for none */
    int    flags;                 /* constraints */
    float  xmin;                  /* default XMIN corner */
    float  xmax;                  /* default XMAX corner */
    float  ymin;                  /* default YMIN corner */
    float  ymax;                  /* default YMAX corner */
    int    isinteger;             /* 1 if integerfractal, 0 otherwise */
    int    tojulia;               /* mandel-to-julia switch */
    int    tomandel;              /* julia-to-mandel switch */
    int    tofloat;               /* integer-to-floating switch */
    int    symmetry;              /* applicable symmetry logic */
    int (*orbitcalc)();           /* function that calculates one orbit */
    int (*per_pixel)();           /* once-per-pixel init */
    int (*per_image)();           /* once-per-image setup */
    int (*calctype)();            /* name of main fractal function */
    int    orbit_bailout;         /* usual bailout value for orbit calc */
} ;

/* defines for symmetry */
#define  NOSYM          0         /* no symmetry at all */
#define  XAXIS_NOPARM  -1         /* X-axis symmetry if no parameters
                                     are given */
#define  XAXIS          1         /* X-axis symmetry */
#define  YAXIS_NOPARM  -2         /* Y-axis symmetry if no parameters
                                     are given */
#define  YAXIS          2         /* Y-axis symmetry */
#define  XYAXIS_NOPARM -3         /* XY-axis symmetry if no
                                     parameters are given */
#define  XYAXIS         3         /* XY-axis symmetry */
#define  ORIGIN_NOPARM -4         /* Origin symmetry if no parameters
                                     are given */
#define  ORIGIN         4         /* Origin symmetry */
#define  PI_SYM_NOPARM -5         /* PI symmetry if no parameters
                                     are given */
#define  PI_SYM         5         /* PI symmetry */
#define  XAXIS_NOIMAG  -6         /* X-axis symmetry if param
                                     has no imag component */
#define  XAXIS_NOREAL   6         /* X-axis symmetry if param has no
                                     real component *
#define  SETUP_SYM    100         /* for formula  fractals - symmetry
                                     declared in the file */

/* bitmask defines for fractalspecific flags */
#define  NOZOOM         1         /* zoombox not allowed at all */
#define  NOGUESS        2         /* solid guessing not allowed */
#define  NOTRACE        4         /* boundary tracing not allowed */
#define  NOROTATE       8         /* zoombox rotate/stretch not
                                     allowed */
#define  NORESUME      16         /* can't interrupt and resume */
#define  INFCALC       32         /* this type calculates forever */
#define  TRIG1         64         /* 1 trig function  in formula */
```

```
#define  TRIG2          128      /* 2 trig functions in formula */
#define  TRIG3          192      /* 3 trig functions in formula */
#define  TRIG4          256      /* 4 trig functions in formula */
#define  WINFRAC        512      /* supported in WinFrac */
#define  PARMS3D        1024     /* uses 3d parameters */


#define STDBAILOUT   4.0
#define NOBAILOUT    0.0
```

Listing 6-2 The Mandelbrot/Julia fractal-specific entries

```
#define NOFRACTAL    -1
#define MANDEL        0
#define JULIA         1
#define MANDELFP      4
#define JULIAFP       6

static char realz0[] = "Real Perturbation of Z(0)";
static char imagz0[] = "Imaginary Perturbation of Z(0)";
static char realparm[] = "Real Part of Parameter";
static char imagparm[] = "Imaginary Part of Parameter";

struct fractalspecificstuff far fractalspecific[] ={
 /*  fractal name, parameter text strings, parameter values,
     helptext, helpformula, flags, xmin  xmax  ymin  ymax int
     tojulia   tomandel tofloat  symmetry orbit fnct     per_pixel
     fnct  per_image fnct  calctype fcnt     bailout   */

   "mandel",       realz0, imagz0,"","",0,0,0,0,
   HT_MANDEL, HF_MANDEL, WINFRAC,
   -2.5,  1.5, -1.5,  1.5, 1, JULIA,      NOFRACTAL, MANDELFP,
   XAXIS_NOPARM,
   JuliaFractal, mandel_per_pixel,MandelSetup,StandardFractal, STDBAILOUT,

   "julia",        realparm, imagparm,"","",0.3,0.6,0,0,
   HT_JULIA, HF_JULIA, WINFRAC,
   -2.0,  2.0, -1.5,  1.5, 1, NOFRACTAL, MANDEL, JULIAFP,  ORIGIN,
   JuliaFractal,  julia_per_pixel, JuliaSetup,StandardFractal, STDBAILOUT,
...
   "*mandel",      realz0, imagz0,"","",0,0,0,0,
   HT_MANDEL, HF_MANDEL, WINFRAC,
   -2.5,  1.5, -1.5,  1.5, 0, JULIAFP,  NOFRACTAL, MANDEL,
   XAXIS_NOPARM,
   JuliafpFractal,mandelfp_per_pixel, MandelfpSetup,StandardFractal, STDBAILOUT,
...
   "*julia",       realparm, imagparm,"","",0.3,0.6,0,0,
   HT_JULIA, HF_JULIA, WINFRAC,
   -2.0,  2.0, -1.5,  1.5, 0, NOFRACTAL, MANDELFP, JULIA,  ORIGIN,
   JuliafpFractal, juliafp_per_pixel, JuliafpSetup,StandardFractal,STDBAILOUT,
```

The Winfract modules that handle the user interface are interested in the following fractalspecific items (the items are not necessarily listed in the order in which they appear in the structure):

name

This is the name of the fractal type. Fractal names can be up to 16 characters long and cannot include spaces. If a particular fractal type has both integer and floating-point algorithms, it has two structure entries. In such cases, one of the entries has a leading '*' in the name field (note that there's a 'mandel' and a '*mandel' entry in Listing 6-2), which the display routines use as a flag indicating that this entry is a duplicate that should not be displayed for user-selection purposes. In these cases, each entry contains flags indicating which type it is (isinteger) and pointing towards its alternative (tofloat) so Winfract can select the appropriate entry automatically.

param[4], paramvalue[4]

These entries contain the names and default values of up to four optional parameters. Fractal types with less than four parameters have null entries in the name fields that aren't relevant. Parameter names should be kept under 40 characters long just so that they'll fit in the dialog boxes. The Mandelbrot/Julia family of fractals all accept two parameters.

xmin, xmax, ymin, ymax

These are the corner values of the default image that is displayed when this fractal type is first selected.

flags

This field contains a bitmask of flags which the Winfract modules query to determine the capabilities and limitations of this fractal type. These flags and their values are detailed in Listing 6-1. Although many of the entries in this field are of interest only to the routines which actually generate the fractal, some of them are of interest to the other modules as well. In particular, the presence of the WINFRAC flag indicates that Winfract has the capability to generate this fractal type. Currently, only the "test" fractal type (a test-mode fractal type of no interest to the nondeveloper) is missing this WINFRAC flag. The Mandelbrot/Julia family of fractals all use only the WINFRAC flag.

helptext, helpformula

These entries contain pointers (defined in HELPDEFS.H) to locations in Fractint's help file describing this particular fractal type. They are not used by Winfract's Windows-style help engine, as that help engine is not currently keyed to the currently selected fractal type. A −1 indicates that no Fractint-style HELP reference is available. When you add fractal types to Winfract, use a value of −1 for these fields.

tojulia, tomandel
These fields contain the entry number of the Julia or Mandelbrot fractals matching this fractal type if any such fractal types exist. These entry numbers are coded as #defines in FRACTYPE.H. Note in Listing 6-2 how the Mandelbrot and Julia set entries point to each other. The main message loop in WINFRACT.C uses these flags when the user requests a Mandelbrot/Julia switch.

The Winfract modules that actually generate the fractal image are interested in the following fractal-specific items (the items are not necessarily listed in the order in which they appear in the structure):

isinteger
This field is nonzero if this fractal type uses an integer algorithm, and zero if this fractal type uses floating point. Many of the fractal types, including the Mandelbrot/Julia fractals in Listing 6-2 have two entries—one of each.

tofloat
This field contains the entry number of the fractal type which is the integer or floating-point equivalent to this one (the name is misleading, as this may be a floating-point fractal type pointing to its integer equivalent). A zero in this entry indicates that there is no such equivalent. Note in Listing 6-2 how the Mandelbrot and Julia set entries point to their sister entries. The calcfracinit() routine in FRACSUBR.C uses this and the isinteger flag to automatically (and silently) select the fractal type appropriate to the user's preference and the current zooming depth (floating-point fractal types can zoom in farther than their integer equivalents). When using fractal types that have only one entry (plasma clouds, for example, have no floating-point equivalent), Winfract uses that one algorithm regardless of any preference the user has indicated on the FLOATING-POINT setting in the FRACTALS / BASIC OPTIONS dialog box.

symmetry
Many fractal types are symmetrical in some respect, and Winfract's fractal engine can recognize and handle many different kinds of symmetry. Listing 6-1 includes an annotated listing of all the symmetry types currently recognized by Winfract. The Mandelbrot fractal, for example, is symmetrical along the x-axis as long as none of its optional parameters has been set to a nonzero value. The Julia fractal is symmetrical about the origin. If a particular fractal type has symmetrical properties, they are indicated here.

flags

This field of bitmasked flags, already mentioned above, also contains a number of flags of interest to the code that actually generates fractals. Some fractal types, for example, don't work correctly with the solid-guessing and/or boundary-tracing options, so the fractal engine must ignore the user's preferences for those options when generating those fractal types. Listing 6-1 includes an annotated listing of the bitmasked flags contained in this field.

orbit_bailout

For escape-time fractal types, this is the comparison value that is used by default to detect that an iteration has escaped from the fractal set. For the Mandelbrot fractals, this value is 4, as the calculation of the fractal ends when the value of $(Z(n)**2)$ is greater than 4. For non-escape-time fractals, this field is meaningless, and is usually set to NOBAILOUT (0.0) as an indicator of that fact.

The four following entries are pointers to functions, and are used by the fractal engine to connect the fractal type to any fractal-specific code it requires. None of these routines is called with any parameters (they all use global variables instead for speed). All return values, although in some cases those values are ignored.

per_image()

This is a pointer to a function specific to this fractal type that handles any initialization that must be taken care of on a "per-image" basis. The per_image() function returns a value of 0 if it has completed the fractal image on its own, or returns a nonzero value if the main fractal engine should continue by calling the calctype() function (described in the next bullet).

Fractal types such as the plasma, IFS, and L-system fractals, which use completely unique calculation logic, traditionally point to the standard StandaloneSetup() routine here and then point to their custom routine in the calctype() pointer, described in the next bullet. Standalone-Setup() calls a routine which starts a timer and then calls the calctype() routine for this fractal type. StandaloneSetup() always returns a 0 to indicate that the calculation process is completed.

The common escape-time fractal types usually point to one of several standard initialization routines. These routines initialize a few variables and handle special cases that affect items like symmetry. The Mandelbrot and Julia fractals, for instance, determine at this point whether they can use their fast assembler algorithms or have to use slower C-based algorithms because some option, such as biomorphs or decomposition, is in effect which the fast assembler algorithms cannot handle. The four most commonly used initialization routines for escape-time fractals are

MandellongSetup(), MandelfpSetup(), JulialongSetup(), and JuliafpSetup(), which handle generic Mandelbrot and Julia-style fractals for the integer and floating-point algorithms, respectively.

Listing 6-8 lists the MandellongSetup() routine used by many of the integer Mandelbrot-like escape-time fractals (and Listing 6-9 shows what this routine would look like without all of its special-case logic).

calctype()

This is a pointer to a function that handles the overall fractal calculation. For some fractal types (plasma clouds, IFS, and L-system fractals, for example), this function is specific to the fractal type and handles the entire image with a single call.

For all of the escape-time fractals, this item points to the StandardFractal() routine. The core fractal logic in CALCFRAC.C recognizes the StandardFractal() entry as being the escape-time fractal routine. When it sees that StandardFractal() is specified as the calctype() entry, the core fractal logic switches to its escape-time logic, enables its escape-time options such as solid-guessing and boundary-tracing, and calls StandardFractal() once for each pixel. The StandardFractal() routine handles the per-pixel options like biomorphs, decomposition, inside and outside colors, and calls the per_pixel() and orbitcalc() functions described in the next two bullets to do the actual work of performing any fractal-specific calculations.

The calctype() routine returns a zero to indicate that it completed the image, or a nonzero value to indicate that it didn't. This returned value is used by the core fractal engine logic to tag the image as being complete or incomplete. StandardFractal() is a special case, and returns the color of the pixel it has just calculated to the escape-time fractal routines that called it (information that the solid-guessing, boundary-tracing, and tesseral algorithms need).

Of all the routines specified in the fractal-specific array, the calctype() routine is by far the most complex for non-escape-time fractals; it's often the only routine specific to the fractal type. If you are adding an escape-time fractal algorithm to Winfract, you must use StandardFractal(). On the other hand, if you're adding a fractal type that is completely unlike anything Winfract currently features, the combination of this entry point and the per_image() one gives you the ability to do so.

per_pixel()

This is a pointer to a function called by StandardFractal() that handles any fractal-specific initialization that must be taken care of on a per-pixel basis (usually pre-calculating $z(0)$). Many escape-time fractal types share common per_pixel() routines, although writing your own is easily done.

Listing 6-11 lists simple per_pixel() routines for integer and floating-point Mandelbrot and Julia fractals. StandardFractal() ignores any value returned by this routine.

Non-escape-time fractal types are free to use this function pointer for their own purposes. Usually, their fractalspecific entries for this function pointer are just set to NULL.

orbitcalc()

This is a pointer to a function called by StandardFractal() that handles a single orbit (iteration) calculation. This function calculates $z(n + 1)$ given the value of $z(n)$, and is often the only routine that is specific to a particular family of escape-time fractal types. This routine returns 0 if the new value has not reached its bailout limit, or 1 if it has. Listing 6-12 lists the orbitcalc() routines used for integer and floating-point Mandelbrot and Julia fractals.

Non-escape-time fractal types are free to use this function pointer for their own purposes. Usually, their fractalspecific entries for this function pointer are just set to NULL.

ADDING NEW FRACTAL TYPES

Let's put all the claims about adding new fractals to Winfract to a test by actually doing it. We're going to add two different kinds of fractals to Winfract.

First, we're going to add a new stand-alone fractal type to Winfract—a simple drunkard's walk. We'll also give this fractal type the ability to generate Mandelbrot images, even though you'd normally generate Mandelbrot fractals using the escape-time fractal engine.

Then, we're going to add a family of four escape-time fractal types—integer and floating-point versions of two fractal types that form a Mandelbrot/Julia pair. In fact, our new fractals are going to be the familiar Mandelbrot and Julia sets.

By the time we have added these fractals, we'll have covered all the basic concepts of adding fractal types to Winfract.

Let's admit to a little cheating here. The entries you have to add are already in their relevant modules. They've just been commented out so as not to show up in the distributed Winfract executable. When the text tells you to add these entries to the relevant modules, all you really have to do is remove the start (/*) and end (*/) of the comments. Nothing eliminates typing errors quite as efficiently as eliminating the typing itself.

Adding Stand-Alone Fractals

Now let's add our stand-alone, drunkard's walk fractal (with its Mandelbrot option) to Winfract.

Adding Entries to the FRACTYPE.H File

The first thing you have to do when adding new fractal types to Winfract is to add their definitions in the FRACTYPE.H file. These definitions point to the fractal's locations in the fractal-specific file. For many fractal types, these definitions are only used in the fractal-specific structure, and in the case of our drunkard's walk fractal, this definition is never actually going to be used anywhere at all. Nevertheless, it's a good practice to always add the definition to FRACTYPE.H so that all of the fractal types are defined in one place. For one thing, it's quite confusing when you're adding fractal types if the last entry in this list isn't also the last entry in the fractal-specific array. The value of this entry will be the location of the entry you will be adding to the end of the fractal-specific structure. You'll need a single entry for the drunkard's walk fractal:

```
#define DEMOWALK              127
```

Adding Eentries to the Fractal-Specific Structure

Having added the entry for this new fractal type to our list in FRACTYPE.H, add its entry to the end of the fractal-specific array in FRACTALP.C, just before the NULL entry indicating the end of the list. (In this case, add the entry just before the four new escape-time fractal entries that are also commented out just prior to the NULL entry. We'll discuss them in the next section.) Listing 6-3 shows the new entry you need to add.

Listing 6-3 The fractal-specific entry for drunkard's walk

```
"demowalk", "Average Stepsize (% of image)",
"Color (0 means rotate colors)","","",5,0.0,0,0,
-1, -1,NORESUME+WINFRAC,
-2.5, 1.5, -1.5, 1.5, 0, NOFRACTAL, NOFRACTAL, NOFRACTAL, NOSYM,
NULL, NULL, StandaloneSetup, demowalk, NOBAILOUT,
```

Refer to Listings 6-1 and 6-2 as we examine this fractal-specific entry (they include the definitions of all of the flags it uses). The fractal type's name, used whenever Winfract needs to identify this fractal type for the user, is "demowalk." This fractal type accepts two optional parameters: an average stepsize expressed as a percentage of the image size, and the color used to display the walk. The first parameter (the stepsize) defaults to 5%, and the second (the color) defaults to zero (the fractal will rotate through all available colors as it walks).

Helptext and helpformula are –1, as this fractal type is not related to any fractint-style help text. This fractal uses two fractal-specific flags. NORESUME indicates that this fractal type is not resumable. If we save one of its images in the middle of a calculation and reload it later, this fractal type doesn't contain any special logic letting it resume its calculations where they left off (the escape-time fractal types rely on logic inside the standard escape-time fractal engine to perform this task). The WINFRAC flag signals that Winfract can invoke this fractal type.

The screen corners are –2.5,1.5,–1.5,1.5, the standard, slightly off-center corner values that display the initial Mandelbrot image well. Isinteger is zero, indicating that this fractal type is a floating-point fractal and the core fractal engine should set up floating-point pixel coordinates when calling it. This fractal has no Julia equivalent, Mandelbrot equivalent, or integer/floating-point equivalent, so those entries are all NOFRACTAL. This fractal has no symmetry (NOSYM).

The demowalk fractal follows the convention of the stand-alone fractal types: the per_image() function points to StandaloneSetup(), the calctype() function points to demowalk's own fractal-specific routine, and the per_pixel() and orbitcalc() functions are unused and set to NULL as an indicator of that fact. Its bailout value has been set to NOBAILOUT because the user can't change the bailout value of its simple Mandelbrot function.

Once you've added (or removed the comments from) these entries in FRACTYPE.H and FRACTALP.C, rebuild Winfract and run it again. You now have a new fractal type, demowalk.

The calctype() Routine

As is the convention with the stand-alone fractal types, the calctype() function is the one that does all the work. Listing 6-4 contains a listing of the demowalk() function found in FRACTALS.C.

Listing 6-4 The demowalk() fractal generation routine

```
demowalk()
{
    extern double param[];       /* optional user parameters */
    extern int maxit;            /* maximum iterations (steps) */
    extern int rflag, rseed;     /* random number seed */
    extern int xdots, ydots;     /* image coordinates */
    extern int colors;           /* maximum colors available */
    extern double far *dx0, far *dy0;  /* arrays of pixel coordinates */
    extern double far *dx1, far *dy1;  /* (... for skewed zoom-boxes) */

    float stepsize;              /* average stepsize */
    int xwalk, ywalk;            /* current position */
    int xstep, ystep;            /* current step */
    int steps;                   /* number of steps */
    int color;                   /* color to draw this step */
    float temp, tempadjust;       /* temporary variables */

if (param[0] != 999) {           /* if 999, do a Mandelbrot instead */

    srand(rseed);                /* seed the random number generator */
    if (!rflag) ++rseed;
    tempadjust = RAND_MAX >> 2;  /* adjustment factor */
```

```
    xwalk = xdots / 2;   /* start in the center of the image */
    ywalk = ydots / 2;

    stepsize = min(xdots, ydots)    /* calculate average stepsize */
            * (param[0]/100.0);   /* as a percentage of
                                        the image */

    color = max(0, min(colors, param[1]));      /* set the initial
                                                    color */

    for (steps = 0; steps < maxit; steps++) {  /* take maxit steps */
        if (keypressed())  /* abort if told to do so */
            return(0);
        temp = rand();      /* calculate the next xstep */
        xstep = ((temp/tempadjust) - 2.0) * stepsize;
        xstep = min(xwalk + xstep, xdots - 1);
        xstep = max(0, xstep);
        temp = rand();       /* calculate the next ystep */
        ystep = ((temp/tempadjust) - 2.0) * stepsize;
        ystep = min(ywalk + ystep, ydots - 1);
        ystep = max(0, ystep);
        if (param[1] == 0.0)  /* rotate the colors? */
            if (++color >= colors)  /* rotate the colors, avoiding */
                color = 1;          /* the background color 0 */
        /* the draw_line function is borrowed from the 3D routines */
        draw_line(xwalk, ywalk,xstep,ystep,color);
        /* or, we could be on a pogo stick and just displaying
           where we landed...
        putcolor(xstep, ystep, color);
        */

        xwalk = xstep;                  /* remember where we were */
        ywalk = ystep;
        }
    return(1);                          /* we're done */

} else {                                /* a simple Mandelbrot routine */

    /* the following routine determines the X and Y values of
       each pixel coordinate and calculates a simple mandelbrot
       fractal with them - slowly, but surely */
    int ix, iy;
    for (iy = 0; iy < ydots; iy++) {
        for (ix = 0; ix < xdots; ix++) {
            int iter;
            double x, y, newx, newy, tempxx, tempxy, tempyy;
            /* first, obtain the X and Y coordinate values of
               this pixel */
            x = dx0[ix]+dx1[iy];
            y = dy0[iy]+dy1[ix];
            /* now initialize the temporary values */
            tempxx = tempyy = tempxy = 0.0;
```

```
        if (keypressed())   /* abort if told to do so */
            return(0);
        /* the inner iteration loop */
        for (iter = 1; iter < maxit; iter++) {
            /* calculate the X and Y values of Z(iter) */
            newx = tempxx - tempyy + x;
            newy = tempxy + tempxy + y;
            /* calculate the temporary values */
            tempxx = newx * newx;
            tempyy = newy * newy;
            tempxy = newx * newy;
            /* are we done yet? */
            if (tempxx + tempyy > 4.0) break;
            }
        /* color in the pixel */
        putcolor(ix, iy, iter & (colors - 1));
        }
    }
return(1);                      /* we're done */
    }


}
```

Let's walk through this routine line-by-line to see what functions a stand-alone fractal type has to perform. Stand-alone routines, because they have no general fractal engine overseeing their function as the escape-time fractals do, have to handle more functions on their own (like updating the actual image and worrying about whether the user is frantically banging on the keyboard attempting to bring up a spreadsheet before the boss arrives).

The first seven lines reference global variables that demowalk( ) needs to access to perform its function. Param[ ] is an array holding up to four optional parameter values, either the default values from the fractal-specific entry or their revised values as modified by the user. Maxit is the maximum number of iterations (MAXIMUM ITERATIONS in the FRACTALS / BASIC OPTIONS menu). Rflag and rseed are values for the random number generator—using these global values instead of its own lets demowalk( ) take advantage of the "rseed=" command-line parameter in case anyone ever needs to replicate random walks. Xdots and ydots give the resolution of the current image, and colors gives the number of colors in the image. Dx0[ ], dy0[ ], dx1[ ], and dy1[ ] are arrays used to determine the floating-point values of each pixel coordinate on the image. The drunkard's walk section of demowalk( ) doesn't need them, but its Mandelbrot option does (and your fractal types probably will).

The next six lines describe local variables that this fractal type needs for its calculations.

For demonstration purposes, we have arbitrarily set up this fractal type to compute a standard Mandelbrot fractal if the first parameter (the stepsize) has been set to 999. Let's ignore the Mandelbrot option for now and concentrate on the drunkard's walk algorithm.

Next, the executable code seeds the random number generator (and bumps up the seed value so that the next random walk will be different from this random walk). Then the routine sets up its initial xwalk and ywalk values to start its walk in the center of the image.

The next few lines of code reference the user-modifiable parameters, param[0] and param[1]. Param[0] is defined in the demowalk fractal-specific structure as the average stepsize in terms of a percentage of the image. Param[1] is defined as the color to use for the walk. Now the routine is ready to begin its main loop, taking a maximum of maxit steps.

Note the call to keypressed( ) at the beginning of this loop, with a return with a zero value if keypressed( ) returns a value. This logic performs several important functions. First, the keypressed( ) routine calls Windows routines to check the message queue. This gives the poor user and your other Windows applications a chance to get the attention of your CPU and Windows. Without this call, demowalk( ) would make Winfract an unfriendly Windows application that completely ignores both the user and his other WinApps for what could be excessive amounts of time. Second, it gives Winfract the ability to force demowalk( ) to exit early. (Maybe the user fired up the demowalk fractal using a maxit of 20,000 and has decided about 10,000 iterations into the image that he wants to see another fractal type instead.)

The next eight lines perform a fairly standard drunkard's walk routine, randomly choosing X and Y directions and handling the case where the poor drunkard smashes into the walls at the edges of the image (in our case, sticking to the wall until the end of that walk step).

The next three lines handle the optional color rotation in the case where param[1] is zero, being careful to avoid using the background color 0 or exceeding the number of colors in the image.

Finally, demowalk() has to update the image. Rather than build our own line drawing routine, we borrowed one from the 3-D logic in PLOT3D.C. Using this routine has one drawback, which you'll only see if you activate the VIEW / PIXEL-BY-PIXEL update option. Its implementation of Bresenham's algorithm sometimes draws the line in to-from fashion instead of from-to fashion. This effect isn't noticeable anywhere else in Winfract, but our drunkard occasionally takes fairly big steps. Ah, well, that's what we get for stealing code from somebody else's modules.

Note that there is alternate, commented-out code that uses the putcolor() routine to display just the endpoints instead of the entire line. This code was added just to show you how to update images a pixel at a time.

The last two lines in the loop replace our drunkard's old location with his new one in preparation for taking the next step.

Finally, if the routine falls out of the bottom of the generation loop, it returns with a value of one indicating to the calling routines that it completed its image normally.

At the end of the drunkard's walk routine is a simple Mandelbrot fractal that is invoked if the user sets the average stepsize parameter to 999. This Mandelbrot routine was inserted to show how a stand-alone fractal type accesses the x- and y-coordinates of each pixel in its image. However, it also serves to demonstrate the disadvantages of implementing an escape-time fractal type as a stand-alone fractal. Because it's not using the escape-time fractal engine, this fractal type does not have automatic access to any of the standard escape-time options like solid-guessing, boundary-tracing, biomorphs, decomposition, any of the inside or outside options, etc. Also, it's incredibly slow.

Note that the floating-point arrays used by the Mandelbrot option are only filled in if a fractal type has been declared to use a floating-point type of algorithm. Integer fractals use long far array equivalents called lx0[ ], ly0[ ], lx1[ ], and ly1[ ].

Adding Escape-Time Fractals

Now let's add a family of four escape-time fractal types to Winfract, integer and floating-point versions of the familiar Mandelbrot and Julia sets.

Adding Entries to the FRACTYPE.H File

The first thing you have to do when adding new fractal types to Winfract is to add definitions in the FRACTYPE.H file. These definitions point to the fractal's locations in the fractal-specific file. For many fractal types, including the ones you're about to add, these definitions are only used inside the fractal-specific structure (and in fact for some fractal types, they aren't even used there), but it's a good practice to always add these definitions to FRACTYPE.H so that they're all in one place. You'll need four entries for the integer and floating-point variations of both the Mandelbrot and Julia types. The values of these entries will be the location of the entries you will be adding to the end of the fractal-specific structure. Listing 6-5 shows the entries you need to add.

Listing 6-5 Adding the demo fractal types to FRACTYPE.H

```
#define DEMOMANDEL      128
#define DEMOJULIA       129
#define DEMOMANDELFP    130
#define DEMOJULIAFP     131
```

Adding Entries to the Fractal-Specific Structure

Having added the entries for these four new fractal types, let's add their entries to the end of the fractal-specific array in FRACTALP.C, just before the NULL entry indicating the end of the list. Listing 6-6 shows the four new entries we need to add.

Listing 6-6 Adding the demo fractal types to FRACTALP.C

```
"demomandel", realz0, imagz0,"","",0,0,0,0,
-1, -1, WINFRAC,
-2.5, 1.5, -1.5, 1.5, 1, DEMOJULIA,  NOFRACTAL, DEMOMANDELFP,
XAXIS_NOPARM,
JuliaFractal, mandel_per_pixel, MandellongSetup, StandardFractal, STDBAILOUT,

"demojulia", realparm, imagparm,"","",0.6,0.55,0,0,
-1, -1, WINFRAC,
-2.0, 2.0, -1.5, 1.5, 1, NOFRACTAL, DEMOMANDEL, DEMOJULIAFP, ORIGIN,
JuliaFractal, julia_per_pixel, JulialongSetup, StandardFractal, STDBAILOUT,

"*demomandel", realz0, imagz0,"","",0,0,0,0,
-1, -1, WINFRAC,
-2.5, 1.5, -1.5, 1.5, 0, DEMOJULIAFP,  NOFRACTAL, DEMOJULIA,
XAXIS_NOPARM,
JuliafpFractal, mandelfp_per_pixel, MandelfpSetup, StandardFractal, STDBAILOUT,

"*demojulia", realparm, imagparm,"","",0.6,0.55,0,0,
-1, -1, WINFRAC,
-2.0, 2.0, -1.5, 1.5, 0, NOFRACTAL, DEMOMANDELFP, DEMOMANDEL, ORIGIN,
JuliafpFractal, juliafp_per_pixel, JuliafpSetup, StandardFractal, STDBAILOUT,
```

Let's go over the demomandel entry. Refer to Listings 6-1 and 6-2 as we do so, as they include the definitions of all flags and parameter strings used by this entry. The fractal type's name, used whenever Winfract needs to identify this fractal type, is "demomandel." It accepts two optional parameters (realparm and imagparm), both of which default to 0. Helptext and helpformula are –1, as this fractal type is not related to any fractint-style help text. Its only flag is WINFRAC, which signals that Winfract can invoke it. Its screen corners are –2.5,1.5,–1.5,1.5, the standard, slightly off-center corner values that display the initial Mandelbrot image well. Isinteger is 1, indicating that this is an integer fractal. Its Julia equivalent, reached by pressing the right mouse button, is DEMOJULIA (being a Mandelbrot fractal, it has no Mandelbrot equivalent so that entry is NOFRACTAL). Its alternative floating-point algorithm is the one in the DEMOMANDELFP entry. Its symmetry (XAXIS_NOPARM) is about the x-axis, but only if its optional parameters are all zero. We'll go into the four function pointers in detail in the following paragraphs. Finally, its bail-out value is the standard bailout value, 4.0.

Once you've added (or removed the comments from) these entries in FRACTYPE.H and FRACTALP.C, rebuild Winfract and run it again. You now have two new fractal types, demomandel and demojulia. These new fractal types have both floating-point and integer versions, and are connected via the Mandelbrot/Julia toggle activated by the right mouse button. Not only do the basic algorithms work, but they also work with all of Winfract's myriad options and doodads.

Now take a look at the entry for the mandel4 fractal type in FRACTALP.C, shown in Listing 6-7. Note that the main difference between this entry and the one for demomandel is the pointer to a different orbitcalc() routine, Mandel4Fractal() (found in FRACTALS.C). All of the other function pointers are identical.

Listing 6-7 The Mandel4 entry in FRACTALP.C

```
"mandel4", realz0, imagz0,"","",0,0,0,0,
HT_MANDJUL4, HF_MANDEL4, WINFRAC,
-2.0,  2.0, -1.5,  1.5, 1, JULIA4,      NOFRACTAL, NOFRACTAL,
XAXIS_NOPARM,
Mandel4Fractal, mandel_per_pixel, MandellongSetup, StandardFractal, STDBAILOUT,
```

The Four Function Pointers
The function pointers are the heart of the actual fractal calculation process, so it's worthwhile to go over the four function pointers in each of these new entries and see what the functions they point to actually do. If you're perusing through the source code while you're reading this chapter, all of the functions referred to in this section reside in the FRACTALS.C module unless noted otherwise.

The per_image() Routines
The new fractal types point to one of four per_image() routines. The routine depends on whether the fractal is a Mandelbrot or a Julia and on whether it uses an integer or floating-point algorithm. In all four cases, we're invoking standardized routines used by a number of escape-time fractal types. The routines are actually quite similar, and they're really simpler than they first appear. In fact, the bulk of the code in these routines covers special cases and variables that don't apply to any of the fractal types in our examples (the usual penalty for writing general-purpose subroutines). Listing 6-8 shows the source code for the MandellongSetup() routine as it appears in the FRACTALS.C module.

Listing 6-9 shows the same routine and its three companions stripped down to the code that affects our new routines. All they do is initialize a pointer to a parameter structure (longparm for the integer types or floatparm for the floating-point types). In the case of the Mandelbrot fractals, this parameter points to a structure containing the current pixel coordinates. In the case of the Julia fractals, it points to a structure containing a parameter value (the parameter value is provided either manually by the user or automatically via the Mandelbrot/Julia toggle function). The Julia fractals also call the get_julia_attractor() routine (located in the FRACSUBR.C module) that checks to see if the finite attractor option has been enabled. If the finite attractor option has been enabled, get_julia_attractor() performs some special initialization. Normally, get_julia_attractor() just returns without doing anything.

Listing 6-8 MandellongSetup() source

```
MandellongSetup()
{
    FgHalf = fudge >> 1;
    c_exp = param[2];
    if(fractype==MARKSMANDEL && c_exp < 1)
        c_exp = 1;
    if(fractype==LMANDELZPOWER && c_exp < 1)
        c_exp = 1;
    if((fractype==MARKSMANDEL    && !(c_exp & 1)) ||
       (fractype==LMANDELZPOWER && c_exp & 1))
        symmetry = XYAXIS_NOPARM;    /* odd exponents */
    if((fractype==MARKSMANDEL && (c_exp & 1)) || fractype==LMANDELEXP)
        symmetry = XAXIS_NOPARM;
    if(fractype==SPIDER && periodicitycheck==1)
        periodicitycheck=4;
    longparm = &linit;
    if(fractype==LMANDELZPOWER)
    {
        if(param[4] == 0.0 && debugflag != 6000  && (double)c_exp == param[2])
            fractal-specific[fractype].orbitcalc = longZpowerFractal;
        else
            fractal-specific[fractype].orbitcalc = longCmplxZpowerFractal;
        if(param[3] != 0 || (double)c_exp != param[2] )
            symmetry = NOSYM;
    }

    return(1);
}
```

Listing 6-9 ...Setup() source simplified

```
MandellongSetup()
{
    /
* initialize the parm pointer to point to the current pixel coordinate values */
    longparm = &linit;
    /* return, indicating that the fractal has yet to be generated */
    return(1);
}
```

```
JulialongSetup()
{
    /* initialize the parm pointer to point to the parameter entry  */
    longparm = &lparm;
    /* invoke the julia attractor option, if its been set */
    get_julia_attractor (0.0, 0.0);
    /* return, indicating that the fractal has yet to be generated */
    return(1);
}
MandelfpSetup()
{
    /
* initialize the parm pointer to point to the current pixel coordinate values */
    floatparm = &init;
    /* return, indicating that the fractal has yet to be generated */
    return(1);
}
JuliafpSetup()
{
    /* initialize the parm pointer to point to the parameter entry */
    floatparm = &parm;
    /* invoke the julia attractor option, if its been set */
    get_julia_attractor (0.0, 0.0);
    /* return, indicating that the fractal has yet to be generated */
    return(1);
}
```

The calctype() Routines

All of the above examples use the same calctype() function. This is the standard escape-time fractal routine, StandardFractal(), located in the CALCFRAC.C module. The core fractal logic in CALCFRAC.C recognizes the StandardFractal() entry as being the escape-time fractal routine. When it sees that StandardFractal() is specified as the calctype() entry, the core fractal logic switches to its escape-time routines, enables its escape-time options such as solid-guessing and boundary-tracing, and calls StandardFractal() once for each pixel. StandardFractal() automatically handles all sorts of options like inside coloring, outside coloring, biomorphs, decomposition, logarithmic palettes, and such, making them a feature of every escape-time fractal type.

The per_pixel() Routines

The examples use one of several per_pixel() routines, depending on whether they are Mandelbrot or Julia fractals and on whether they use the integer or floating-point algorithms. As in the case of the per_image() routines, these are all standardized routines used by a number of escape-time fractal types. Listing 6-10 shows the mandel_per_pixel() routine called by many of the Mandelbrot-style functions.

This routine has special logic to handle the inversion option (with inversion, the initial pixel value is really from a different (everted) location) and several of the esoteric inside options. Listing 6-11 shows the same routine and its sister routines stripped of those options and down to fighting trim for comparison purposes.

Aside from those option checks, all the routines do is initialize a few variables so that the first call to the orbitcalc() routines can calculate z(1). The old/lold structures hold the results of the previous iteration—z(0) in this case, and the value of the current pixel coordinate position. For the Mandelbrot fractals, z(0) may be modified by an optional parameter. The tempsqrx/tempsqry variables contain the square of the real and imaginary components of the previous calculation. Normally, they are leftover values from the previous iteration, so they have to be explicitly calculated here because on the first call to the per_orbit() routines there won't have been a previous iteration.

Listing 6-10 The mandel_per_pixel() routine

```
int mandel_per_pixel()
{
    /* mandel */

    if(invert)
    {
        invertz2(&init);

        /* watch out for overflow */
        if(bitshift <= 24)
            if (sqr(init.x)+sqr(init.y) >= 127)
            {
                init.x = 8;  /* value to bail out in one iteration */
                init.y = 8;
            }
        if(bitshift >  24)
            if (sqr(init.x)+sqr(init.y) >= 4)
            {
                init.x = 2;  /* value to bail out in one iteration */
                init.y = 2;
            }

        /* convert to fudged longs */
        linit.x = init.x*fudge;
        linit.y = init.y*fudge;
    }
    else
        linit.x = lx0[col]+lx1[row];
    switch (fractype)
        {
            case MANDELLAMBDA:  /* Critical Value 0.5 + 0.0i  */
```

```
                lold.x = FgHalf;
                lold.y = 0;
                break;
            default:
                lold = linit;
                break;
        }

   /* alter init value */
   if(useinitorbit == 1)
      lold = linitorbit;
   else if(useinitorbit == 2)
      lold = linit;

   if(inside == -60 || inside == -61)
   {
      /* kludge to match "Beauty of Fractals" picture since we start
         Mandelbrot iteration with init rather than 0 */
      lold.x = lparm.x; /* initial pertubation of parameters set */
      lold.y = lparm.y;
      color = -1;
   }
   else
   {
      lold.x += lparm.x; /* initial pertubation of parameters set */
      lold.y += lparm.y;
   }
   ltmp = linit; /* for spider */
   ltempsqrx = multiply(lold.x, lold.x, bitshift);
   ltempsqry = multiply(lold.y, lold.y, bitshift);
   return(1); /* 1st iteration has been done */
}
```

Listing 6-11 The ...per_pixel functions simplified

```
int mandel_per_pixel()
{
   /* Z(0) is the value of the pixel coordinates */
   lold = linit;
   /* add in the optional parameter, if any */
   lold.x += lparm.x;
   lold.y += lparm.y;
   /* precalculate temporary values for the next iteration */
   ltempsqrx = multiply(lold.x, lold.x, bitshift);
   ltempsqry = multiply(lold.y, lold.y, bitshift);
   /* return - we're done */
   return(0);
}
int julia_per_pixel()
{
   /* Z(0) is the value of the pixel coordinates */
   lold.x = lx0[col]+lx1[row];
```

```
    lold.y = ly0[row]+ly1[col];
    /* precalculate temporary values for the next iteration */
    ltempsqrx = multiply(lold.x, lold.x, bitshift);
    ltempsqry = multiply(lold.y, lold.y, bitshift);
    /* return - we're done */
    return(0);
}

int mandelfp_per_pixel()
{
    /* Z(0) is the value of the pixel coordinates */
    old = init;
    /* add in the optional parameter, if any */
    old.x += parm.x;
    old.y += parm.y;
    /* precalculate temporary values for the next iteration */
    tempsqrx = sqr(old.x);
    tempsqry = sqr(old.y);
    /* return - we're done */
    return(0);
}

int juliafp_per_pixel()
{
    /* Z(0) is the value of the pixel coordinates */
    old.x = dx0[col]+dx1[row];
    old.y = dy0[row]+dy1[col];
    /* precalculate temporary values for the next iteration */
    tempsqrx = sqr(old.x);
    tempsqry = sqr(old.y);
    /* return - we're done */
    return(0);
}
```

The orbitcalc() Routines

The Mandelbrot and Julia examples use the same orbitcalc() logic. Given that the longparm/floatparm pointer has already been redirected by the per_image() routine, once you get those fractal types initialized with $z(0)$, they use the same formula to calculate $z(n+1)$ from $z(n)$. There are floating-point and integer variants of this routine, JuliaFractal() and JuliafpFractal(). Listing 6-12 shows both of them and the bailout routines they call. This is one case where the floating-point algorithms are easier to follow, as the integer algorithms have to include some fairly contorted logic to ensure that they detect all the overflow possibilities.

Listing 6-12 The JuliaFractal and JuliafpFractal routines and their bailout functions

```
JuliaFractal()
{
    lnew.x  = ltempsqrx - ltempsqry + longparm->x;
    lnew.y = multiply(lold.x, lold.y, bitshiftless1) + longparm->y;
```

```
        return(longbailout());
   }
   JuliafpFractal()
   {
      new.x = tempsqrx - tempsqry + floatparm->x;
      new.y = 2.0 * old.x * old.y + floatparm->y;
      return(floatbailout());
   }

   static int near floatbailout()
   {
      if ( ( magnitude = ( tempsqrx=sqr(new.x) )
                     + ( tempsqry=sqr(new.y) ) ) >= rqlim ) return(1);
      old = new;
      return(0);
   }
   int longbailout()
   {
     /* the real routine is in assembler for speed: this is the C
        equivalent */
     ltempsqrx = lsqr(lnew.x);
     ltempsqry = lsqr(lnew.y);
     lmagnitud = ltempsqrx + ltempsqry;
     if (lmagnitud >= llimit || lmagnitud < 0 || labs(lnew.x) > llimit2
           || labs(lnew.y) > llimit2 || overflow) {
                 overflow=0;
                 return(1);
                 }
     lold = lnew;
   }
```

Algorithmically, the routines only perform the function listed below. The actual code is contorted to save calculation time: this iteration's new.x is also next iteration's old.x, so there's no reason to recalculate the squares of the old values given that you've already calculated them (as the squares of the new values) in the previous iteration.

```
/*   algorithm notes:
     old.x and old.y are the values of the x and y results of the
          prior iteration
     new.x and new.y are the values of the x and y results of this
          iteration
     tempsqrx and tempsqry are temporary values for x squared and
          y squared. The real routines, being clever, re-use these
          values when they calculate new.x in the next iteration.
     bailoutlimit is the bailout value (usually 4) defined by the
          orbit_bailout entry in the fractal-specific structure, but
          perhaps changed to a different value as a user option.
*/
new.x = (old.x * old.x) - (old.y * old.y) + param.x;
new.y = 2 * old.x * old.y + param.y;
tempsqrx = new.x * new.x;
tempsqry = new.y * new.y;
if  ( (tempsqrx + tempsqry ) >= bailoutlimit)
     return(1);
else
     return(0);
```

A

Winfract
and Windows
Video Drivers

Have you had any of these questions lately?

- Why won't Winfract let me color cycle my images?

- When I use Winfract to display a nonfractal GIF file, why do some of the colors look funny?

- Why do I get all these "sparklies" on my screen when Winfract is color cycling?

- Why do the colors and the display change on me when I copy a Winfract image to the clipboard and then switch back and forth between the two applications?

These question illustrate some typical, video-related problems people have when running Winfract, and this appendix will answer some of those questions.

WINDOWS VIDEO DRIVERS

Graphics programs running under MS-DOS generally contain their own video routines, bypassing any graphics support provided by the video adaptor's BIOS. This approach gives the MS-DOS application the advantage of having the ability to deliver every last ounce of speed and capability, with the disadvantage that every MS-DOS application must reinvent the wheel when it comes to supporting every individual graphics adaptor in the PC world.

Windows applications don't have this option. All access to the screen is handled by the video driver that the user installed either as part of the original Windows installation or during a later running of the Windows Setup program. This is because Windows applications, unlike their MS-DOS counterparts, do not own the screen—they share it with other applications, including Windows' own Program Manager. Some other process has to match the demands of all of these applications to the capabilities of the physical adaptor. Often, it is the Windows video driver that performs this task.

This approach has the advantage of isolating the idiosyncrasies of the video adaptor from the Windows application. The disadvantage is that the Windows application just has to live with any limitations of the installed video driver.

COLORS AND PALETTES

One of the areas where Windows applications differ from their MS-DOS equivalents is in their use of colors and color palettes. Because Windows has to deal with multiple applications on the screen at the same time, individual programs do not always have the luxury of dictating which colors are being used to display their images. Often the application is reduced to suggesting which colors it would like to display—and hoping for the best. Winfract, in particular, uses device-independent bitmaps internally to hold its images, and asks Windows and its installed video driver to map those images (and their associated colors) to the screen as best it can.

In the case of 16-color drivers (the standard EGA and VGA video drivers that come with Windows 3.x are 16-color drivers), a Windows application has no control at all over the 16 colors that are used for the display. When Winfract asks Windows about the capabilities of the active video driver, Windows reports back that the video driver is a 16-color video driver and that these colors cannot be changed. (To use the Windows phrase, the video is not "palette-based.") Winfract can (and does) still ask Windows to display specific colors, but Windows responds by mapping Winfract's colors to the 16 available colors using a best-fit algorithm—a best-fit that doesn't always fit very well. Winfract disables its color-cycling capabilities when it detects that it is being run using a non-palette-based Windows video driver such as these 16-color drivers.

256-color Windows video drivers, on the other hand, are "palette-based," and a Windows application can ask Windows to modify some—but not all—of these colors. Windows reserves 20 palette values for its own use, leaving the individual Windows application with 236 modifiable colors. When Winfract asks Windows to use an alternate set of 256 colors, Windows uses the first 236 colors as requested, but maps the last 20 to whatever is available on a best-fit basis. Winfract enables its color-cycling capabilities when it is being run using a 256-color video driver.

If Winfract is the only WinApp attempting to use all 256 colors, Winfract's image will look consistent whether or not it is the application with the "focus" (the application you are working with at the moment). If another application is requesting control over some or all of these same colors, the Windows video driver gives the application you're working with at the moment (the one with the "focus") first choice as to the colors being displayed. All other applications have their colors temporarily mapped to those colors using Windows' "best-fit" algorithm. In some cases, the display of the application that does not have the focus can look particularly weird; the colors can even be all black. This is true even in cases when Winfract has just sent its image to the clipboard, and two applications are supposedly using the same 256 colors.

"True-color" video drivers (those with the ability to display 32,000 or more colors simultaneously on the screen) are yet another breed. With true-color video drivers, Windows gives every Windows application exactly the colors it wants, as the video adaptor is not using palettes and every pixel on the screen has its color value set independently. The good news is that with these video drivers Winfract is free to dictate exactly what each of its 256 color values will look like on the screen. The bad news is that there is no real palette to manipulate (the only way to modify the "palette" is to completely redisplay the image), so Winfract has to disable its color-cycling routines.

COLOR CYCLING AND "SPARKLIES"

When an applications program is color cycling, it is modifying the hardware color palette rapidly. With many graphics adaptors, modifying the palette while an image is being displayed causes temporary (and non-harmful) interference with the image display. This interference shows up as "snow" or "sparklies," as the display of different pixels gets temporarily interfered with each time the palette is modified.

MS-DOS-based programs have ways to avoid this interference. The most commonly used trick is to wait for the brief period during the vertical retrace when the image on your display is not being modified and update the palette during that interval.

Windows applications don't have this control over the hardware, and must rely on the Windows video driver to take care of it. Unfortunately, not all Windows video drivers do so. This is not a flaw in your video driver, but rather a design decision. This interference is only noticeable if an application is constantly modifying the palette. Waiting 1/60th of a second and doing nothing before modifying the palette is not always considered good behavior in a multitasking environment. At any rate, there is not much that Winfract can do about it. In fact, Winfract isn't even aware of the problem.

If you get sparklies all over the screen when you use Winfract's color-cycling option, all you can do is console yourself with the fact that there is no harm being done to your system.

B

The Graphics Interchange Format

Winfract uses a standard format for saving and loading its images that is very popular. It is called the Graphics Interchange Format, or GIF (pronounced "jif"). CompuServe created and maintains this machine-independent standard format for distributing graphics images. All files saved in this format end with the .GIF extension. This graphics standard is supported by a wide range of software. You can display a GIF image on any computer with graphics hardware using GIF decoder software written for that machine. Many different GIF programs have been written for the PC. Decoders are available for the Mac II, Atari, Amiga, C-64, TI Professional, DEC Rainbow, Sun Workstations, and X-Windows. Various GIF decoders can be downloaded from CompuServe's PICS forum, library 3.

An image stored as a GIF file is composed of two different tables. One short table contains a list of gun colors for each of the color index values similar to the .MAP files described in Chapter 4. The other table contains the image data. The image data table is comprised of color index numbers. This table is compressed using an LZW (after Liv, Zempel, and

Welch, the originators) compression algorithm to keep the size of the file as small as possible. Therefore, compression utilities such as PKZIP will usually store a GIF file without compression—it's already compressed! At the most these utilities will provide 2 percent compression by squeezing down the header and color table.

There are two GIF formats. The first format, called GIF87a, is the original 1989 GIF format. Virtually all GIF decoders can read this format. In 1989 the format was revised and some additional features added. One of these features was the designation of areas within a GIF file for storing application data. Winfract takes advantage of this to store all the information needed to duplicate the image. When you open a Winfract-created GIF89a file, the fractal parameters are set for you and Winfract is ready to regenerate the image. In fact, if you save a partially complete image in GIF89a format, when you open the file later, Winfract can continue the calculation right where it left off. Therefore, you should save files using the GIF89a format. The only reason that Winfract gives you the option of using the GIF87a format is that even at this late date there are still GIF decoders that cannot accept the newer format.

The complete GIF89a standard is available on CompuServe in a file called GIF89A.DOC or GIF89A.ARC in the PICS forum (GO PICS). You can also find many software packages in the same library that support viewing and manipulating GIF images.

The Stone Soup Group and the Winfract Authors

Winfract is the product of an informal association of program mers and fractal enthusiasts know as the Stone Soup Group. Here is the explanation of the origin of that name and an introduction to the Fractint authors.

THE FABLE OF STONE SOUP

Once upon a time, somewhere in Eastern Europe, there was a great famine. People jealously hoarded whatever food they could find, hiding it even from their friends and neighbors. One day a peddler drove his wagon into a village, sold a few of his wares, and began asking questions as if he planned to stay for the night.

"There's not a bite to eat in the whole province," he was told. "Better keep moving on."

"Oh, I have everything I need," he said. "In fact, I was thinking of making some stone soup to share with all of you." He pulled an iron cauldron from his wagon, filled it with water, and built a fire under it.

Then, with great ceremony, he drew an ordinary-looking stone from a velvet bag and dropped it into the water.

By now, hearing the rumor of food, most of the villagers had come to the square or watched from their windows. As the peddler sniffed the "broth" and licked his lips in anticipation, hunger began to overcome their skepticism.

"Ahh," the peddler said to himself rather loudly, "I do like a tasty stone soup. Of course, stone soup with *cabbage*—that's hard to beat."

Soon a villager approached hesitantly, holding a cabbage he'd retrieved from its hiding place, and added it to the pot. "Capital!" cried the peddler. "You know, I once had stone soup with cabbage and a bit of salt beef as well, and it was fit for a king."

The village butcher managed to find some salt beef...and so it went, through potatoes, onions, carrots, mushrooms, and so on, until there was indeed a delicious meal for all. The villagers offered the peddler a great deal of money for the magic stone, but he refused to sell and traveled on the next day. And from that time on, long after the famine had ended, they reminisced about the finest soup they'd ever had.

THE ORIGIN OF WINFRACT

Winfract has grown and developed just like the soup in the fable, with quite a bit of magic, although without the element of deception. You don't have to deceive programmers to make them think that hours of painstaking, often frustrating work is fun—they think that already!

The original "stone" was the program Fra386.exe written by Bert Tyler, which may still be found on some computer bulletin boards. In some ways, it is a little unfair to describe Bert's original program as a humble stone, since Fra386 is a highly polished and capable fractal generator. Its claim to fame is that it is "blindingly fast." But a comparison between the original program and the copy of Winfract packaged with this book (and its sister, DOS program Fractint) shows why the "stone" metaphor is apt. If Fra386 is a tasty morsel, then Winfract and Fractint are a gourmet feast! The reason is that for several years now fractal enthusiasts from around the world have been sending Bert programming onions, potatoes, and spices to add to the soup! You are a beneficiary of this enthusiastic outpouring of creativity because Winfract is the state of the art of PC fractal programming. It would take a mammoth software development project to duplicate Winfract's features in a commercial program, and by then Winfract would have added still more features. And the software with this book has this unique advantage; it comes with free updates forever!

A WORD ABOUT THE AUTHORS

Winfract is the result of a synergy between the main authors, many contributors, and published sources. All four of the main authors have had a hand in many aspects of the code. At the time of writing, none of the four had ever met; the intense collaboration resulting in Winfract has been conducted entirely by electronic conferencing in the COMART (short for "Computer Art") forum of the CompuServe Information Service. You are welcome to join the discussions of Winfract and fractals; just type GO COMART when you log onto CompuServe.

Here is some background on each of the four main authors.

Tim Wegner

Tim Wegner

Tim Wegner considers himself more of a "math type" than a programmer, although some of the programming skills of the rest of the team may have rubbed off a little on him. He first discovered Bert's Fra386 program in late 1988, and remembers pestering Bert to alter the program so it would run on low-end PCs. Tim's reasons were entirely selfish: he wanted to modify Bert's code to add features, and he only had a lowly 80286-based PC. As soon as Fractint version 6 came out in January of 1989, Tim began to barrage Bert with ideas and code. These included support for super VGA graphics boards, the now-famous color-cycling feature, new fractal types, and 3-D transformation capabilities. Together, Tim and Bert hammered out the main outlines of Fractint's "StandardFractal" architecture and data structures. Tim has been labeled by his cohorts as being "obsessed with options," but he has now paid the price: as a co-author of this book, Tim had to document all the options he so enthusiastically added!

Tim has BA and MA degrees in mathematics from Carleton College and the University of California Berkeley. He worked for seven years overseas as a volunteer, doing things like working with Egyptian villagers building water systems. Since returning to the United States in 1982, he has written shuttle navigation software, a flight scheduling prototype, and supported strategic information planning, all at NASA's Johnson Space Center. He currently is a member of the Technical Staff of MITRE Houston.

Tim is a co-author of the Stone Soup Group's first book, *The Waite Group's Fractal Creations*.

Bert Tyler

Bert Tyler

Bert Tyler is Winfract's original author. He wrote the "blindingly fast" Intel 80386, specific-integer math code and the original, video-mode logic that was the basis of the Fractint program. When Windows 3.0 was released, Bert decided to dive into the mysterious world of Windows programming. At the time it was widely believed that DOS programs could not be ported to Windows, but had to be rewritten from the ground up. Bert bought a copy of the Windows Software Development Kit, and was determined to prove that Fractint could be ported to Windows. Several months later he released the first version of Winfract. To this day, the Fractint and Winfract programs are maintained in parallel, sharing many thousands of lines of C and assembler code.

When asked what his best contributions to Fractint have been, Bert answered that they were his decisions to distribute the program with full source code, and give full credit to anyone who sent him improvements. The authors receive major improvements from people they've never heard of before on an almost daily basis.

Bert has a BA in mathematics from Cornell University. He has been in programming since he got a job at the computer center in his sophomore year at college. Bert has been known to pass himself off as a PC expert, a UNIX expert, a statistician, and even a financial modeling expert. He is currently an independent PC consultant, supporting PC-to-Mainframe communications. Winfract is Bert's first effort at building a Windows program. Then again, Fractint was Bert's first effort at building a graphics program.

Mark Peterson

Mark Peterson

The Fractint team first heard from Mark in early 1989 when Mark sent an electronic mail message about an "artificial intelligence" algorithm for greatly speeding up fractal calculations. Bert and Tim didn't take him very seriously at first, but Mark's persistence paid off. What is now called the "periodicity checking" speedup became a feature of Fractint that made it even faster. In short order, Mark began coming up with significant and unique Fractint enhancements. Mark didn't just look in fractal texts for new fractal types, he invented brand new ones. Among his new fractal types are the unity type and the four-dimensional Julibrot. Mark wrote the formula parser, and greatly speeded up the Fractint code with a library of hand-coded assembler routines for calculating transcendental functions such as sine and cosine.

Mark's interest in fractals started when he read the book *Chaos* by James Gleick. Mark currently works for Northeast Utilities and also as a free-lance programming consultant in the Hartford, CT area. Mark is a co-author of *Fractal Creations*, and he has since written another book, *The Borland C++ Developer's Bible*.

Pieter Branderhorst

Pieter Branderhorst

Pieter was the last of the four authors to join the team, but his impact has already been extensive. Pieter first tried a couple of fractal programs in 1989, but he didn't explore them much because they were too slow. Then a friend sent him a copy of Fractint, and he was impressed with the speed. But Pieter has never seen a program he didn't think he could make a little faster, so he obtained the source code and dived in. As a result, Fractint will never be the same! Pieter sees himself as one of the no-holds-barred programming types in the group. He has already touched so many parts of the Fractint code that it would be impossible to list all his contributions, but they include major code speedups, rotating zoom box support, the save-and-resume logic, and the lion's share of the colorful point-and-shoot user interface.

Pieter has been programming computers for twenty years, since he left high school. He has worked on more types of computers and in more languages than he can remember. He currently works as an independent consultant. When asked to describe his work in one sentence, he answers with a wry smile, "I've never designed any hardware."

When asked to describe his work in one sentence, he answers with a wry smile, "I've never designed any hardware."

HOW THE STONE SOUP TEAM WORKS

Whenever anyone comes up with ideas for Winfract or Fractint, those ideas are shared and passed around in the CompuServe COMART forum. A feature makes it into the program if someone cares enough to incorporate the feature by writing the code. Since the source code is available, many ideas are sent to the authors as fully integrated source code. Other features start life as suggestions and are eventually coded by one of the authors.

One of the Fractint authors wrote this statement, which sums up the experience of being a "Stone Souper":

> There is something unique about the way this group works. We get along well without a formal structure or responsibilities, without clashes, and somehow everyone's efforts come together. Don't ask me how—I think some kind of magic is involved, and certainly some good humor.

ACCESSING THE AUTHORS

Communication between the authors for development of the next version of Fractint takes place in COMART (Computer Art) Section 15 (Fractals) of CompuServe (CIS). Access to this area is open to any and all who are interested in computer generated images. Stop on by if you have any questions or just want to take a peek at what's getting tossed into the soup! This is a good way to get your Fractint questions answered. The authors are always happy to help Fractint users and to hear suggestions for improving the program.

Bert Tyler	[73477,433] on CIS
Timothy Wegner	[71320,675] on CIS
Mark Peterson	[70441,3353] on CIS
Pieter Branderhorst	[72611,2257] on CIS

Index

WINFRACT.H, 310
WINFRACT.HLP, 306
WINFRACT.MAK, 306
WINFRACT.PRJ, 306
WINFRACT.RC, 307
WINFRACT.RTF, 306, 309
WINSRC.EXE, 305
WINTEXT.C, 309
Wire-Frame option, 107
WRITE COLOR-MAP command,
    159–160

X

x/y adjusts, 113–114
x/y shifts, 113–114, 145

Y

Yellow Leaves (RHS-20) recipe, 89–90

Z

ZOOM BAR option, 152–153
zoom box
    deleting, *xviii*, 151
    moving, 151
    using, 48–50
ZOOM.DLG, 307
zooming
    In box, 150–151
    in on Mandelbrot set, 28–29, 48–50
    Out box, 151–152
zpixel, 176

Environmental Awareness

Books have a substantial influence on the destruction of the forests of the Earth. For example, it takes 17 trees to produce one ton of paper. A first printing of 30,000 copies of a typical 480 page book consumes 108,000 pounds of paper which will require 918 trees!

Waite Group Press™ is against the clear-cutting of forests and supports reforestation of the Pacific Northwest of the United States and Canada, where most of this paper comes from. As a publisher with several hundred thousand books sold each year, we feel an obligation to give back to the planet. We will therefore support and contribute a percentage of our proceeds to organizations which seek to preserve the forests of planet Earth.

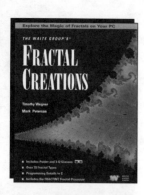

WAITE GROUP PRESS™

IMAGE LAB

Explore, Manipulate, and Create Images on Your PC

by Tim Wegner

Image Lab is a complete IBM PC-based "digital darkroom" in a unique book disk package that covers virtually all areas of graphic processing and manipulation, and comes with the finest graphics shareware available today: *PICLAB, CSHOW, IMPROCES, Image Alchemy,* and others. The software included in Image Lab lets you size images, remove colors, adjust palettes, combine, crop, transform, ray trace, convert from one graphics file format to another, and render your images. Graphics expert Tim Wegner shows how to make 3-D fractals and combine them to make photorealistic scenes. The powerful POV-Ray program and clever examples are worth the price of the book alone. Full color stereo glasses are available along with detailed directions for making your own stereoscopic full color images. Best on MS/PC DOS 386 machines with a VGA video board.

ISBN 1-878739-11-5, 350 pp, 1 HD 3.5" disk, color poster, $39.95 US/$49.95 Can., Available now

MULTIMEDIA CREATIONS

Hands On Workshop for Exploring Animation

by Philip Shaddock

Contemplating the jump into multimeida? Do it with **Multimedia Creations** and its powerful bundled *GRASP* program. Whether novice or programmer, you can create your own animated interactive audio-visual programs: from concept through post production, renderings to video tape. After a brief primer on PC video systems and animation fundamentals, you can start working with *GRASP*, creating everything from educational programs to your own multimedia cartoons. Work through the entire book/disk package to learn tricks like windowing, color cycling, sprite animation, delta compression techniques, and classical flipbook-style animation. And there are advanced chapters with in-depth coverage and reference sources for power users. Accompanying shareware programs provide you with the basic tools for creating complete multimedia presentations on the PC. For MS/PC DOS machines.

ISBN 1-878739-26-3, 450 pp, 2 5.25" disks, $44.95 US/$56.95 Can., Available November1992

WAITE GROUP PRESS™

LIMITED WARRANTY

The following warranties shall be effective for 90 days from the date of purchase: (i) The Waite Group, Inc. warrants the enclosed disk to be free of defects in materials and workmanship under normal use; and (ii) The Waite Group, Inc. warrants that the programs, unless modified by the purchaser, will substantially perform the functions described in the documentation provided by The Waite Group, Inc. when operated on the designated hardware and operating system. The Waite Group, Inc. does not warrant that the program will meet purchaser's requirements or that operation of the program will be uninterrupted or error-free. The program warranty does not cover any program that has been altered or changed in any way by anyone other than The Waite Group, Inc. The Waite Group, Inc. is not responsible for problems caused by changes in the operating characteristics of computer hardware or computer operating systems that are made after the release of the program, nor for problems in the interaction of the program with each other or other software.

THESE WARRANTIES ARE EXCLUSIVE AND IN LIEU OF ALL OTHER WARRANTIES OF MERCHANTABILITY OR FITNESS FOR A PARTICULAR PURPOSE OR OF ANY OTHER WARRANTY, WHETHER EXPRESS OR IMPLIED.

EXCLUSIVE REMEDY

The Waite Group, Inc. will replace any defective disk without charge if the defective disk is returned to The Waite Group, Inc. within 90 days from date of purchase.

This is Purchaser's sole and exclusive remedy for any breach of warranty or claim for contract, tort, or damages.

LIMITATION OF LIABILITY

THE WAITE GROUP, INC. AND THE AUTHORS OF THE PROGRAM SHALL NOT IN ANY CASE BE LIABLE FOR SPECIAL, INCIDENTAL, CONSEQUENTIAL, INDIRECT, OR OTHER SIMILAR DAMAGES ARISING FROM ANY BREACH OF THESE WARRAN-TIES EVEN IF THE WAITE GROUP, INC. OR ITS AGENT HAS BEEN ADVISED OF THE POSSIBILITY OF SUCH DAMAGES.

THE LIABILITY FOR DAMAGES OF THE WAITE GROUP, INC. AND THE AUTHORS OF THE PROGRAMS UNDER THIS AGREEMENT SHALL IN NO EVENT EXCEED THE PURCHASE PRICE PAID.

COMPLETE AGREEMENT

This Agreement constitutes the complete agreement between The Waite Group, Inc. and the authors of the program, and you, the purchaser.

Some states do not allow the exclusion or limitation of implied warranties or liability for incidental or consequential damages, so the above exclusions or limitations may not apply to you. This limited warranty gives you specific legal rights; you may have others, which vary from state to state.